Exciting news about Don's mate

1. Over 22,000 copies of the Japanese translation of Don's bo̲o̲k̲ "C̲a̲l̲c̲u̲l̲u̲s̲ By and For Young People (ages 7, yes 7 and up)", were sold by Kodansha Ltd., August 1998-Dec. 2001.

2. A JUKU teacher in Japan had Don's worksheet book translated and put the English and Japanese versions on a CD-ROM.

3. Kodansha Ltd. published the Japanese version of Don's book "Changing Shapes With Matrices" on April 20, 2001. They sold 5,490 in 8 months!

"..And that's what this series is all about. Playing with interesting aspects of math--The Fibonacci Sequence, for example--and learning to think mathematically. None of these materials offer a step-by-step instructional sequence, like a regular math course. Instead, these are "explorations" in math, a veritable hands-on museum of activities for young children in areas where high-school students fear to tread." ..**Mary Pride**, in her new 2000 issue of "***The Big Book of Home Learning***"

".. Much lip-service is given to education as it ought to be. Your materials guide us to education at its best. It's always exciting and rewarding to work with your materials." - **Debbie Reese**, former teacher of grades 6-8, IA

In case you missed it, below is the review of Don's book "Calculus By and For Young People (ages 7, yes 7 and up)" by **Phylis and Philip Morrison**, which appeared in the Dec. '88 issue of

Scientific American

"Trying to divide six cookies fairly among seven people? Third-grader Brad had the right idea: cut each one in half, share out as many as you can; again halve the pieces not shared until there are pieces enough to share, and continue. He quit at sixteenths, amidst lots of crumbs. But he could see that everyone got $1/2 + 1/4 + 0/8 + 1/16 + 1/32 + 0/64 +...$of a cookie. The sum is not hard to express in terms of more familiar series, once you notice that the missing portion of unity is itself a geometric series for $1/(1- (1/8))$. Iteration is more powerful and more intuitive than dividing a round cookie into seven equal parts.

This spiral-bound book the size of your hand reports with infectious enthusiasm the work of many beginners in one fine teacher's class over the decades, some of them highly gifted kids and some of them grown-ups with no particular mathematical bent. All were on their way to an understanding of slope and integral, natural logarithm and exponential. En route a good many famous problems were encountered, among them the proof of the snaillike divergence of the harmonic series (its first million terms add up to about 14.4, a sum given here to a dozen decimals), the Fibonacci sequence in pineapples and that glorious relation among, e, i, pi, 0 and 1.

The crossings between recreational mathematics, modern calculators and the track of such pioneers as Newton and Euler make this breezy and personal account, more notebook than book, good fun for the mathematically inclined young person and helpful for any adults who seek freer and solid arithmetic teaching".

What people are saying about Don's videotapes

"What to conventional wisdom appears either impossible or unlikely, this tape and my class's experiences with it, demonstrate that the math concepts presented here are not only possible with young children but fun, engaging and eminently practical. The tape integrates a wide spectrum of math concepts with critical thinking to solve really important math problems. Don uses concrete examples to help children find patterns in the process". ---**Douglas Elrick, 4th-5th grade teacher,** and father of three of Don's former students.

"..seldom do I see students so excited about their discoveries and sharing their methods.. What's more exciting, they want to get ahold of some little kids and try it out on them..". --**Bruce Hamilton, HS math teacher** , Colorado Springs School, CO

"The Cohen videotape on infinite series is an excellent inservice for teachers. The tape demonstrates how to engage children's minds and shows alternate ways to study mathematics other than workbook fill-in-the-blanks".-- **Marjorie Klein, kindergarten teacher** and mother of two of Don's students.

".. Especially appealing is your non-threatening approach where analytical concepts, such as geometrical series, are made visually understandable to young children in terms of what they can grasp... Congratulations on an excellent achievement. I can strongly recommend and endorse this educational tool to all ages. Even my university level students could benefit from an exposure to your concepts".--**Richard E. Klein, Ph.D., Associate Professor of Mechanical Engineering**, University of Illinois, and father of two of Don's students.

ORDER FORM:

1. "Calculus By and For Young People (ages 7, yes 7 and up)"................$ 13.95

2. "Calculus By and For Young People -- Worksheets" ....$ 25.95

3. VT #1 "Infinite Series with 6 year-olds and up" ....$ 42.95

4. VT #2 "Iteration to infinite Sequences with 6 to11 year-olds " ....$ 42.95

5. A "Map to Calculus"- a 15"x18" poster-map, overview...........................$ 7.95

6. "Changing Shapes With Matrices"..$ 9.95

Save! All 6 items above ordered together.....................................…..........$ 127.90

7. CD-ROM with Don's "Calculus By and For Young People - Worksheets" in Japanese and English...$ 25.95

add for shipping and handling.....$ 5.00

* IL residents add 7 1/4% sales tax; outside US call or email for S&H, pay in USD on a US bank.

TOTAL $_____*

"On Thinking About & Doing Mathematics"- an 11"x17" poster, free with any purchase above, $1.99 alone, no s&h.

Ask Don about his Math By Mail/Email, using Instant Messenger, and coming to study with him in Champaign, IL

Check; V/MC #_____ Exp. date_____

Name_____Tel. No._____

Address_____Zip:_____

Email address:_____

Send order to: Don Cohen, 809 Stratford Dr., Champaign, IL 61821-4140
Or call toll free US & CAN: 1-800-356-4559; Fax: 1-217-356-4593 or order on
Don's web site at: http://www.shout.net/~mathman ; or Don's email: mathman@shout.net

On January 15, 2002, Don received this email: "Dear Don: Your materials are being used by a parent in our school to work with our GATE students [within a month there were 3 classes]. The kids are loving it!!" --BC, principal of a K-4 public school in CA, who had purchased 2 sets of Don's materials in Nov. '01.

Calculus By and For Young People -- Worksheets©

by Don Cohen

to accompany Don's book
"Calculus By and For Young People (ages 7, yes 7 and up)"
(reviewed in the Dec. '88 *Scientific American*, Oct '89 *Mathematics Teacher*, and
'00 *The Big Book of Home Learning* by Mary Pride, among others);
"A Map to Calculus"- 15"x18" poster-flowchart; videotapes
"Infinite Series By and For 6 year-olds and up" (Chapter 1) and
"Iteration to Infinite Sequences with 6 to 11 year-olds" (Chapter 8) and
"Changing Shapes With Matrices"

Jane, age 8, works on the tower puzzle, which led her to an exponential function
(see ch. 6).

Published by Don Cohen - **The Mathman**
809 Stratford Dr., Champaign, IL 61821-4140
Call toll-free 1 800 356 4559; email: mathman@shout.net
Math by Mail/Email & IM; website: http://www.shout.net/~mathman
ISBN 09621674-5-2

Acknowledgements

I would like to thank Dr. Robert B. Davis, my mentor and friend (now deceased).

I would like to thank Phylis and Philip Morrison for their wonderful review of my book,
Calculus By and For Young People
(ages 7, yes 7 and up)
in the Dec. 1988 issue of *Scientific American* magazine. They really brought me to a new awareness of the quality of my work and what I could be doing for young people and adults.

I would like to thank the owner of some Jukus, who made me realize that a more creative approach to teaching mathematics using these worksheets, would be useful in a changing Japanese educational system. Hiroshi Takimoto, one of these Juku owners, found Kodansha who published my original book in Japanese and he put this worksheet book on a CD-ROM in Japanese and English. All 3 of my books have been published in Japan as of this printing in April, 2001.

I would like to thank all the people who have purchased my book and videotapes, who have asked for and encouraged me to do these worksheets.

I would like to thank
    All my students and their parents with whom I have worked in The Math Program
    My Math by Mail students around the country
    My own children and grandchildren
all of whom have made my life and my teaching, so interesting and exciting.

I would like to thank Ian Robertson, Jenny Kearns and Dan Lichtblau for helping me edit this book.

I would like to dedicate this book to Marilyn L. Cohen, my wife of 48 years, for her constant encouragement, assistance, smarts, common sense, loyalty, humor, love...

What is this book?

This is a book of problems to work on and think about. Archimedes, Newton, Euler, my students and I have worked on them also -- they are important. Important mathematically and important for understanding problems in your life. Get out some paper, a pencil and a calculator. Expect chaos and confusion, then you'll be on your way. This is **not** a linear book, but do get started on the ideas in chapters 1 and 2 first, then you could jump to chapter 6 or 8 or 13. *If you are a parent or teacher please allow your child to look at the answer sheets and to work with other people on the problems!*
This book is **not** a 1 year course! One could spend two months on one problem.

On thinking about and doing mathematics

You can do it! You must tell yourself that. Don't think because you haven't done a problem before, that you can't do it, or that someone else must show you how to do it first (a myth some people want to use to keep others in ignorance). You can do it! Don't be afraid. You've learned how to do the hardest things you'll ever do, walking and talking--mostly by yourself. This stuff is much easier!

Don't worry about making mistakes.. we all do. I make a lot of mistakes. My brighter students usually make more mistakes because they try an answer, it doesn't work, they change it until they get a solution.

Stay with it, don't give up, and have fun! This is going to take time. Keep a journal or diary of your work. Write down what you are doing, what you're thinking about, what's easy, what you don't understand, questions you have. Make up your own problems, your own tests.

Talk to someone else about what you are doing; teach it to a friend

Don't get discouraged if you are confused or don't understand it; most of us are confused about **most** things, but we don't want others to think we are.

Look for patterns; look at differences and ratios. Don't write one number for an answer, but write it so you can tell where it came from and how to get the next answer and all answers. Try to predict what will happen next.

Don't just memorize...try to understand; think about what you are doing. Ask yourself often..What am I doing? Where am I going? What am I trying to do? Be able to get the answer later on; come back to it again.

Ask a lot of questions; you might get a lot of questions answered by others. Ask questions like: What happens if I change this number? What happens if I change this graph? Can I predict what happens next?

Guess. Try a number.. see if it works. This will get you going. Don't wait.

Write a program on a calculator or computer to help solve the problem. Use your calculator to do the "dirty work".

Graph everything. Look for patterns!

Try to find 2 or 3 ways to do everything. Be able to check your work, that builds confidence. Do problems more than once, but in a different way

If a problem is difficult, work hard on it, take a break by working on a different problem, but then come back to the original problem. Change it to one like it, but easier, solve that one, then go back to the harder one.

All the problems were done by the author, his students, or what the author understood of the mathematician's works at this time.

This learning will never be finished..there will always be new questions and new problems...enjoy!

(This page has been expanded and comes free with any purchase of my materials).

The Table of Contents

Page #

Chapter 1: 7 Year-Olds Do $\frac{A}{B}+\left(\frac{A}{B}\right)^2+\left(\frac{A}{B}\right)^3+\left(\frac{A}{B}\right)^4+\cdots$ 1

Chapter 2: Brad's: Share 6 Cookies With 7 People 35

Chapter 3: Ian's Proof : Infinity = ⁻1 63

Chapter 4: The Snowflake curve--Its Area and perimeter........................... 71

Chapter 5: The Harmonic Series 83

Chapter 6: On Thin Spaghetti and Nocturnal Animals (functions and graphs)........... 87

Chapter 7: The Fibonacci Numbers, Pineapples,
            Sunflowers and The Golden Mean... 129

Chapter 8: Solving Equations and Iteration 145

Chapter 9: The Binomial Expansion and Infinite Series................................183

Chapter 10: Pi and Square Roots 205

Chapter 11: Compound Interest to e and **i**...213

Chapter 12: The Two Problems of the Calculus 239

Chapter 13: Area Under Curves--The Integral 241

Chapter 14: Slopes and The Derivative 273

Appendix 1-- The important mathematics 305

Appendix 2-- Activities for a parent/teacher workshop 307

Appendix 3-- On writing computer programs and
            the use of calculators and computers 309

Appendix 4-- Sheets to copied 313

Bibliography--Books, Videotapes, Materials, Computer Software & Websites of note.........322

Question worksheets for chapter 1

"7 Year-Olds Do $\frac{A}{B} + \left(\frac{A}{B}\right)^2 + \left(\frac{A}{B}\right)^3 + \left(\frac{A}{B}\right)^4 + \cdots$ "

(also see Don's videotape "Infinite Series By and For 6 year-olds and up")

Try to find patterns in all your work. Make a picture of everything possible! Have some graph paper (see appendix 5) ready to use now.

1. The first problem is to add up these fractions

$\frac{1}{2} + \frac{1}{4} + \frac{1}{8} + \frac{1}{16} + \frac{1}{32} + \cdots$ *forever !*

and answer the question: What happens to the sum if we go on forever? Very exciting!

Our strategy will be to add $\frac{1}{2} + \frac{1}{4}$, then $\frac{1}{2} + \frac{1}{4} + \frac{1}{8}$, then $\frac{1}{2} + \frac{1}{4} + \frac{1}{8} + \frac{1}{16}$ and so on, until we find a pattern that will help us go *forever,* without having to actually do it. These are called the partial sums.

Start with an 8x8 square on graph paper, like that at the right and call it one cake. Shade in $\frac{1}{2}$ (one-half or one-twoth) of the cake. What does $\frac{1}{2}$ mean? Share the cake between 2 people, you and someone else, then shade in one of the two shares.

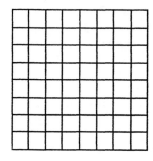

There are lots of ways to show $\frac{1}{2}$,
compare yours with your friend's way.

You can use your own way as we go
along.

We'll start with $\frac{1}{2}$ as shown in this
picture:

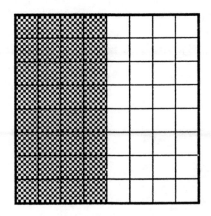

Now color in $\frac{1}{2}$ of $\frac{1}{2}$ of the cake or $\frac{1}{4}$ (one-fourth) of the cake, a **different** color. Don't
overlap the $\frac{1}{2}$ you did. What does $\frac{1}{4}$ mean? We share the cake with 4 people and shade in
one of the pieces. $\frac{1}{4}$ of the cake is $\frac{1}{2}$ of $\frac{1}{2}$ of the cake $= \frac{1}{2} \times \frac{1}{2} = \left(\frac{1}{2}\right)^{2} = \frac{1}{4}$

This is $\frac{1}{2}$ and $\frac{1}{4}$ of the cake.

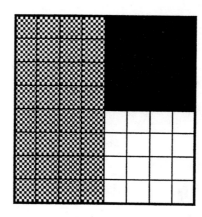

Now add $\frac{1}{2}$ and $\frac{1}{4}$ of the cake, in other words we want to name $\frac{1}{2} + \frac{1}{4}$ with one fraction.

One way to write $\frac{1}{2} + \frac{1}{4}$ with one fraction

is $\frac{1\frac{1}{2}}{2}$ (one and one-half halves or one half

and a half of a half). Another way to write

$\frac{1}{2} + \frac{1}{4}$ is $\frac{3}{4}$ because 3 quarters or 3 out of

4 pieces of the cake are now shaded in.

Another way to think about this is $\frac{1}{2}$ is $\frac{2}{4}$,

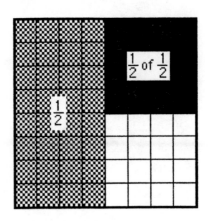

so $\frac{1}{2} + \frac{1}{4} = \frac{2}{4} + \frac{1}{4} = \frac{3}{4}$. You could also think about $\frac{1}{2}$ of a dollar plus $\frac{1}{4}$ of a dollar is three

quarters of a dollar or 75 cents. So $\frac{1}{2} + \frac{1}{4} = \frac{3}{4} = \frac{1\frac{1}{2}}{2} = .75$

Try to write things different ways! Each different way will help you understand what you are doing .

What are we trying to do? and where are we so far? One has to keep asking oneself these questions, because we start off and get into the fine details and sometimes forget what it is we set out to do. Our problem was to add

$$\frac{1}{2} + \frac{1}{4} + \frac{1}{8} + \frac{1}{16} + \frac{1}{32} + \cdots \quad \text{and keep going forever.}$$

So far we have $\frac{1}{2} + \frac{1}{4} = \frac{3}{4}$. What's the next question?

Add $\frac{1}{2} + \frac{1}{4} + \frac{1}{8}$.

So we need to shade in $\frac{1}{8}$ of the cake in a different color (don't overlap the other pieces). What does $\frac{1}{8}$ mean? $\frac{1}{8}$ is $\left(\frac{1}{2}\right)^3$ or $\frac{1}{2}$ of $\frac{1}{2}$ of $\frac{1}{2}$, or $\frac{1}{2}$ of $\frac{1}{4}$, or we share the cake with 8 people and shade in one of the pieces. Shade in $\frac{1}{8}$ of the cake.

This is a picture of $\frac{1}{2}$, $\frac{1}{4}$, and $\frac{1}{8}$ of the cake.

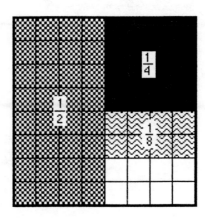

Now add these and find a single fraction name for $\frac{1}{2}+\frac{1}{4}+\frac{1}{8}$.

How many $\frac{1}{8}$'s are in the whole cake? $\frac{8}{8}$ make the whole cake or $\frac{8}{8} = 1$, just as $\frac{4}{4} = 1$,

(4 quarters make 1 dollar) and $\frac{2}{2} = 1$ (two half-dollars make 1 dollar).

How many $\frac{1}{8}$'s are not shaded in? How many $\frac{1}{8}$'s are shaded in?

So we can say $\frac{1}{2} + \frac{1}{4} + \frac{1}{8} = \frac{7}{8}$.

Or we can also say the shaded part is $\frac{3\frac{1}{2}}{4}$ because $\frac{1}{2}$ is $\frac{2}{4}$, plus the $\frac{1}{4}$, plus the $\frac{1}{8}$ which is

$\frac{1}{2}$ of $\frac{1}{4}$, or $\frac{\frac{1}{2}}{4}$ and $\frac{2}{4} + \frac{1}{4} + \frac{\frac{1}{2}}{4} = \frac{3\frac{1}{2}}{4}$

Or we can also say the shaded part is $\frac{1\frac{3}{4}}{2}$. Does this make sense? Look carefully at the picture. Talk to your friends about this.

So $\frac{1}{2} + \frac{1}{4} + \frac{1}{8} = \frac{7}{8} = \frac{3\frac{1}{2}}{4} = \frac{1\frac{3}{4}}{2}$.

Where are we so far?

$$\frac{1}{2} = \frac{2}{4},$$

$$\frac{1}{2} + \frac{1}{4} = \frac{3}{4} = \frac{1\frac{1}{2}}{2} \quad \text{and the other partial sum,}$$

$$\frac{1}{2} + \frac{1}{4} + \frac{1}{8} = \frac{7}{8} = \frac{3\frac{1}{2}}{4} = \frac{1\frac{3}{4}}{2}$$

Look at these partial sums $\frac{1}{2}$, $\frac{3}{4}$, $\frac{7}{8}$; do you see a pattern in these numbers? **Can you predict the next one?**

Can you find a pattern for these same sums when they are written as $\frac{1}{2}$'s?

$$\frac{1}{2}, \quad \frac{1\frac{1}{2}}{2}, \quad \frac{1\frac{3}{4}}{2}, \quad \text{... Predict the next two of these.}$$

Can you find a pattern for these same sums when they are written as $\frac{1}{4}$'s?

$$\frac{2}{4}, \quad \frac{3}{4}, \quad \frac{3\frac{1}{2}}{4} \quad \text{... Predict the next two of these. Talk about these with your friends.}$$

Now we need to shade in $\frac{1}{16}$ of the cake in a different color (don't overlap the other pieces). What does $\frac{1}{16}$ mean? $\frac{1}{16}$ means share the cake between 16 people and shade in one share, or $\frac{1}{16} = \frac{1}{2}$ of $\frac{1}{8} = \frac{1}{2} \times \frac{1}{8} = \frac{1}{2}$ of $\left(\frac{1}{2} \text{ of } \frac{1}{4} \right) = \frac{1}{2} \times \frac{1}{2} \times \frac{1}{4} = \frac{1}{2}$ of $\frac{1}{2}$ of $\frac{1}{2}$ of $\frac{1}{2} = \frac{1}{2} \times \frac{1}{2} \times \frac{1}{2} \times \frac{1}{2} = \left(\frac{1}{2} \right)^4$. These are all names for $\frac{1}{16}$!

$\frac{1}{2}$, $\frac{1}{4}$, $\frac{1}{8}$, and $\frac{1}{16}$ are shown in this picture:

Now find one fraction name for $\frac{1}{2} + \frac{1}{4} + \frac{1}{8} + \frac{1}{16}$.

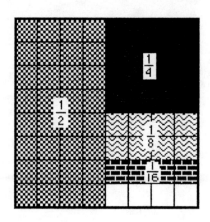

The total shaded portion now is

$\frac{1}{2} + \frac{1}{4} + \frac{1}{8} + \frac{1}{16}$ and can be named as,

$$\frac{1}{2} + \frac{1}{4} + \frac{1}{8} + \frac{1}{16} = \frac{15}{16} \text{ or as}$$

$$\frac{4}{8} + \frac{2}{8} + \frac{1}{8} + \frac{\frac{1}{2}}{8} = \frac{7\frac{1}{2}}{8} = \frac{3\frac{3}{4}}{4} = \frac{1\frac{7}{8}}{2}.$$

Predict the next partial sum: $\frac{1}{2} + \frac{1}{4} + \frac{1}{8} + \frac{1}{16} + \frac{1}{32} = ?$

Can you find a pattern in the partial sums $\frac{1}{2}, \frac{3}{4}, \frac{7}{8}, \frac{15}{16}, \frac{31}{32}, \frac{63}{64}, \frac{127}{128}, \ldots$

Can you write the next 4 terms?

2. What's happening to the partial sums?

Are these sums getting bigger, smaller or staying the same size?

Are the numbers you are adding each time getting bigger or smaller?

Will the square ever get filled in if we keep going on?

What is this series getting close to? What is the **smallest** number that the series gets closer to?

3. Graph these partial sums. The first point on the graph is $(1, \frac{1}{2})$, that is the first partial sum, $\frac{1}{2}$. Try graphing the 2nd partial sum (2 terms added), $\frac{3}{4}$, at $(2, \frac{3}{4})$ and so on.

What happens when you continue the graph?

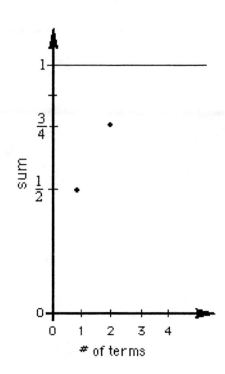

In the sequence $\frac{1}{2}, \frac{1}{4}, \frac{1}{8}, \frac{1}{16}, \ldots \frac{1}{2^n} \ldots$ as n gets bigger and bigger what happens to the fraction $\frac{1}{2^n}$?

In the sequence $\left(1 - \frac{1}{2}\right), \left(1 - \frac{1}{4}\right), \left(1 - \frac{1}{8}\right), \left(1 - \frac{1}{16}\right), \ldots \left(1 - \frac{1}{2^n}\right), \ldots$ as n gets bigger and bigger what happens to $\left(1 - \frac{1}{2^n}\right)$?

4. Exponents

This is a little side trip. A few questions about exponents, those little numbers up above, like $\frac{1}{2}$ to the third power $= \left(\frac{1}{2}\right)^3 = \frac{1}{2} \times \frac{1}{2} \times \frac{1}{2} = \frac{1 \cdot 1 \cdot 1}{2 \cdot 2 \cdot 2} = \frac{1}{8}$ as we did above. 10 to the third

power is $10^3 = 10 \times 10 \times 10 = 1000$. In the table below the powers of ten are shown from 10^4 down to 10^{-3}. Notice that in going from 10^4 to 10^3 we're dividing by 10. Just keep that pattern! So $10^1 = 10$ and $10^0 = \frac{10}{10} = 1$ and $10^{-1} = \frac{1}{10} = .1$; fill in the rest of the table below:

$10^4 = 10000$	$2^4 = 16$	$3^4 =$	$5^4 =$
$10^3 = 1000$	$2^3 = 8$	$3^3 =$	$5^3 =$
$10^2 = 100$	$2^2 =$	$3^2 =$	$5^2 =$
$10^1 = 10$	$2^1 =$	$3^1 =$	$5^1 =$
$10^0 = 1$	$2^0 =$	$3^0 =$	$5^0 =$
$10^{-1} = \frac{1}{10} = \frac{1}{10^1} = .1$	$2^{-1} =$	$3^{-1} =$	$5^{-1} =$
$10^{-2} = \frac{1}{100} = \frac{1}{10^2} = .01$	$2^{-2} =$	$3^{-2} =$	$5^{-2} =$
$10^{-3} = \frac{1}{1000} = \frac{1}{10^3} = .001$	$2^{-3} =$	$3^{-3} =$	$5^{-3} =$
$10^{-4} = \frac{1}{10000} = \frac{1}{10^4} = .0001$	$2^{-4} =$	$3^{-4} =$	$5^{-4} =$

What goes in for x to make these true?

a) $2^1 \cdot 2^3 = 2^x$ ___   b) $2^5 \cdot 2^8 = 2^x$ ___

c) $2^x \cdot 2^4 = 2^1$ ___   d.) $\left(2^3\right)^5 = 2^x$ ___

Check with other people; then you make up some like these, for them. What can you make different?

5. A new problem, add

$\frac{1}{3} + \frac{1}{9} + \frac{1}{27} + \frac{1}{81}$ ... or written with exponents,

$\frac{1}{3} + \left(\frac{1}{3}\right)^2 + \left(\frac{1}{3}\right)^3 + \left(\frac{1}{3}\right)^4 + \cdots$ on a 9x9 or 27x27

grid and see what happens.

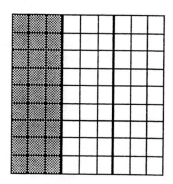

Shown at the right is $\frac{1}{3}$ of the cake.

Now color in $\frac{1}{3}$ of $\frac{1}{3}$ of the cake, or $\frac{1}{9}$ of the cake (don't overlap pieces).

Add the fractions $\frac{1}{3} + \frac{1}{9}$.

Then color in $\frac{1}{3}$ of $\frac{1}{3}$ of $\frac{1}{3}$ of the cake, or $\frac{1}{27}$ of the cake. Add $\frac{1}{3} + \frac{1}{9} + \frac{1}{27}$ and so on.
Use a calculator to do it with decimals also. What is happening? Is this series getting closer and closer to some number? What is the smallest number that is too big? _____

Graph the number of terms vs the partial sums (plot at least 5 points).

So $\frac{1}{3} + \frac{1}{9} + \frac{1}{27} + \frac{1}{81}$ ... goes to what number? _____

6. Now add these: $\frac{1}{4} + \frac{1}{16} + \frac{1}{64} + \frac{1}{256} \cdots$

or $\frac{1}{4} + \left(\frac{1}{4}\right)^2 + \left(\frac{1}{4}\right)^3 + \left(\frac{1}{4}\right)^4 + \cdots$ on an 8x8 or 16x16 grid and see what happens.

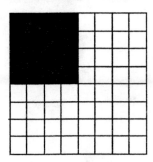

Shown at the right is $\frac{1}{4}$ of the cake.

Now color in $\frac{1}{4}$ of $\frac{1}{4}$ of the cake, or $\frac{1}{16}$ of the cake (don't overlap pieces). Add the fractions $\frac{1}{4} + \frac{1}{16}$.

Then color in $\frac{1}{4}$ of $\frac{1}{4}$ of $\frac{1}{4}$ of the cake, or $\frac{1}{64}$ of the cake. Add $\frac{1}{4} + \frac{1}{16} + \frac{1}{64}$ + and so on. Use a calculator to do it with decimals also. What is happening? Is this series getting closer and closer to some number? What is the smallest number that is too big? _____

Graph the number of terms vs the partial sums.

So $\frac{1}{4} + \frac{1}{16} + \frac{1}{64} + \frac{1}{256} \cdots$ goes to what number?

7. What do we have so far?

$\frac{1}{2} + \frac{1}{4} + \dots$ goes to 1

$\frac{1}{3} + \frac{1}{9} + \dots$ goes to $\frac{1}{2}$

$\frac{1}{4} + \frac{1}{16} + \dots$ goes to $\frac{1}{3}$

Look for a pattern in the numbers above!

Predict : what $\frac{1}{5} + \frac{1}{25} + \dots$ will go to? _____

Try it and test out your prediction.

Can you generalize what $\frac{1}{x} + \left(\frac{1}{x}\right)^2 + \left(\frac{1}{x}\right)^3 + \left(\frac{1}{x}\right)^4 + \cdots$ goes to?

8. Now try a series with the top number of the fraction to start with is not 1, like $\frac{2}{5}$ and $\frac{3}{7}$. So you would have the following series

$$\frac{2}{5} + \left(\frac{2}{5}\right)^2 + \left(\frac{2}{5}\right)^3 + \left(\frac{2}{5}\right)^4 + \cdots = \underline{\hspace{3cm}}$$

Remember, if we raise fractions to powers, we get

$$\left(\frac{2}{5}\right)^2 = \frac{2}{5} \times \frac{2}{5} = \frac{2 \cdot 2}{5 \cdot 5} = \frac{4}{25} \text{ and } \left(\frac{2}{5}\right)^3 = \frac{2}{5} \times \frac{2}{5} \times \frac{2}{5} = \frac{2 \cdot 2 \cdot 2}{5 \cdot 5 \cdot 5} = \frac{8}{125}.$$

$$\frac{3}{7} + \left(\frac{3}{7}\right)^2 + \left(\frac{3}{7}\right)^3 + \left(\frac{3}{7}\right)^4 + \cdots = \underline{\hspace{3cm}}$$

Before you start, **predict** what these sums are going to, and write it as a simple fraction.

9. Do a bunch like these, write the answer as a simple fraction, then try to generalize $\frac{A}{B} + \left(\frac{A}{B}\right)^2 + \left(\frac{A}{B}\right)^3 + \left(\frac{A}{B}\right)^4 + \cdots = \underline{\hspace{3cm}}$

What happens if the top number is larger than the bottom, like $\frac{7}{5} + \left(\frac{7}{5}\right)^2 + \left(\frac{7}{5}\right)^3 + \left(\frac{7}{5}\right)^4 + \cdots$?!?

—————————————————————————————

10. Write a program for a computer or calculator to add up the terms of the infinite series

$\frac{A}{B} + \left(\frac{A}{B}\right)^2 + \left(\frac{A}{B}\right)^3 + \left(\frac{A}{B}\right)^4 + \cdots$, starting with any fraction $\frac{A}{B}$, that is, be able put in any numbers for A and B someone else chooses, then have the machine give the partial sums. How could this program start..hmmm...

Writing a program to do $\frac{A}{B} + \left(\frac{A}{B}\right)^2 + \left(\frac{A}{B}\right)^3 + \left(\frac{A}{B}\right)^4 + \cdots$ will go something like this:

Put a number in for A.

Put a number in for B.

A ÷ B will give the fraction, but we have to raise it to a power, call it N. N will have to be 1 when we start, then increase by 1 afterwards.

We have to add $\left(\frac{A}{B}\right)^N$ to the sum we had before, call that S. Then we need to print S. S will have to be 0 to start.
Then we have to go back to do this procedure again and again.

Let's write this in basic:
```
10 N=1
20 S=0
30 INPUT A
40 INPUT  B
50 S = (A/B)^N +  S
60 PRINT S
70 N = N + 1
80 GOTO 50
```

or.. with a "for-next" loop
```
10 S=0
20 INPUT A
30 INPUT  B
40 for N=1 to 10
50 S = (A/B)^N +  S
60 PRINT S
70 next N
```

11. Assorted problems:
Is .999999... = 1 ? In _____, Mo., a 7th grade class, in a small building, had a great discussion about this. Students came in each day for a week with arguments that it is or it is not. What do you think? Can you give arguments one way or another? What do your friends think?

Change this infinite repeating decimal to a common fraction: .999...

We can write .9999... using an infinite series like one of those above, then find a simple fraction that is equal to it. What does this decimal mean? Using the place values we can write

.9999... = .9 + .09 + .009 + .0009 + ...

$$= \frac{9}{10} + \frac{9}{100} + \frac{9}{1000} + \frac{9}{10000} + \dots$$ If we then factor the 9 out, we get

$$= 9 \cdot \left(\frac{1}{10} + \frac{1}{100} + \frac{1}{1000} + \frac{1}{10000} + \dots \right),$$ and then using exponents

$$= 9 \cdot \left(\frac{1}{10} + \left(\frac{1}{10}\right)^2 + \left(\frac{1}{10}\right)^3 + \left(\frac{1}{10}\right)^4 + \dots \right)$$ and now you finish it from here!

Notice that we can write the sequence of partial sums: .9, .99, .999, .9999, ...
Change the following infinite repeating decimals to common fractions

a) 0.55555...   _____

b) 0.343434... _____

c) 0.1027027... _____

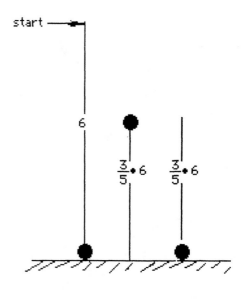

A rubber ball is dropped from a height of 6 feet above a hardwood floor. When it hits the floor it bounces back $\frac{3}{5}$ of the previous height. What is the **total distance** the ball travels before coming to rest?

This picture will get you started:
When the ball drops it travels 6 feet. When it bounces, it goes up $\frac{3}{5}$×6 feet. (Remember, leave it this way, don't get one number). Now when it comes down it travels the same distance it went up, $\frac{3}{5}$×6 feet.

The total distance will be 6 + $\frac{3}{5}$×6 + $\frac{3}{5}$×6 + ... keep going until you find a pattern and an infinite series.

The total distance you get: _____

According to Dunham, Huygens suggested to Leibnitz (circa 1670), that he find the sum of the reciprocals of the triangular numbers.

The first 4 triangular numbers

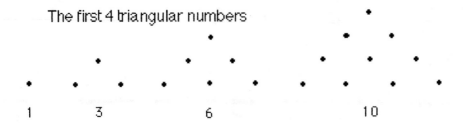

1   3   6   10

The triangular numbers are 1, 3, 6, 10, 15, ... So the problem for Leibnitz was to find

$$S = 1 + \frac{1}{3} + \frac{1}{6} + \frac{1}{10} + \frac{1}{15} + \frac{1}{21} + ...$$

See if you can do it. It's different from the ones we've done before..watch out!

Often when one is trying to solve one problem, it often is necessary to solve a different problem. When Angela started the problem of $\frac{1}{2} + \frac{1}{4}$, she made the $\frac{1}{2}$ this way. This turned out fine because there were 32 squares out of 64 and $\frac{32}{64} = \frac{1}{2}$

32

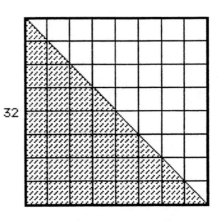

24

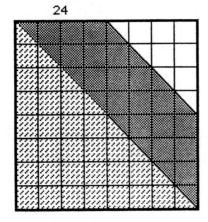

Then she tried to do $\frac{1}{4}$ the same way, diagonally. This new shaded part turned out to be 24 squares, so it was $\frac{24}{64}$ of the cake, which is not $\frac{1}{4}$; $\frac{16}{64} = \frac{1}{4}$ and $\frac{24}{64} > \frac{1}{4}$.

Show $\frac{1}{4}$ of the cake diagonally. How far from the upper-right corner, across the top, must we go to draw it?

In each case below, find the part of the outside square that is shaded in, if you go on forever with the pattern. Take a guess first, then use an infinite series to do it.

a) Area = _____   b) Area = _____

The infinite series for the area in a):

The infinite series for the area in b):

Answer worksheets for **chapter 1**

"7 Year-Olds $\frac{A}{B}+\left(\frac{A}{B}\right)^2+\left(\frac{A}{B}\right)^3+\left(\frac{A}{B}\right)^4+\cdots$ "

(also see Don's videotape "Infinite Series By and For 6 year-olds and up")

1. The first problem is to add up these fractions

$\frac{1}{2}+\frac{1}{4}+\frac{1}{8}+\frac{1}{16}+\frac{1}{32}+\cdots$ *forever !*

Different ways to write $\frac{1}{2}+\frac{1}{4}+\frac{1}{8}$ are $\frac{7}{8}=\frac{3\frac{1}{2}}{4}=\frac{1\frac{3}{4}}{2}$. You can find each of these in the picture if you look carefully!

Different ways to show $\frac{1}{16}$. Since $\frac{1}{16}$ means share the cake with 16 people and shade in one share, or $\frac{1}{16}$ it is also $\frac{1}{2}$ of $\frac{1}{8}=\frac{1}{2}\times\frac{1}{8}=\frac{1}{2}$ of $\frac{1}{2}$ of $\frac{1}{4}=\frac{1}{2}\times\frac{1}{2}\times\frac{1}{4}=\frac{1}{2}\times\frac{1}{2}\times\frac{1}{2}\times\frac{1}{2}=\left(\frac{1}{2}\right)^4$, all names for $\frac{1}{16}$.

A pattern for the partial sums when they are written as $\frac{1}{2}$'s:

$\frac{1}{2},\ \frac{1\frac{1}{2}}{2},\ \frac{1\frac{3}{4}}{2},\ \frac{1\frac{7}{8}}{2},\ \frac{1\frac{15}{16}}{2}$ ... The tops form a sequence which is going to 2, so the whole fraction is going to 1.

A pattern for these partial sums when they are written as $\frac{1}{4}$'s:

$\frac{2}{4},\ \frac{3}{4},\ \frac{3\frac{1}{2}}{4},\ \frac{3\frac{3}{4}}{4},\ \frac{3\frac{7}{8}}{4}$,...The tops form a sequence which is going to 4, so the whole fraction is going to 1.

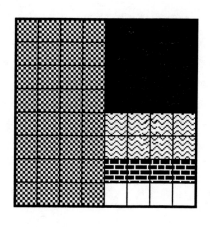

The total shaded portion now is $\frac{1}{2}+\frac{1}{4}+\frac{1}{8}+\frac{1}{16}$ and can be renamed as

$$\frac{15}{16}=\frac{7\frac{1}{2}}{8}=\frac{3\frac{3}{4}}{4}=\frac{1\frac{7}{8}}{2}.$$

$\frac{1}{2} + \frac{1}{4} + \frac{1}{8} + \frac{1}{16}$ can be renamed as

$\frac{8}{16} + \frac{4}{16} + \frac{2}{16} + \frac{1}{16} = \frac{15}{16}$, **or, as**

$\frac{4}{8} + \frac{2}{8} + \frac{1}{8} + \frac{\frac{1}{2}}{8} = \frac{7\frac{1}{2}}{8} = \frac{3\frac{3}{4}}{4} = \frac{1\frac{7}{8}}{2}$.

$\frac{1}{2} + \frac{1}{4} + \frac{1}{8} + \frac{1}{16} + \frac{1}{32} = \frac{31}{32} = \frac{15\frac{1}{2}}{16} = \frac{7\frac{3}{4}}{8} = \frac{3\frac{7}{8}}{4} = \frac{1\frac{15}{16}}{2}$

2. What's going on?

If we look at the partial sums

$\frac{1}{2}, \frac{3}{4}, \frac{7}{8}, \frac{15}{16}, \frac{31}{32}, \frac{63}{64}, \frac{127}{128}, \frac{255}{256}, \frac{511}{512}, \frac{1023}{1024}, \ldots$ there are lots of patterns.

These numbers are getting larger. Why? Because we are adding a new piece each time.

The pieces we're adding are getting smaller, like $\frac{1}{8} < \frac{1}{4}$ and $\frac{1}{16} < \frac{1}{8}$.

The bottom number is doubling each time and are powers of 2; $16 = 2^4$, $32 = 2^5$.

If we add the top and bottom number of each fraction, this sum will be the top number of

the next fraction, like in $\frac{7}{8}$, $7+8 = 15$, which is the top number in $\frac{15}{16}$.

The top number is 1 less than the bottom number.

Will this number ever get as big as 2? Is it getting closer to 2? Yes. Will it ever get bigger

than 1? No. Because the top number is always 1 less than the bottom number since $\frac{15}{16}$ is

less than $\frac{16}{16}$ or 1.

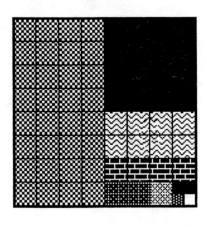

Will the square ever get filled in if we keep going on? No, there will always be 1 of the fraction left, not filled in. Since the bottom numbers are powers of 2, we

could write $\frac{63}{64}$ as $\frac{2^6 - 1}{2^6}$, the sum of the first 6 terms of

the series and generalize these $\frac{1}{2}, \frac{3}{4}, \frac{7}{8}, \frac{15}{16}, \frac{31}{32}, \frac{63}{64},$

$\frac{127}{128}$ as some people $\frac{2^n - 1}{2^n}$, or as others have written

the nth term of this sequence $1 - \frac{1}{2^n}$. As n gets bigger

and bigger, $\frac{1}{2^n}$ goes to zero, so $1 - \frac{1}{2^n}$ goes to 1.

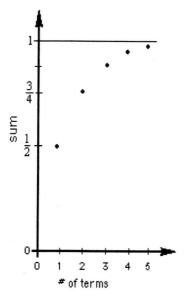

# of terms

3. The graph of the partial sums
$\frac{1}{2}$, $\frac{3}{4}$, $\frac{7}{8}$, $\frac{15}{16}$, and $\frac{31}{32}$ are shown on the left.

These sums as decimals
are .5, .75, .875, .9375, .96875, .984375, .9921875, ...
which is going to .999... or 1.

In the sequence $\frac{1}{2}$, $\frac{1}{4}$, $\frac{1}{8}$, $\frac{1}{16}$, .. $\frac{1}{2^n}$, ... as n gets bigger and bigger, the fraction $\frac{1}{2^n}$ goes to zero.

In the sequence $\left(1-\frac{1}{2}\right)$, $\left(1-\frac{1}{4}\right)$, $\left(1-\frac{1}{8}\right)$, $\left(1-\frac{1}{16}\right)$, .. $\left(1-\frac{1}{2^n}\right)$, as n gets bigger and bigger, $\left(1-\frac{1}{2^n}\right)$ goes to 1.

4. Exponents
The rest of the table is filled in below:

$10^4 = 10000$	$2^4 = 16$	$3^4 = 81$	$5^4 = 625$
$10^3 = 1000$	$2^3 = 8$	$3^3 = 27$	$5^3 = 125$
$10^2 = 100$	$2^2 = 4$	$3^2 = 9$	$5^2 = 25$
$10^1 = 10$	$2^1 = 2$	$3^1 = 3$	$5^1 = 5$
$10^0 = 1$	$2^0 = 1$	$3^0 = 1$	$5^0 = 1$
$10^{-1} = \frac{1}{10^1} = \frac{1}{10} = .1$	$2^{-1} = \frac{1}{2^1} = \frac{1}{2}$	$3^{-1} = \frac{1}{3^1} = \frac{1}{3}$	$5^{-1} = \frac{1}{5^1} = \frac{1}{5}$
$10^{-2} = \frac{1}{10^2} = \frac{1}{100} = .01$	$2^{-2} = \frac{1}{2^2} = \frac{1}{4}$	$3^{-2} = \frac{1}{3^2} = \frac{1}{9}$	$5^{-2} = \frac{1}{5^2} = \frac{1}{25}$
$10^{-3} = \frac{1}{10^3} = \frac{1}{1000} = .001$	$2^{-3} = \frac{1}{2^3} = \frac{1}{8}$	$3^{-3} = \frac{1}{3^3} = \frac{1}{27}$	$5^{-3} = \frac{1}{5^3} = \frac{1}{125}$
$10^{-4} = \frac{1}{10^4} = \frac{1}{10000} = .0001$	$2^{-4} = \frac{1}{2^4} = \frac{1}{16}$	$3^{-4} = \frac{1}{3^4} = \frac{1}{81}$	$5^{-4} = \frac{1}{5^4} = \frac{1}{625}$

What goes in for x to make these true?

a) $2^1 \cdot 2^3 = 2^x$ {4}

 b) $2^5 \cdot 2^8 = 2^x$ {13}

c) $2^x \cdot 2^4 = 2^1$ { -3}

d.) $\left(2^3\right)^5 = 2^x$ {15}

Make up more of these equations for your friends to make true.

5. In finding the sum of the infinite series

$$\frac{1}{3} + \left(\frac{1}{3}\right)^2 + \left(\frac{1}{3}\right)^3 + \left(\frac{1}{3}\right)^4 + \cdots \quad \text{or}$$

$$\frac{1}{3} + \frac{1}{9} + \frac{1}{27} + \frac{1}{81} + \cdots$$

The first term is $\frac{1}{3}$

The sum of the first 2 terms $\frac{1}{3} + \left(\frac{1}{3}\right)^2 = \frac{1}{3} + \frac{1}{3} \times \frac{1}{3} = \frac{1}{3} + \frac{1}{9} = \frac{3}{9} + \frac{1}{9} = \frac{4}{9}$

So the first 2 partial sums are $\frac{1}{3}$ and $\frac{4}{9}$.

The sum of the first 3 terms

$$\frac{1}{3} + \left(\frac{1}{3}\right)^2 + \left(\frac{1}{3}\right)^3 =$$

$$\frac{1}{3} + \frac{1}{9} + \frac{1}{3} \times \frac{1}{3} \times \frac{1}{3} =$$

$$\frac{4}{9} + \frac{1}{27} =$$

$$\frac{4}{9} \times \frac{3}{3} + \frac{1}{27} =$$

$$\frac{12}{27} + \frac{1}{27} = \frac{13}{27}$$

So the first 3 partial sums are

$$\frac{1}{3}, \frac{4}{9}, \frac{13}{27}$$

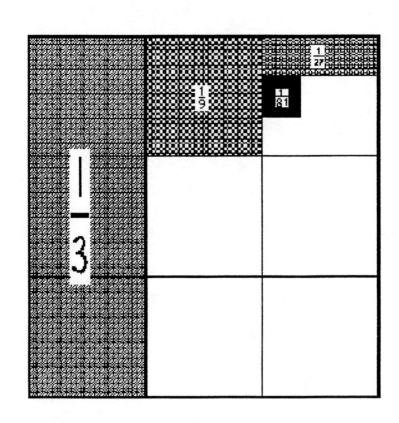

The sum of the first 4 terms is $\frac{1}{3} + \left(\frac{1}{3}\right)^2 + \left(\frac{1}{3}\right)^3 + \left(\frac{1}{3}\right)^4 =$

$$\frac{1}{3} + \frac{1}{3} \times \frac{1}{3} + \frac{1}{3} \times \frac{1}{3} \times \frac{1}{3} + \frac{1}{3} \times \frac{1}{3} \times \frac{1}{3} \times \frac{1}{3} =$$

$$\frac{1}{3} + \frac{1}{9} + \frac{1}{27} + \frac{1}{81} =$$

$$\frac{13}{27} + \frac{1}{81} = \frac{40}{81}$$

The first 6 partial sums are $\quad \frac{1}{3}, \frac{4}{9}, \frac{13}{27}, \frac{40}{81}, \frac{121}{243}, \frac{364}{729}$

Lucas, gr. 7, saw that each partial sum is $\frac{1}{2}$ of the fraction less than $\frac{1}{2}$; for example,

$\frac{1}{2} - \frac{1}{2} \times \frac{1}{81} = \dfrac{40\frac{1}{2}}{81} - \dfrac{\frac{1}{2}}{81} = \frac{40}{81}$ From this fine observation, his work could be generalized to

$\frac{1}{2} - \frac{1}{2} \times \frac{1}{3^n}$, where n is the number of terms. Then as n gets bigger and bigger

$\frac{1}{3^n} \to 0$ and $\frac{1}{2} \times \frac{1}{3^n} \to 0$, so $\frac{1}{2} - \frac{1}{2} \times \frac{1}{3^n} \to \frac{1}{2}$. So $\frac{1}{3} + \frac{1}{9} + \frac{1}{27} + \frac{1}{81} + \bullet\bullet\bullet$ **goes to** $\frac{1}{2}$

6. $\frac{1}{4} + \left(\frac{1}{4}\right)^2 + \left(\frac{1}{4}\right)^3 + \left(\frac{1}{4}\right)^4 + \cdots = \frac{1}{4} + \frac{1}{16} + \frac{1}{64} + \frac{1}{256} + \cdots$

Let's go!

$\frac{1}{4} = .25$

$\frac{1}{4} + \frac{1}{16} = \frac{5}{16} = .3125$

$\frac{1}{4} + \frac{1}{16} + \frac{1}{64} = \frac{21}{64} = .328125$

$\frac{1}{4} + \frac{1}{16} + \frac{1}{64} + \frac{1}{256} = \frac{85}{256} = .33203125$

The partial sums are: $\frac{1}{4}, \frac{5}{16}, \frac{21}{64}, \frac{85}{256}, \frac{341}{1024}, \frac{1365}{4096}, \ldots$ Each term is getting bigger. The top number in the fraction is the sum of the top and bottom of the previous fraction. The decimals seem to go towards .33333... which equals $\frac{1}{3}$.

Hmmm.. Does Lucas' idea still work? Is each partial sum $\frac{1}{3}$ of the fraction less than $\frac{1}{3}$?

For the third partial sum, since $\frac{1}{3} \times 64 = 21\frac{1}{3}$, $\frac{1}{3} - \frac{1}{3} \times \frac{1}{64} = \dfrac{21\frac{1}{3}}{64} - \dfrac{\frac{1}{3}}{64} = \frac{21}{64}$ Yes! This could be generalized to $\frac{1}{3} - \frac{1}{3} \times \frac{1}{4^n}$, where n is the number of terms. Then as n gets bigger and bigger $\frac{1}{4^n} \to 0$ and $\frac{1}{3} \times \frac{1}{4^n} \to 0$, and $\frac{1}{3} - \frac{1}{3} \times \frac{1}{4^n} \to \frac{1}{3}$. This series is getting closer and closer to $\frac{1}{3}$ and the smallest number that is too big is $\frac{1}{3}$.

The graph of the number of terms vs the first
4 partial sums $\frac{1}{4}$, $\frac{5}{16}$, $\frac{21}{64}$, $\frac{85}{256}$, ...for the series

$$\frac{1}{4}+\left(\frac{1}{4}\right)^2+\left(\frac{1}{4}\right)^3+\left(\frac{1}{4}\right)^4+\cdots \quad \text{looks like this:}$$

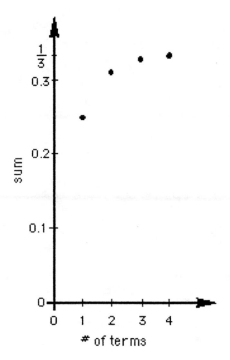

So far we have the series

$\frac{1}{2} + \frac{1}{4} + ...$ goes to 1

$\frac{1}{3} + \frac{1}{9} + ...$ goes to $\frac{1}{2}$

$\frac{1}{4} + \frac{1}{16} + ...$ goes to $\frac{1}{3}$

Did you predict what $\frac{1}{5}+\frac{1}{25}+...$ will go to? $\frac{1}{4}$ right, looking at the pattern.

Generalizing from the pattern above, we get the sum of

$$\frac{1}{x}+\left(\frac{1}{x}\right)^2+\left(\frac{1}{x}\right)^3+\left(\frac{1}{x}\right)^4+\cdots \quad -> \quad \frac{1}{x-1}$$

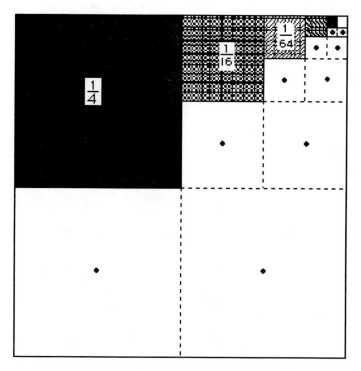

At the left is how Lisa, a high school student in Colorado thought about

$$\frac{1}{4}+\left(\frac{1}{4}\right)^{2}+\left(\frac{1}{4}\right)^{3}+\left(\frac{1}{4}\right)^{4}+\cdots$$ She put

dots in the squares that could never have any part filled and then noticed that the ratio of shaded to not-shaded was 1:2. Since the sum of 1 and 2 is 3, she concluded that the series converges to $\frac{1}{3}$.

How about that!
Do you think Lisa's method works for

$$\frac{1}{3}+\left(\frac{1}{3}\right)^{2}+\left(\frac{1}{3}\right)^{3}+\left(\frac{1}{3}\right)^{4}+\cdots \quad ?$$

Try Lisa's method for

$$\frac{2}{3}+\left(\frac{2}{3}\right)^{2}+\left(\frac{2}{3}\right)^{3}+\left(\frac{2}{3}\right)^{4}+\cdots$$

Try Lucas' method for this also.

8. Starting with fractions with the top not equal to 1:

$$\frac{2}{5}+\left(\frac{2}{5}\right)^{2}+\left(\frac{2}{5}\right)^{3}+\left(\frac{2}{5}\right)^{4}+\cdots \ =\ \frac{2}{3}$$

$$\frac{3}{7}+\left(\frac{3}{7}\right)^{2}+\left(\frac{3}{7}\right)^{3}+\left(\frac{3}{7}\right)^{4}+\cdots \ =\ \frac{3}{4}$$

There is a pattern here $\frac{2}{5} \rightarrow \frac{2}{3} = \frac{2}{5-2}$ and

$$\frac{3}{7} \rightarrow \frac{3}{4} = \frac{3}{7-3} \text{ and generalizing}$$

$$\frac{A}{B} \rightarrow \frac{A}{B-A}, \text{ so } \frac{A}{B}+\left(\frac{A}{B}\right)^{2}+\left(\frac{A}{B}\right)^{3}+\left(\frac{A}{B}\right)^{4}+\cdots \quad \rightarrow \frac{A}{B-A}$$

Jeff, an 11th grader, when asked to $\frac{2}{5}+\left(\frac{2}{5}\right)^{2}+\left(\frac{2}{5}\right)^{3}+\left(\frac{2}{5}\right)^{4}+\cdots$, divided top and bottom of

the fraction by 2 to make it into an equivalent fraction with top 1! Then he used his rule $\frac{1}{x}$

$\rightarrow \frac{1}{x-1}$ to get the sum. So using Jeff's way, $\frac{2}{5} = \frac{2 \div 2}{5 \div 2} = \frac{1}{2.5}$, then using the generalization

for sums with top number 1, he gets $\frac{1}{2.5} \rightarrow \frac{1}{2.5-1} = \frac{1}{1.5} = \frac{2}{3}$. I think Jeff, who hasn't been very

successful trying to memorize the school math, did an elegantly simple and wonderful thing to solve this problem. In more than 15 years working with these infinite series, I had never seen this done so simply. I think this is important because he used something he had just figured out for an easier problem, to solve a harder problem. That to me is really learning to learn.

What happens if the top number is larger than the bottom,

$$\frac{7}{5} + \left(\frac{7}{5}\right)^2 + \left(\frac{7}{5}\right)^3 + \left(\frac{7}{5}\right)^4 + \cdots \quad ?$$

In this case the series doesn't converge to a certain value, it diverges, gets bigger and bigger; or $-1 < \frac{A}{B} < 1$

10. A program for a computer or calculator to add up the terms of the infinite series

$$\frac{A}{B} + \left(\frac{A}{B}\right)^2 + \left(\frac{A}{B}\right)^3 + \left(\frac{A}{B}\right)^4 + \cdots$$

starting with any fraction you choose, $\frac{A}{B}$, where N stands for the exponent, S stands for the partial sum, A for the numerator of the fraction, B for the denominator, T for each term

For Casio FX7000G	For Apple or IBM, in basic
0 -> S :	10 S = 0
? -> A :	20 INPUT A
? -> B :	30 INPUT B
1 -> N :	40 For N = 1 to 20
Lbl 7 :	
(A÷B) x⁄N + S-> S∆	50 S = S + (A/B)^N
N+1->N	60 PRINT S
Goto 7 :	70 Next N

To do $\frac{1}{2} + \frac{1}{4} + \frac{1}{8} \ldots$ on a non-programmable calculator, just press the keys 1÷2 + (1÷2) x^y 2 + (1÷2) x^y 3 + (1÷2) x^y 4 and stop whenever you want. If your calculator doesn't have an exponent key (x^y) then use parentheses and multiplication, like 1÷2 + (1÷2) x(1÷2) + (1÷2) x(1÷2) x(1÷2) and so on. If your calculator doesn't have parentheses, try to do the above, but be careful how your calculator handles the division then multiplication. I would check the calculator against pencil and paper for the first few, to see if they agree.

11. Assorted problems:

Is .999999... = 1? My students came in each day for a week, with arguments like:

$\frac{1}{3}$ = .33333... and

$\frac{2}{3}$ = .66666... so

$\frac{1}{3} + \frac{2}{3} = \frac{3}{3}$ = 1, and .33333... + .66666... = .99999... = 1

and "My father says you need calculus!" To finish the story, one day the whole class, spontaneously, made signs to put around their necks. They were going to march around the school, half the signs saying .999... = 1, the other half of the signs saying .999... is not equal to 1. That was a most exciting and unforgettable day; marching around the school about a math problem! There is a sad ending to this story, however. The principal, upon seeing this excitement, said we couldn't do this, it would upset the school!

Change this infinite repeating decimal to a common fraction: 0.999...
We can write 0.999... using an infinite series like one of those above, then find a simple fraction that is equal to it. What does this decimal mean? Using the place values we can write

.9999... = .9 + .09 + .009 + .0009 + ...

$$= \frac{9}{10} + \frac{9}{100} + \frac{9}{1000} + \frac{9}{10000} + \dots \text{ If we then factor the 9 out, we get}$$

$$= 9 \cdot \left(\frac{1}{10} + \frac{1}{100} + \frac{1}{1000} + \frac{1}{10000} + \dots\right) \text{, and then using exponents}$$

$$= 9 \cdot \left(\frac{1}{10} + \left(\frac{1}{10}\right)^2 + \left(\frac{1}{10}\right)^3 + \left(\frac{1}{10}\right)^4 + \dots\right)$$

Now the infinite series above in the parentheses $= \frac{1}{10-1} = \frac{1}{9}$ from above

So .999... $= 9 \times \frac{1}{9} = 1$

The sequence of partial sums .9, .99, .999, ... goes to 1 also.
Change the following infinite repeating decimals to common fractions

a. $0.55555... = \frac{5}{9}$

b. $0.343434... = \frac{34}{99}$ (the only difference here is that we get powers of $\frac{1}{100}$)

$$0.3434... = \frac{34}{100} + \frac{34}{10000} + \frac{34}{1000000} + \dots$$

$$0.3434... = 34 \cdot \left(\frac{1}{100} + \frac{1}{10000} + \frac{1}{1000000} + \dots\right), \text{ and then using exponents}$$

$$0.3434... = 34 \cdot \left(\frac{1}{100} + \left(\frac{1}{100}\right)^2 + \left(\frac{1}{100}\right)^3 + \left(\frac{1}{100}\right)^4 + \dots\right)$$

$$0.3434... = 34 \times \frac{1}{100-1} = \frac{34}{99}$$

c. $0.1027027... = \frac{1026}{9990}$

$$0.1027027... = 0.1 + 0.0027027027...$$

$$0.1027027... = 0.1 + \frac{1}{10} \times (0.027027027...)$$

$$0.1027027... = 0.1 + \frac{1}{10} \times 27 \times \left(\frac{1}{1000} + \left(\frac{1}{1000}\right)^2 + \left(\frac{1}{1000}\right)^3 + \left(\frac{1}{1000}\right)^4 + \dots\right)$$

$$0.1027027... = 0.1 + \frac{1}{10} \times 27 \times \left(\frac{1}{1000-1}\right) = 0.1 + \frac{1}{10} \times 27 \times \left(\frac{1}{999}\right)$$

$$0.1027027... = 0.1 + \frac{27}{9990} = \frac{1}{10} + \frac{27}{9990} = \frac{999}{9990} + \frac{27}{9990}$$

$$0.1027027... = \frac{1026}{9990}$$

A rubber ball is dropped from a height of 6 feet above a hardwood floor. When it hits the floor it bounces back $\frac{3}{5} \times 6$ of the previous height. What is the total distance the ball travels? When the ball drops, it travels 6 feet. When it bounces, it goes up $\frac{3}{5} \times 6$ feet. Then when it comes down again it comes down the same distance as it went up, $\frac{3}{5} \times 6$ feet. When it

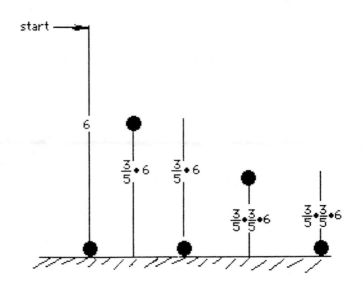

bounces again, it goes up $\frac{3}{5} \times \frac{3}{5} \times 6$ feet. Then when it comes down again it comes down the same distance as it went up, $\frac{3}{5} \times \frac{3}{5} \times 6$ feet. So the total distance will be

$6 \ + \ 2 \times \frac{3}{5} \times 6 \ + \ 2 \times \frac{3}{5} \times \frac{3}{5} \times 6 \ + \ 2 \times \frac{3}{5} \times \frac{3}{5} \times \frac{3}{5} \times 6 \ + ...$ which is an infinite series. What's the next term? If we factor 2×6 out of the 2nd term on, we get

$6 \ + \ 2 \times 6 \times \left(\frac{3}{5} + \left(\frac{3}{5}\right)^2 + \left(\frac{3}{5}\right)^3 + \left(\frac{3}{5}\right)^4 + \cdots \right)$

Since the infinite series $\frac{3}{5} + \left(\frac{3}{5}\right)^2 + \left(\frac{3}{5}\right)^3 + \left(\frac{3}{5}\right)^4 + \ ...$ goes to $\frac{3}{5-3} = \frac{3}{2}$

Then $6 + 2 \times 6 \times \frac{3}{2} = 6 + 18$. The total distance the ball travels is 24 feet.

===

Leibnitz did this to find the sum of the reciprocals of the triangular numbers:

$S = 1 + \frac{1}{3} + \frac{1}{6} + \frac{1}{10} + \frac{1}{15} + \frac{1}{21} + ...$

He took $\frac{1}{2}$ of both sides to get

$\frac{1}{2} \times S \ = \ \frac{1}{2} + \frac{1}{6} + \frac{1}{12} + \frac{1}{20} + \frac{1}{30} + \frac{1}{42} + \ ...$

Leibnitz noticed that $\frac{1}{2} = 1 - \frac{1}{2}$ and $\frac{1}{6} = \frac{1}{2} - \frac{1}{3}$ and so on, so he wrote

$\frac{1}{2} \times S = \left(1 - \frac{1}{2}\right) + \left(\frac{1}{2} - \frac{1}{3}\right) + \left(\frac{1}{3} - \frac{1}{4}\right) + \left(\frac{1}{4} - \frac{1}{5}\right) + ...$ and

$\frac{1}{2} \times S = 1 - \frac{1}{2} + \frac{1}{2} - \frac{1}{3} + \frac{1}{3} - \frac{1}{4} + \frac{1}{4} - \frac{1}{5} + \frac{1}{5} - ...$, so everything after the 1 goes to zero

$\frac{1}{2} \times S = 1$ and $S = 2$. So $1 + \frac{1}{3} + \frac{1}{6} + \frac{1}{10} + \frac{1}{15} + \frac{1}{21} + ... \rightarrow 2$

Often when one is trying to solve one problem, it is necessary to solve a different problem. Angela, in trying to get $\frac{1}{4}$ diagonally, realized the 24- square piece was too big because $\frac{24}{64} > \frac{16}{64} = \frac{1}{4}$. The 14- square piece was too small because $\frac{14}{64} < \frac{16}{64} = \frac{1}{4}$

24

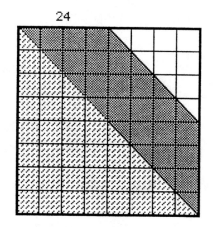

14

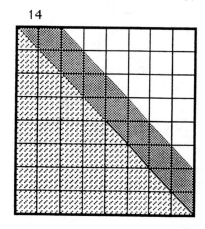

Then Angela saw a pattern in the area of the diagonal strips, and realized we couldn't get a 16-square piece if we stayed on whole number of squares.

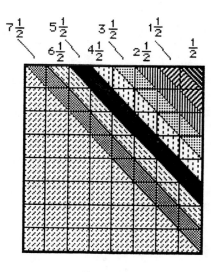

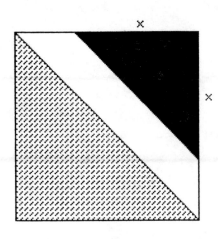

We used the following argument to see how far over along the top of the square we would have to cut diagonally to get $\frac{1}{4}$ of the cake. We agreed that the area of the black triangle is $\frac{1}{4}$ of 64 or $\frac{1}{2}$ of 32 or 16 squares. We let x be the distance from the upper right corner and the length of the two equal sides of the triangle.

The area of the triangle $\frac{1}{2} \cdot x \cdot x = 16$; $\frac{1}{2} x^2 = 16$

So $x^2 = 32$ and $x = \sqrt{32} = 4\sqrt{2} \approx 5.6$. So we would have to go a distance of $\sqrt{32}$ or about 5.6 units from the upper right hand corner of the square in order to shade in $\frac{1}{4}$ of the square.

The shaded portion of the square at the right, if you keep going forever, is:

$4 \times \frac{1}{8} + 4 \times \frac{1}{4} \times \frac{1}{8} + 4 \times \frac{1}{4} \times \frac{1}{4} \times \frac{1}{8} + 4 \times \frac{1}{4} \times \frac{1}{4} \times \frac{1}{4} \times \frac{1}{8} +$

... (because there are 4 of each piece, the largest piece is $\frac{1}{8}$ of the whole square, and each smaller piece is $\frac{1}{4}$ of the previous one--why?)

$= 4 \times \frac{1}{8} + 4 \times \frac{1}{8} \times \left(\frac{1}{4} + \left(\frac{1}{4}\right)^2 + \left(\frac{1}{4}\right)^3 + \left(\frac{1}{4}\right)^4 + \cdots \right) =$

$= \frac{4}{8} + \frac{4}{8} \times \frac{1}{3} = \frac{1}{2} + \frac{1}{6} = \frac{2}{3}$. The shaded portion at the

right, if you keep going forever, is $\frac{2}{3}$ of the whole square.

Intuitively, it looks like this shaded portion at the left will be $\frac{1}{4}$ of the square; let's do it:

The largest piece is $\frac{1}{8}$ of the whole square, as before, and the next smaller piece is $\frac{1}{2}$ of the previous piece (why?). So we have

$\frac{1}{8} + \frac{1}{2} \times \frac{1}{8} + \frac{1}{2} \times \frac{1}{2} \times \frac{1}{8} + \frac{1}{2} \times \frac{1}{2} \times \frac{1}{2} \times \frac{1}{8} + \ldots =$

$\frac{1}{8} + \frac{1}{8} \times \left(\frac{1}{2} + \left(\frac{1}{2}\right)^2 + \left(\frac{1}{2}\right)^3 + \left(\frac{1}{2}\right)^4 + \cdots \right) = \frac{1}{8} + \frac{1}{8} \times 1 = \frac{2}{8} =$

$\frac{1}{4}$. So you were right if you said $\frac{1}{4}$ at the start.

Questions worksheets for **chapter 2**
"Brad's: Share 6 cookies with 7 people"

Major suggestion: Use 3x5 cards for the cookies and scissors to cut them. **Don't** use round cookies or pies, because the size of the pieces gets impossible to determine. You have to have an easy way to answer the question "How many of these pieces make a whole cookie?" **Try to find patterns in all your work.**

1. Try this: You have **5 cookies** to share between **3 people** (including yourself).

If we each are to get the same amount, how many cookies will we each get?

_____

Now try sharing **5 cookies** between **3 people** *another way*. See how many ways you can do it! Compare your method with your friend's and the two ways shown below.

Tara's way of sharing **5 cookies** between **3 people** :

Tara, age 5, shared 1 cookie with each person. Then she cut the 2 leftover cookies into 2 equal pieces each.

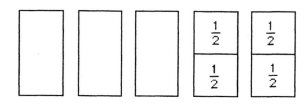

She shared $\frac{1}{2}$ of a cookie with each person. Each person then then had 1 + $\frac{1}{2}$ of a cookie, with $\frac{1}{2}$ of a cookie left over.

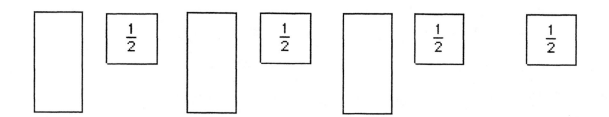

Then Tara cut the left-over $\frac{1}{2}$ of a cookie into 3 pieces. She named these new pieces. Since 3 of them make a $\frac{1}{2}$ cookie, 6 make a whole cookie, so each piece is $\frac{1}{6}$ of a cookie.

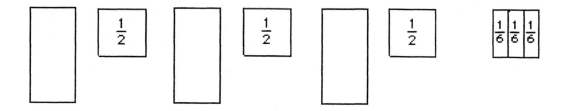

Now each person gets one of these $\frac{1}{6}$'s and all the cookies are shared equally.

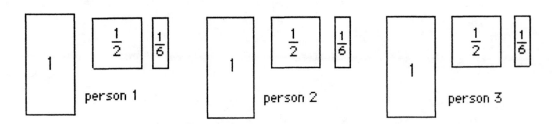

So each person gets $1 + \frac{1}{2} + \frac{1}{6}$ of a cookie using Tara's method.

Tara, at one point said: "If I had a cookie and I split it into pieces sometimes people think it's more than one cookie, but it really isn't more than one cookie. It is math".

2. Brad's way of sharing **5 cookies** between **3 people**. This is very exciting because it leads to an infinite series! Brad had just finished 2nd grade when he did a cookie-sharing problem like this.

Brad's method works this way, pretend **your scissors can only cut into 2 equal pieces**. Share the cookies when you can, then you must cut all leftover pieces into 2 **equal** pieces. Here we go, same problem--share **5 cookies** between **3 people.**

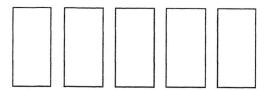

Can we share these 5 cookies with 3 people? Yes.

Each person gets 1 cookie, and there are 2 cookies leftover. Can we share the 2 leftover pieces with 3 people? No.

What do we have to do?

Cut each leftover piece into 2 equal pieces.

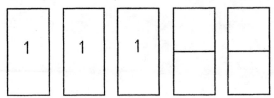

How many of each of these new pieces make a whole cookie? 2, so each is $\frac{1}{2}$ of a

cookie.

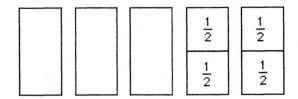

Can we share four $\frac{1}{2}$'s with three people?

Sure. Each person gets $\frac{1}{2}$ (one-half, or better, one-twoth) of a cookie.

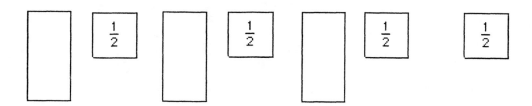

So far each person now has $1 + \frac{1}{2}$ of a cookie and we have one leftover $\frac{1}{2}$. We aren't finished yet because we haven't used up all the cookies.

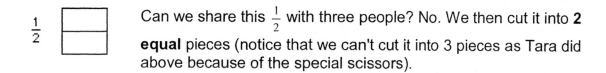

$\frac{1}{2}$ Can we share this $\frac{1}{2}$ with three people? No. We then cut it into **2 equal** pieces (notice that we can't cut it into 3 pieces as Tara did above because of the special scissors).

We'll name these new pieces first. How many make a whole cookie?

Well 2 of them make $\frac{1}{2}$ of a cookie, and 4 make a whole cookie. So each of these 2 new

pieces is $\frac{1}{4}$ of a cookie.

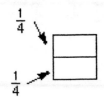

$\frac{1}{4}$

$\frac{1}{4}$

Do we have enough of these $\frac{1}{4}$'s to share with 3 people?

Since we have only 2 pieces, we don't have enough $\frac{1}{4}$'s to share

with 3 people. So each person gets $\frac{0}{4}$.

So far each person has $1 + \frac{1}{2} + \frac{0}{4}$ of a cookie. Notice, if we can't share one size piece,
we write zero of them anyway. This will help us find a pattern.

What do we have to do now?

We have to cut each $\frac{1}{4}$ into 2 equal pieces.

We'll name these new smallest pieces.

How many make a whole cookie?

Well 4 of them make $\frac{1}{2}$ of a cookie, and 8 make a whole cookie. So each of these 4 new pieces is $\frac{1}{8}$ of a cookie.

$\frac{1}{8}$ ⟶

Can we share these four $\frac{1}{8}$'s with 3 people? Sure. Each person gets one of these $\frac{1}{8}$'s and there is one of the $\frac{1}{8}$'s leftover..

Now what does each person have?

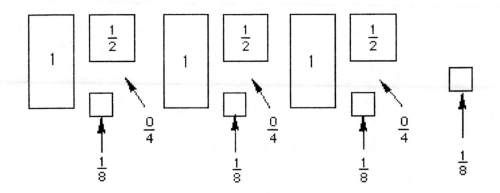

So far each person has $1 + \frac{1}{2} + \frac{0}{4} + \frac{1}{8}$ of a cookie, with $\frac{1}{8}$ of a cookie leftover.

Look at what each person has so far, look at this sum. Can you predict, without much work, what the next 4 terms will be? Look for a pattern in the tops of the fractions, look for a pattern in the bottoms.

Since there is only one $\frac{1}{8}$, cutting it into 2 equal parts, each $\frac{1}{16}$, there will not be enough $\frac{1}{16}$'s to share, so each person will get $\frac{0}{16}$. Cutting the two $\frac{1}{16}$'s, gives four $\frac{1}{32}$'s, which can be shared, and so on. The tops go 1, 0, 1, 0, and continue that way. The bottoms double each time-- 2, 4, 8, 16, 32, 64, 128, 256, and so on.

So, if we do this **forever**, each person will get

$$1 + \frac{1}{2} + \frac{0}{4} + \frac{1}{8} + \frac{0}{16} + \frac{1}{32} + \frac{0}{64} + \frac{1}{128} + \ldots \text{ cookies!}$$

(A lot of crumbs, right?). The 3 dots means the series or sum goes on forever and the sum is called an infinite series.

Sharing 5 cookies between 3 people is the same as saying 5 divided by 3, written as $3\overline{)5}$ or

$5 \div 3$ or

$\frac{5}{3} = 1 + \frac{1}{2} + \frac{1}{6} = 1 + \frac{2}{3} = 1 + \frac{1}{2} + \frac{0}{4} + \frac{1}{8} + \frac{0}{16} + \frac{1}{32} + \frac{0}{64} + \frac{1}{128} + \ldots$ = other names you

might have found.

Use your calculator to do $5 \div 3$.

Write your answer down -- it will be a decimal.   _____

Now on your calculator do $1 + 1 \div 2 + 0 \div 4 + 1 \div 8 + 0 \div 16 + 1 \div 32 + 0 \div 64 + 1 \div 128 + \ldots$, going at least to $1 \div 2048$ to see if the sum is going to $5 \div 3$.

$1 + \frac{1}{2} + \frac{0}{4} + \frac{1}{8} + \frac{0}{16} + \frac{1}{32} + \frac{0}{64} + \frac{1}{128} + \frac{0}{256} + \frac{1}{512} + \frac{0}{1024} + \frac{1}{2048}$ as a decimal is

_____

You make up some cookie-sharing problems now, using the **cut-only-into-2-pieces scissors.**

Make up some cookie-sharing problems for a friend and have them make some for you.

When we shared 5 cookies with 3 people, two ways of writing the answer were:

$$1 + \frac{2}{3} = 1 + \frac{1}{2} + \frac{0}{4} + \frac{1}{8} + \frac{0}{16} + \frac{1}{32} + \frac{0}{64} + \frac{1}{128} + \ldots$$

Since there is a 1 on each side, the $\frac{2}{3}$ must equal the infinite series that's left

$$\frac{2}{3} = \frac{1}{2} + \frac{0}{4} + \frac{1}{8} + \frac{0}{16} + \frac{1}{32} + \frac{0}{64} + \frac{1}{128} + \ldots$$

In chapter 1 we found that $\frac{2}{3} = \frac{2}{5} + \left(\frac{2}{5}\right)^2 + \left(\frac{2}{5}\right)^3 + \left(\frac{2}{5}\right)^4 + \cdots$

How about that!

The following questions assume the cutting scissors are **cut-only-into-2-equal- pieces** scissors; in other words, we are only using halves (twoths), quarters (fourths), eighths and so on.

Now if $\dfrac{2}{3} = \dfrac{1}{2} + \dfrac{0}{4} + \dfrac{1}{8} + \dfrac{0}{16} + \dfrac{1}{32} + \dfrac{0}{64} + \dfrac{1}{128} + \ldots$

what would the infinite series be for $\dfrac{1}{3}$? (Clue: how is $\dfrac{1}{3}$ related to $\dfrac{2}{3}$?)

_____

Look for patterns, what do you see in the $\dfrac{1}{3}$'s?

What would the infinite series be for $\frac{1}{5}$ (share 1 cookie with 5 people using the special 2-equal-cut scissors)? $\frac{2}{5}$? $\frac{3}{5}$? $\frac{4}{5}$? $\frac{5}{5}$?

$$\frac{1}{5} = \underline{\hspace{4cm}}$$

$$\frac{2}{5} = \underline{\hspace{4cm}}$$

$$\frac{3}{5} = \underline{\hspace{4cm}}$$

$$\frac{4}{5} = \underline{\hspace{4cm}}$$

$$\frac{5}{5} = \underline{\hspace{4cm}}$$

What patterns do you see in the infinite series for the fifths?

Make up some questions about these infinite series. Like, what happens if we add two infinite series. What would you get if you added the infinite series for $\frac{1}{3}$ and the infinite series for $\frac{2}{3}$? Write the answer as an infinite series.

3. Write infinite series as a bimal

In writing the infinite series I find it easier after a while, to write the series as a **bimal**. A bimal is analogous to a decimal--in a decimal the places are powers of ten, here they are powers of two.

So for $\frac{2}{3} = \frac{1}{2} + \frac{0}{4} + \frac{1}{8} + \frac{0}{16} + \frac{1}{32} + \frac{0}{64} + \ldots$ we could also write this as a bimal

$$\frac{2}{3} = .101010\ldots$$

See if you can write bimals for the infinite series in fifths you found above.

$$\frac{1}{5} = \underline{\hspace{4cm}}$$

$$\frac{2}{5} = \underline{\hspace{4cm}}$$

What would the infinite series (& bimal) be for $\frac{1}{7}$? $\frac{2}{7}$? Is there a patterns for the $\frac{1}{7}$'s ?

Do lots of problems like these. Make up some for your friends. Get them to make some for you. Share your discoveries.

4. Write a program on a calculator or computer which when you put in the top and bottom of a fraction, the machine will give the 0's and 1's in the infinite series or bimal.

5. Other special scissors
What if you did the original problem-- share **5** cookies between **3** people, but this time your special scissors cut only into **ten** pieces...What would you end up with as an answer?

_____

What if you did the original problem-- share **5** cookies between **3** people, but this time your special scissors cut only into **five** pieces...What would you end up with as an answer?

_____

Make up new problems like these. See what you find out.

6. Find the simple fraction equal to an infinite series.
Here's another thing I've been working on. Let's go backwards. Suppose I give you the infinite series

$$\frac{1}{2} + \frac{1}{4} + \frac{0}{8} + \frac{1}{16} + \frac{1}{32} + \frac{0}{64} + \ldots$$ or its bimal, .110110... , find the **simple fraction** equal

to this infinite series.

If I'm dealing with infinite repeating **decimals**, I know that

$.1111... = \frac{1}{9} = \frac{1}{10-1}$ and $.4444... = \frac{4}{9} = \frac{4}{10-1}$

$.010101... = \frac{1}{99} = \frac{1}{100-1}$ and $.212121... = \frac{21}{99} = \frac{21}{100-1}$ and $.1 \times .123 = .0123$ and so on.

Lots of patterns.
Similar patterns exist for **bimals**.
To change .110110... to a simple fraction, I get the repeating group, .110, or

$\frac{1}{2} + \frac{1}{4} + \frac{0}{8}$. I change these to eighths and add them, $\frac{4}{8} + \frac{2}{8} + \frac{0}{8} = \frac{6}{8}$, then I take the

same top number, 6, and the bottom number less 1, and the answer is

$\frac{6}{8-1} = \frac{6}{7} = .110110...$

Here are a couple of others to try:

a) 0.100100... =_____   b) 0.1001110011...= _____   c) 0.100100... = _____

You make up some problems like these for someone else.

Have a friend make some for you.

Explore !! Send me your discoveries.

Try multiplying the infinite series for, say $\frac{1}{3} \times \frac{1}{5}$, what infinite series do you get. This is

something I've just started working on!

Answer worksheets for **chapter 2**
"Brad's: Share 6 cookies with 7 people"

1. Other ways to share **5 cookies**
between **3 people**

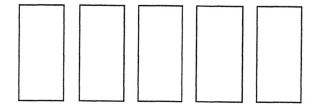

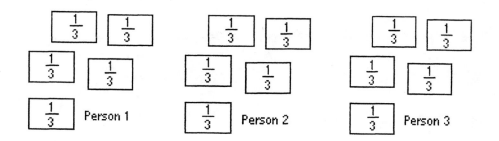

Cut each original piece into 3 pieces, each piece being $\frac{1}{3}$ of a cookie.

Then each of the **3** people gets $\frac{5}{3}$ of a cookie, or $\frac{5}{3} = \frac{3}{3} + \frac{2}{3} = 1 + \frac{2}{3} = 1\frac{2}{3}$. Make sure you can write these fractions different ways like this. Notice that $3 \times \frac{5}{3} = \frac{5}{3} + \frac{5}{3} + \frac{5}{3} = \frac{15}{3} = 5$, the number of cookies we had to start with.

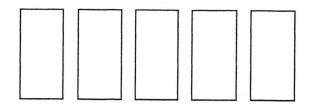

Julie's way to share **5 cookies** between **3 people**:

Each person gets 1 cookie.

Julie took one of the left-over cookies and cut it into 3 pieces, each piece being $\frac{1}{3}$ of a cookie. She shared these pieces with each person.

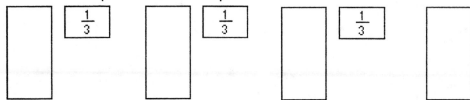

So each person now had $1 + \frac{1}{3}$ of a cookie, with one left over.

She then cut the left-over cookie into 4 pieces, $\frac{1}{4}$'s, and shared 3 of these pieces, one for each person.

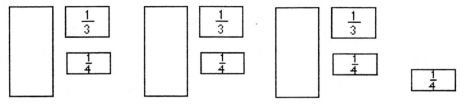

The remaining $\frac{1}{4}$ she cut into 3 equal pieces. Since 12 of these make a whole cookie, each is $\frac{1}{12}$ of a cookie and she shared these equally with each person.

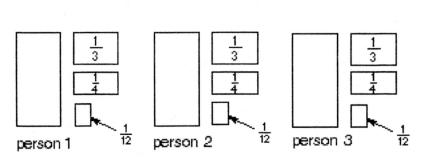

So each person gets $1 + \frac{1}{3} + \frac{1}{4} + \frac{1}{12}$ of a cookie.

So there are **many ways** to share 5 cookies between 3 people.

Here are some other problems young people have done:
Marie (age 7) saw a pattern when she shared different numbers of cookies between 3 people:

Share **5 c, 3 p** -- each person gets $1\frac{2}{3} = \frac{5}{3}$ cookies

Share **4 c, 3 p** -- each person gets $1\frac{1}{3}$ = $\frac{4}{3}$ cookies

Share **3 c, 3 p** -- each person gets 1 = $\frac{3}{3}$ cookie

Share **7 c, 3 p** -- each person gets $2\frac{1}{3}$ = $\frac{7}{3}$ cookies

Share **100 c, 3 p** each person gets $33\frac{1}{3}$ = $\frac{100}{3}$ cookies, then she generalized

Share **n cookies, 3 p** each person gets $\frac{n}{3}$ cookies!

Share **5 cookies, 4 people,** by Robin
-- a very interesting sequence.
Robin, age 7, shared 1 cookie with each
person, then cut the remaining one this
way:

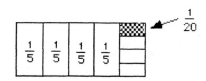

Each person received $1 + \frac{1}{5} + \frac{1}{20}$ of a

cookie.

The next week she did the same problem,
but cut the remaining cookie this way:

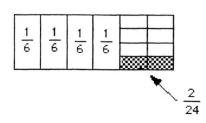

So each person got $1 + \frac{1}{6} + \frac{2}{24}$ of a cookie !

The first way was $1 + \frac{1}{5} + \frac{1}{20}$. Can you

predict what she'll do next? I could not
predict what Robin would do next, but I
see a pattern in what she has done so far
and from that I can predict a next one.
Can you?

2. Brad's way

What would the infinite series be for $\frac{1}{3}$? $\frac{2}{3}$ = $\frac{1}{2}$ + $\frac{0}{4}$ + $\frac{1}{8}$ + $\frac{0}{16}$ + $\frac{1}{32}$ + $\frac{0}{64}$ + $\frac{1}{128}$ + ...

Since $\frac{1}{3}$ is $\frac{1}{2}$ of $\frac{2}{3}$, we could take $\frac{1}{2}$ of each term in the series for $\frac{2}{3}$:

$\frac{2}{3}$ = $\frac{1}{2}$ + $\frac{0}{4}$ + $\frac{1}{8}$ + $\frac{0}{16}$ + $\frac{1}{32}$ + $\frac{0}{64}$ + $\frac{1}{128}$ + ... (since $\frac{1}{2}$ of $\frac{1}{2}$ = $\frac{1}{4}$ and $\frac{1}{2}$ of $\frac{1}{8}$ = $\frac{1}{16}$ and so on)

$\frac{1}{2}$ of $\frac{2}{3}$ = $\frac{1}{2}$ x $\frac{1}{2}$ + $\frac{1}{2}$ x $\frac{0}{4}$ + $\frac{1}{2}$ x $\frac{1}{8}$ + $\frac{1}{2}$ x $\frac{0}{16}$ + ..., so $\frac{1}{3}$ = $\frac{0}{2}$ + $\frac{1}{4}$ + $\frac{0}{8}$ + $\frac{1}{16}$ + $\frac{0}{32}$ + $\frac{1}{64}$ + $\frac{0}{128}$ + ...

Or we could have started with the problem "Share 1 cookie with 3 people" and using the
special scissors, arrived at this same answer. Notice in the infinite series for $\frac{1}{3}$, the tops of
the fractions are 0, 1, 0, 1, ... and in the bottoms 2, 4, 8, 16, 32, ... doubling each time,
these numbers are powers of 2. $2 = 2^1$, $4 = 2^2$, $8 = 2^3$, $16 = 2^4$, $32 = 2^5$, and so on.
What would the infinite series be for $\frac{1}{5}$ (share 1 cookie with 5 people and use the

special scissors)?
Cut the 1 cookie into 2 equal pieces. 2 pieces are not enough to share with 5 people. So

each person gets $\frac{0}{2}$. Cut the 2 pieces each into 2 equal pieces, getting 4 pieces, each $\frac{1}{4}$. Can you share 4 pieces with 5 people? No. So each person gets $\frac{0}{4}$. Cut each of the 4 pieces into 2 equal pieces, getting 8 pieces, each $\frac{1}{8}$. We can share 8 pieces with 5 people. Each person gets $\frac{1}{8}$ of a cookie, with 3 of the eighths left over. So far each person has $\frac{0}{2} + \frac{0}{4} + \frac{1}{8}$ of a cookie, with 3 of the eighths left over. Cut each of these 3 pieces into two equal pieces, getting 6 pieces, each $\frac{1}{16}$. We can share 6 pieces with 5 people. Each person gets $\frac{1}{16}$ of a cookie, with 1 of the sixteenths left over. So far each person has $\frac{0}{2} + \frac{0}{4}$ $+ \frac{1}{8} + \frac{1}{16}$ of a cookie, with 1 of the sixteenths left over. Since we have 1 piece left, that's like starting from the beginning when we had 1 cookie. Now, however, when we cut , we'll have $\frac{1}{32}$'s , then $\frac{1}{64}$'s , then $\frac{1}{128}$'s and $\frac{1}{256}$'s and so on, but the pattern **0, 0, 1, 1** will be the same. So if we share 1 cookie with 5 people each person will get $\frac{0}{2} + \frac{0}{4} + \frac{1}{8} + \frac{1}{16} + \frac{0}{32} + \frac{0}{64} +$ $\frac{1}{128} + \frac{1}{256} + \ldots$ of a cookie. If we used the regular scissors, we could cut the cookie into 5 equal pieces and each person would get $\frac{1}{5}$ of a cookie.

So $\frac{1}{5} = \frac{0}{2} + \frac{0}{4} + \frac{1}{8} + \frac{1}{16} + \frac{0}{32} + \frac{0}{64} + \frac{1}{128} + \frac{1}{256} + \ldots$ The infinite series for

$\frac{2}{5} = \frac{0}{2} + \frac{1}{4} + \frac{1}{8} + \frac{0}{16} + \frac{0}{32} + \frac{1}{64} + \frac{1}{128} + \frac{0}{256} + \ldots$ This can be written as the bimal

.011001100110... or $.\overline{0110}$, with the part under the line repeating forever.

$\frac{3}{5} = \frac{1}{2} + \frac{0}{4} + \frac{0}{8} + \frac{1}{16} + \frac{1}{32} + \frac{0}{64} + \frac{0}{128} + \frac{1}{256} + \ldots = .\overline{1001}$; $\frac{4}{5} = \frac{1}{2} + \frac{1}{4} + \frac{0}{8} + \frac{0}{16} + \frac{1}{32} + \frac{1}{64} + \frac{0}{128} + \frac{0}{256} +$

$\ldots = .\overline{1100}$; and $\frac{5}{5} = \frac{1}{2} + \frac{1}{4} + \frac{1}{8} + \frac{1}{16} + \frac{1}{32} + \frac{1}{64} + \frac{1}{128} + \frac{1}{256} + \ldots = .\overline{1111} = 1$

What would the infinite series (& bimal) be for $\frac{1}{7}$? $\frac{2}{7}$? Is there a patterns for the $\frac{1}{7}$'s ?

$\frac{1}{7} = \frac{0}{2} + \frac{0}{4} + \frac{1}{8} + \frac{0}{16} + \frac{0}{32} + \frac{1}{64} + \ldots = .\overline{001}$ $\frac{4}{7} = \frac{1}{2} + \frac{0}{4} + \frac{0}{8} + \frac{1}{16} + \frac{0}{32} + \frac{0}{64} + \ldots = .\overline{100}$

$\frac{2}{7} = \frac{0}{2} + \frac{1}{4} + \frac{0}{8} + \frac{0}{16} + \frac{1}{32} + \frac{0}{64} + \ldots = .\overline{010}$ $\frac{5}{7} = \frac{1}{2} + \frac{0}{4} + \frac{1}{8} + \frac{1}{16} + \frac{0}{32} + \frac{1}{64} + \ldots = .\overline{101}$

$\frac{3}{7} = \frac{0}{2} + \frac{1}{4} + \frac{1}{8} + \frac{0}{16} + \frac{1}{32} + \frac{1}{64} + \ldots = .\overline{011}$ $\frac{6}{7} = \frac{1}{2} + \frac{1}{4} + \frac{0}{8} + \frac{1}{16} + \frac{1}{32} + \frac{0}{64} + \ldots = .\overline{110}$

4. A program to change any fraction $\frac{T}{B}$ to its bimal; it gives a decimal whole number

first if T>B, then the 0's and 1's for the numerators of the terms of the binary series:

FX7000G	Basic
? -> T △	10 c=0
? -> B △	20 INPUT t
INT(T ÷ B) △	30 INPUT b
T - B* INT(T ÷ B) -> N:	40 PRINT INT (t/b);
Lbl 5:	50 n= t- b*INT(t/b)
N * 2 -> N:	60 n=n * 2
N > B => Goto 7:	70 c=c+1
N ≤ B => Goto 9:	80 IF c>10 THEN STOP
Lbl 7:	90 IF n>b THEN GOTO 110
1->X △	100 IF n<=b THEN GOTO 150
N-B ->N:	110 x=1
Goto 5:	120 PRINT x;
Lbl 9 :	130 n=n-b
0->X △	140 GOTO 60
Goto 5	150 x=0
N.B. This type of program can be used	160 PRINT x;
with any new programmable calculator.	170 GOTO 60
	180 END

5. Using the **special scissors that cut into 10-equal pieces**: Share 5 cookies with 3 people, but this time your special scissors cut only into **ten** equal pieces...Each person gets 1 whole cookie, with 2 leftover.

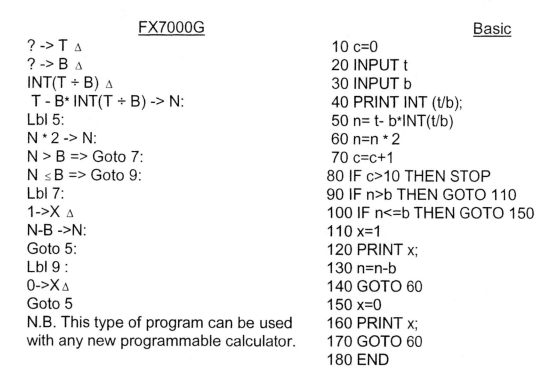

Then cut the 2 leftovers cookies, each into **ten** equal pieces, called $\frac{1}{10}$'s . There are 20 of these $\frac{1}{10}$'s.

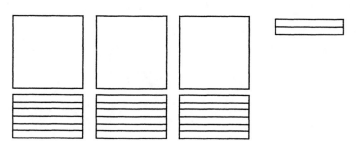

Each of the 3 people can get 6 tenths, with 2 tenths left over. So at this point each person has

$1 + \frac{6}{10}$ of a cookie. The 2 tenths are then cut into **ten** pieces each. These 20 smaller pieces are each $\frac{1}{10}$ of $\frac{1}{10} = \frac{1}{100}$ of a cookie. These again can be shared, each person getting 6, with 2 of these hundredths left over.

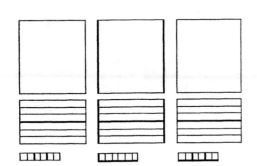

So each person gets

$1 + \frac{6}{10} + \frac{6}{100}$ and this pattern keeps

going forever. Each person gets

$1 + \frac{6}{10} + \frac{6}{100} + \frac{6}{1000} + \frac{6}{10000} + \frac{6}{100000}$ ... or as

a **decimal**, 1.6666...

Notice, now we have different names for $\frac{2}{3}$ using different, but equal infinite series !

$$\frac{2}{3} = \frac{6}{10} + \frac{6}{100} + \frac{6}{1000} + \frac{6}{10000} + \frac{6}{100000} \ldots = .66666...\text{(a decimal)} = \frac{1}{2} + \frac{0}{4} + \frac{1}{8} + \frac{0}{16} + \frac{1}{32} + \frac{0}{64} +$$

$$\frac{1}{128} + \ldots = .1010...\text{(a bimal)}$$

Using the **special scissors that cut into 5-equal pieces**: Share **5 cookies with 3 people**, but this time your special scissors cut only into **five** equal pieces...Each person gets 1 whole cookie, with 2 leftover.

We cut each whole cookie into 5 pieces, each $\frac{1}{5}$. We now have 10 of these which we can share with 3 people.

Each person can get 3 of the $\frac{1}{5}$'s, with $\frac{1}{5}$ left over. At this point each person has $1 + \frac{3}{5}$ of a cookie.

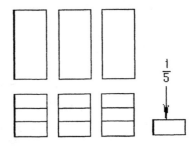

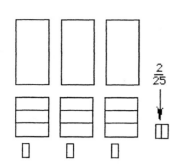

We then cut the $\frac{1}{5}$ into 5 equal pieces, each $\frac{1}{25}$ of a cookie. There are 5 of these $\frac{1}{25}$'s, which can be shared with 3 people.

Each person now has $1 + \frac{3}{5} + \frac{1}{25}$ of a cookie with $\frac{2}{25}$ left over.

We cut each $\frac{1}{25}$ of a cookie into 5 pieces, each $\frac{1}{125}$. We now have 10 of these, which we can share between 3 people, with $\frac{1}{125}$ left over.

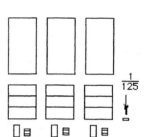

At this point each person has
$1 + \frac{3}{5} + \frac{1}{25} + \frac{3}{125}$ of a cookie.

Notice a pattern emerges, we can predict the infinite series; each person gets
$1 + \frac{3}{5} + \frac{1}{25} + \frac{3}{125} + \frac{1}{625} + \dots$ of a cookie. Now we have another name for $\frac{2}{3}$ an using infinite series !

$\frac{2}{3} = \frac{6}{10} + \frac{6}{100} + \frac{6}{1000} + \frac{6}{10000} + \frac{6}{100000} \dots = .66666\dots$(a decimal) $= \frac{1}{2} + \frac{0}{4} + \frac{1}{8} + \frac{0}{16} + \frac{1}{32} + \frac{0}{64} + \frac{1}{128} + \dots$

$= .1010\dots$(a bimal) $= \frac{3}{5} + \frac{1}{25} + \frac{3}{125} + \frac{1}{625} + \dots = .3131_5\dots$ (as a pentamal?)

6. Change the following infinite bimals to simple fractions:
a) $0.10011001\dots = .1001\dots = \frac{1}{2} + \frac{0}{4} + \frac{0}{8} + \frac{1}{16} + \dots = \frac{9}{16-1} = \frac{9}{15} = \overline{.1001}$

b) $0.1001110011\dots = .10011\dots = \frac{1}{2} + \frac{0}{4} + \frac{0}{8} + \frac{1}{16} + \frac{1}{32}\dots =$
$\frac{16}{32} + \frac{0}{32} + \frac{0}{32} + \frac{2}{32} + \frac{1}{32} + \dots = \frac{19}{32-1} = \frac{19}{31} = .1001110011\dots$

c) $0.100100\dots = \frac{1}{2} + \frac{0}{4} + \frac{0}{8}\dots = \frac{4}{8} + \frac{0}{8} + \frac{0}{8} + \dots = \frac{4}{8-1} = \frac{4}{7} = \overline{.100}$

Let's multiply $\frac{1}{3}$ x $\frac{1}{5}$ by multiplying the infinite series for each:

$\frac{1}{5} = \frac{0}{2} + \frac{0}{4} + \frac{1}{8} + \frac{1}{16} + \frac{0}{32} + \frac{0}{64} + \frac{1}{128} + \ldots$ and

$\frac{1}{3} = \frac{0}{2} + \frac{1}{4} + \frac{0}{8} + \frac{1}{16} + \frac{0}{32} + \frac{1}{64} + \frac{0}{128} + \ldots$ we'll use the distributive property, multiplying each

term in the infinite series for $\frac{1}{3}$ by each term in the infinite series for $\frac{1}{5}$.

Here we go!

Line 1: $\frac{0}{2}$ x $\left(\frac{0}{2} + \frac{0}{4} + \frac{1}{8} + \frac{1}{16} + \frac{0}{32} + \frac{0}{64} + \frac{1}{128} + \ldots \right)$ +

Line 2: $\frac{1}{4}$ x $\left(\frac{0}{2} + \frac{0}{4} + \frac{1}{8} + \frac{1}{16} + \frac{0}{32} + \frac{0}{64} + \frac{1}{128} + \ldots \right)$ +

Line 3: $\frac{0}{8}$ x $\left(\frac{0}{2} + \frac{0}{4} + \frac{1}{8} + \frac{1}{16} + \frac{0}{32} + \frac{0}{64} + \frac{1}{128} + \ldots \right)$ +

Line 4: $\frac{1}{16}$ x $\left(\frac{0}{2} + \frac{0}{4} + \frac{1}{8} + \frac{1}{16} + \frac{0}{32} + \frac{0}{64} + \frac{1}{128} + \ldots \right)$ +

Line 5: $\frac{0}{32}$ x $\left(\frac{0}{2} + \frac{0}{4} + \frac{1}{8} + \frac{1}{16} + \frac{0}{32} + \frac{0}{64} + \frac{1}{128} + \ldots \right)$ +

Line 6: $\frac{1}{64}$ x $\left(\frac{0}{2} + \frac{0}{4} + \frac{1}{8} + \frac{1}{16} + \frac{0}{32} + \frac{0}{64} + \frac{1}{128} + \ldots \right)$ + ...

The first, third, and fifth line above are all equal to zero ($\frac{0}{2} = 0$ and 0 times anything is 0).

Looking at the second line, the first term that is not zero is $\frac{1}{4}$ x $\frac{1}{8}$ = $\frac{1}{32}$ and we get

Line 2: $\frac{1}{32} + \frac{1}{64}$ +	$\frac{1}{512} + \frac{1}{1024}$ +	$\frac{1}{8192} + \frac{1}{16384}$ +
Line 4:	$\frac{1}{128} + \frac{1}{256}$ +	$\frac{1}{2048} + \frac{1}{4096}$ +
Line 6:	$\frac{1}{512} + \frac{1}{1024}$ +	$\frac{1}{8192} + \frac{1}{16384}$ +
Line 8:	$\frac{1}{2048} + \frac{1}{4096}$ +	
Line 10:		$\frac{1}{8192} + \frac{1}{16384}$ +

    1   1   1   1   2   2   2   2   3   3   3 <- these
are the number of each of the fractions above. I looked at the results above and wondered
how to proceed....

About a month later I tackled the problem again. I knew that multiplying $\frac{1}{3}$ **x** $\frac{1}{5}$ the answer

should be $\frac{1}{15}$, which from the program to change the fractions to bimals, I also knew that

$\frac{1}{15}$ = .0001000100010001...

What I had above was

$$\frac{0}{2} + \frac{0}{4} + \frac{0}{8} + \frac{0}{16} + \frac{1}{32} + \frac{1}{64} + \frac{1}{128} + \frac{1}{256} + \frac{2}{512} + \frac{2}{1024} + \frac{2}{2048} + \frac{2}{4096} \text{ ... or}$$

.00001111222233334444... assuming the pattern would continue. Could I show these are the same? Now the hard work. These are powers of 2, and $\frac{2}{512} = \frac{1}{256}$, or 2 of one digit in the bimal equals 1 of the things to its left. After a couple of false starts, I organized my numbers and changed .00001111222233334444... to .0001000100010001... out to 16 places! I started with 512ths.

```
0  0  0  0  1  1  1  1  2  2  2  2  3  3  3  3  4  4  4  4  5  5  5  5
0  0  0  0  1  1  1  2  0  2  2  2  3  3  3  3  4  4  4  4  5  5  5  5
0  0  0  0  1  1  2  0  0  2  2  2  3  3  3  3  4  4  4  4  5  5  5  5
0  0  0  1  0  0  0  0  0  0  2  2  2  3  3  3  4  4  4  4  5  5  5  5
0  0  0  1  0  0  0  0  1  0  2  2  3  3  3  3  4  4  4  4  5  5  5  5
0  0  0  1  0  0  0  0  1  1  0  2  3  3  3  3  4  4  4  4  5  5  5  5
0  0  0  1  0  0  0  0  1  1  1  0  3  3  3  3  4  4  4  4  5  5  5  5
0  0  0  1  0  0  0  0  1  1  1  1  1  3  3  3  4  4  4  4  5  5  5  5
0  0  0  1  0  0  0  1  0  0  0  0  0  1  3  3  4  4  4  4  5  5  5  5
0  0  0  1  0  0  0  1  0  0  0  0  1  0  1  3  4  4  4  4  5  5  5  5
0  0  0  1  0  0  0  1  0  0  0  0  1  1  0  1  4  4  4  4  5  5  5  5
0  0  0  1  0  0  0  1  0  0  0  0  1  1  1  1  0  4  4  4  5  5  5  5
0  0  0  1  0  0  0  1  0  0  0  1  0  0  0  0  0  0  4  4  5  5  5  5
0  0  0  1  0  0  0  1  0  0  0  1  0  0  0  0  1  0  0  4  5  5  5  5
0  0  0  1  0  0  0  1  0  0  0  1  0  0  0  0  1  1  0  0  5  5  5  5
0  0  0  1  0  0  0  1  0  0  0  1  0  0  0  0  1  1  1  0  1  5  5  5
0  0  0  1  0  0  0  1  0  0  0  1  0  0  0  0  1  1  1  1  1  1  5  5
0  0  0  1  0  0  0  1  0  0  0  1  0  0  0  1  0  0  0  0  0  1  1  5
```

Whew! That took a lot of mistakes, a lot of careful organization and time. I quit after I was able to prove to myself that the first 16 places agreed with the bimal for $\frac{1}{15}$ = .00010001...

Try one of these yourself, probably not more than one though! It takes time and perseverance.

Question worksheets for **chapter 3**
"Ian's Proof: Infinity = -1 "

When Ian was 11, he came back to town from winter vacation with the following problem he found in The Mathematics Calendar (see bibliography). He had solved it of course, and very elegantly; you try it:

$$\text{Solve for x}: \quad \sqrt{x + \sqrt{x + \sqrt{x + \sqrt{x + \ldots}}}} = 3$$

Using what you found in chapter 1 and 2, can you write as a fraction the sum of this infinite series :

$$1 + a^1 + a^2 + a^3 + a^4 + a^5 + \ldots = \,?$$

When you get your answer for this infinite series, put a = 2. What happens on the left side and on the right side of this equation?

$$1 + a^1 + a^2 + a^3 + a^4 + a^5 + \ldots =$$

The really big mathematicians like Gauss, Newton and Leibnitz, who invented the calculus, made a lot of mistakes with these infinite series. They were confused as you and I are about them. Don't worry about making mistakes.

Answer worksheets to parallel **chapter 3**
"Ian's Proof: Infinity = -1 "

Solve for x :

$$\sqrt{x + \sqrt{x + \sqrt{x + \sqrt{x + \ldots}}}} = 3$$

Ian argued, what's under the biggest square root is 9, because $\sqrt{9}$ is 3.

He set what's under the biggest radical then, equal to 9

$$x + \underbrace{\sqrt{x + \sqrt{x + \sqrt{x + \ldots}}}}_{} = 9$$

but this much is the original problem (!)
and equals 3

So   x + 3 = 9

and $\boxed{x = 6}$ the answer.

Ian found the sum of this infinite series like this:

$$1 + a^1 + a^2 + a^3 + a^4 + a^5 + \ldots = ?$$

Ian called this C

$$1 + a^1 + a^2 + a^3 + a^4 + a^5 + \ldots = C$$

He factored an **a** out of all the terms after the first

$$1 + a(\underbrace{1 + a + a^2 + a^3 + a^4 + a^5 + \ldots}_{\text{this is C}}) = C$$

so $1 + a(C) = C$ now solve for C;
      subtract C and add -1

$aC - C = -1$ factor out C

$C(a-1) = -1$ divide by a-1

multiplying top and

bottom by -1

$$\text{So } 1 + a^1 + a^2 + a^3 + a^4 + a^5 + \ldots = \frac{1}{1-a}$$

Ian then put 2 in for a

$$1 + 2^1 + 2^2 + 2^3 + 2^4 + 2^5 + \ldots = \frac{1}{1-2}$$

$$1 + 2 + 4 + 8 + 16 + 32 + \ldots = \frac{1}{1-2} = -1$$

Since the left side 1 + 2 + 4 + 8 + 16 + 32 + ... goes to infinity,

he concluded that $\infty = {}^-1$

What's wrong with Ian's argument? Nothing, except the infinite series

$$1 + a^1 + a^2 + a^3 + a^4 + a^5 + \dots$$

converges only for certain numbers. If we put 1 -> a , the fraction on the right $\dfrac{1}{1-a}$

blows up, there is no answer, because we get $\dfrac{1}{0}$ and we're dividing by zero.

It turns out that the series converges when |a| < 1, like $\dfrac{1}{2}$ and $\dfrac{^-3}{4}$ which are numbers we have been using in chapters 1 and 2.

We must accept the fact that Euler, Newton, Leibnitz and other great mathematicians made many mistakes in working with infinite series. So it's OK if you make mistakes!
Another way, not as elegant , to get this sum $1 + a^1 + a^2 + a^3 + a^4 + a^5 + \dots$
From chapter 1 we'll start with:

$$\frac{A}{B} + \left(\frac{A}{B}\right)^2 + \left(\frac{A}{B}\right)^3 + \left(\frac{A}{B}\right)^4 + \dots \; = \; \frac{A}{B-A} \quad \text{Now divide both sides by } \frac{A}{B}$$

$$1 + \frac{A}{B} + \left(\frac{A}{B}\right)^2 + \left(\frac{A}{B}\right)^3 + \dots \; = \; \frac{A}{B-A} \div \frac{A}{B}$$

$$1 + \frac{A}{B} + \left(\frac{A}{B}\right)^2 + \left(\frac{A}{B}\right)^3 + \dots \; = \; \frac{B}{B-A} =$$

$$\frac{1}{1-\frac{A}{B}} \quad \text{by dividing top and bottom by B}$$

Then let $\dfrac{A}{B}$ = a, and we get

$$1 + a^1 + a^2 + a^3 + a^4 + a^5 + \dots = \; \frac{1}{1-a}, \text{ which is what Ian had.}$$

Question worksheets for **chapter 4**
"The Snowflake Curve - its Area and Perimeter "

Some very interesting and surprising things happen here.

 Make three copies of the blank triangular graph paper in appendix 4. To build the snowflake curve start with an equilateral triangle (27 units along on each side). The succeeding figures are made by dividing each **side** of the figure into **3** equal parts, then adding a triangular piece of the same shape (smaller however), on each of the center sections of **every** side. Make all four snowflake pictures; the first three are shown below.

There are two problems to solve, to find the **area** and **perimeter** of each figure **compared to the original triangle**, then tell what happens to the area and perimeter if this process goes on forever. If you write an expression for the area and perimeter, at least partly in the form $\frac{A}{B} + \left(\frac{A}{B}\right)^2 + \left(\frac{A}{B}\right)^3 + \left(\frac{A}{B}\right)^4 + \cdots$, then you can use what you know about these infinite series from chapter 1, to tell if the series converges or diverges and find the limit if it converges. I would start with the area first. I recommend calling the area of the first figure 1.

Snowflake curve #1

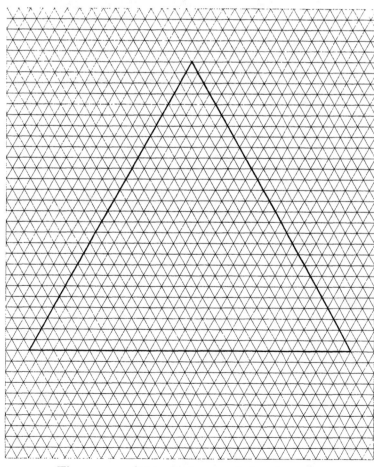

The area of this first snowflake $A_1 = 1$

Snowflake curve #2

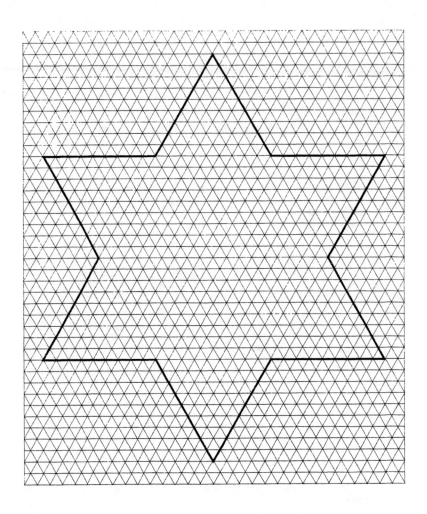

What do you get for A_2 ?

$$A_2 = \underline{\hspace{3cm}}$$

The area of this second snowflake then is $A_2 = 1 + \frac{3}{9}$ because the area of the small

triangles are each $\frac{1}{9}$ of the original one and there are 3 of these added on to the original.

Notice we're not writing this as one number, like $1\frac{1}{3}$. This is important. We want an answer which will help us find a pattern, then generalize, and it's better left as a sum so we can find an infinite series. If you didn't use 1 for the area of the first snowflake, your answer will just be a multiple of this answer.

Snowflake curve #3

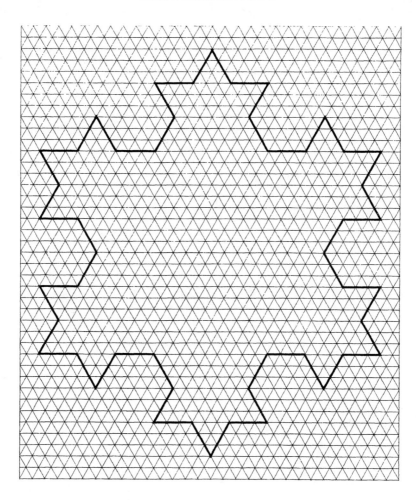

What do you get for the area of #3 snowflake?

$$A_3 = \underline{\hspace{5cm}}$$

Make the picture and find the area for snowflake #4 (picture in appendix #4).

$$A_4 = \underline{\hspace{5cm}}$$

$A_3 = 1 + \dfrac{3}{9} + \dfrac{12}{81}$

$A_4 = 1 + \dfrac{3}{9} + \dfrac{12}{81} + \dfrac{48}{729}$

Since this goes on forever, find a pattern for the area of the snowflake in this infinite series and find its limit if it converges:

$1 + \dfrac{3}{9} + \dfrac{12}{81} + \dfrac{48}{729} + \ldots$

Now find the **perimeter** of the snowflake curve using the figures above to do it.

The same argument holds here as in the area, you probably want to call the first perimeter 1.

$$P_1 = 1$$

$$P_2 = \underline{\hspace{5cm}}$$

$$P_3 = \underline{\hspace{5cm}}$$

$$P_4 = \underline{\hspace{5cm}}$$

So for the perimeter we get the infinite series

$$P = 1 + \frac{1}{3} + \frac{4}{9} + \frac{48}{81} + \ldots$$

Now see if you can write this in such a way as to include an infinite series like we had in chapter 1.

P = _____

Does the infinite series converge or diverge? What is its limit if it converges?

The second curve, called a **Sierpinski curve**, is sometimes called a space-filling curve. The same game applies here as for the snowflake curve, find the perimeter and area of each compared to the **outside square** and see what happens if you continue this forever. Copy the $\frac{1}{4}$" graph paper in appendix 4 to make the four figures.

Sierpinski curve #1

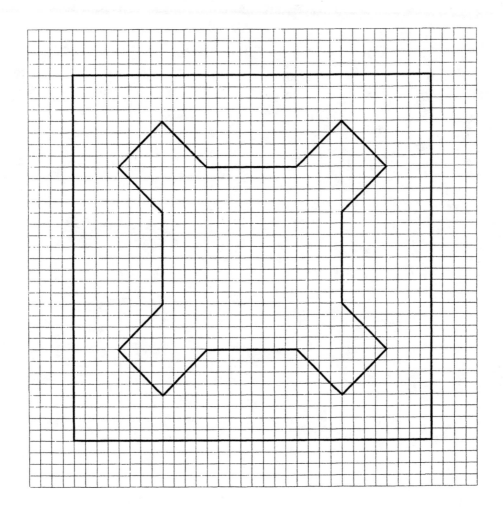

The area of the outside square is 1 (32x32=1024 squares). The area within the first

Sierpinski curve is $A_1 = $ _____

The area of the first Sierpinski curve is $A_1 = \dfrac{22}{64} = \dfrac{11}{32} = \dfrac{11}{2^5} = .34\dfrac{3}{8}$

The perimeter of the outside square we'll call 1 (128 lengths of sides of the small squares).
The perimeter of the first Sierpinski curve is

$P_1 = \dfrac{32 + 48\sqrt{2}}{128}$

The length of the diagonal of the smallest square is $\dfrac{\sqrt{2}}{128}$.

Sierpinski curve #2

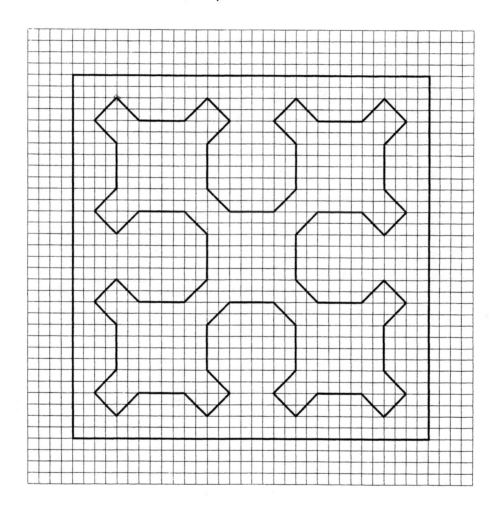

Sierpinski A_2 = _____ Sierpinski P_2 = _____

Sierpinski curve #3

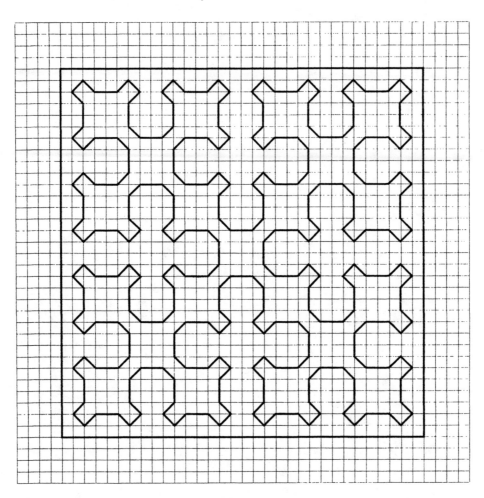

Sierpinski A_3 = _____   Sierpinski P_3 =_____
Make the fourth Sierpinski curve. Look carefully at the first three. The 4th Sierpinski curve
is in appendix #4 if you need help.

Sierpinski A_4 = _____   Sierpinski P_4 = _____

Write a series for the area and the perimeter. What happens to each? Do they each
converge? If so, to what.

Look up fractals, fractal geometry and chaos theory. Try to find out how these are related to
the snowflake and Sierpinski curves. Look up Mandelbrot's book and Gleick's book from
the bibliography. Also check out chapter 8 on iteration.

Answer worksheets for **Chapter 4**
"The Snowflake Curve - its Area and Perimeter "

The area of **the snowflake curve**:

$A_1 = 1$

$A_2 = 1 + \dfrac{3}{9}$

$A_3 = 1 + \dfrac{3}{9} + \dfrac{12}{81}$

$A_4 = 1 + \dfrac{3}{9} + \dfrac{12}{81} + \dfrac{48}{729} + \ldots$

Looking at these another way, after the first one, there are 4 times as many smaller triangles and the area of each smaller triangle is $\dfrac{1}{9}$ the area of the previous triangle, so the new added area is $\dfrac{4}{9}$ of the previous added area.

$$A = 1 + 3 \times \dfrac{1}{9} + 4 \times 3 \times \dfrac{1}{9} \times \dfrac{1}{9} + 4 \times 4 \times 3 \times \dfrac{1}{9} \times \dfrac{1}{9} \times \dfrac{1}{9} + \ldots \ =$$

$$A = 1 + 3 \times \dfrac{1}{9} + 3 \times \dfrac{1}{9} \times \dfrac{4}{9} + 4 \times 3 \times \dfrac{1}{9} \times \dfrac{1}{9} \times \dfrac{4}{9} + \ldots$$

after the first term, to get the same number of factors of 4 on top as 9's on the bottom, we'll multiply by 4 and divide by 4 so as not to change the value of the numbers. We get

$$A = 1 + \dfrac{3}{4} \times \dfrac{4}{9} + \dfrac{3}{4} \times \dfrac{4}{9} \times \dfrac{4}{9} + \dfrac{3}{4} \times \dfrac{4}{9} \times \dfrac{4}{9} \times \dfrac{4}{9} + \ldots$$

factoring out $\dfrac{3}{4}$ and writing the terms with exponents

$$A = 1 + \dfrac{3}{4} \times \left(\dfrac{4^1}{9^1} + \dfrac{4^2}{9^2} + \dfrac{4^3}{9^3} + \ldots \right)$$

In the parentheses is the infinite series

$\dfrac{4^1}{9^1} + \dfrac{4^2}{9^2} + \dfrac{4^3}{9^3} + \ldots$, from chapter 1, goes to $\dfrac{4}{9-4} = \dfrac{4}{5}$, and we can write the area of the snowflake curve as

$A = 1 + \dfrac{3}{4} \times \dfrac{4}{5} = 1 + \dfrac{3}{5} = \dfrac{8}{5}$. So the **area** of the snowflake converges to $\dfrac{8}{5} = 1\dfrac{3}{5}$ of the original triangle.

Now let's find the **perimeter** of the snowflake:

$P_1 = 1$

$P_2 = 1 + \dfrac{3}{9}$ because each side of the new figure is $\dfrac{1}{3}$ of $\dfrac{1}{3}$ **or** $\dfrac{1}{9}$ of the original perimeter and since there are 12 of these, the perimeter of the second snowflake is $\dfrac{12}{9} = 1 + \dfrac{3}{9}$; leave this as ninths or thirds?...I don't know yet. Let's see what happens next.

$P_3 = 1 + \frac{3}{9} + \frac{4}{9} = 1 + \frac{1}{3} + \frac{4}{9}$. Each of the smallest sides is $\frac{1}{3}$ of $\frac{1}{3}$ of $\frac{1}{3}$ or $\frac{1}{27}$ of the original

perimeter and since there are 48 of these, the perimeter of the third snowflake is $\frac{48}{27} = 1\frac{21}{27}$

$= 1\frac{7}{9} = 1 + \frac{1}{3} + \frac{12}{27} = 1 + \frac{1}{3} + \frac{4}{9}$.

$P_4 = \frac{192}{81} = 1 + \frac{1}{3} + \frac{4}{9} + \frac{48}{81}$ The smallest side of figure 4 is $\frac{1}{3}$ of $\frac{1}{3}$ of $\frac{1}{3}$ of $\frac{1}{3}$ or $\frac{1}{81}$ of the original perimeter and there are 192 of these.

This will go on forever. Now lets write it so we can see a pattern in this, what is now an infinite series.

$P = 1 + \frac{1}{3} + \frac{4}{9} + \frac{48}{81} + \ldots = 1 + \frac{1}{3} + \frac{4}{3^2} + \frac{3 \times 16}{3^4} + \ldots$

$P = 1 + \left(\frac{1}{3} + \frac{4}{3^2} + \frac{4^2}{3^3} + \ldots \right)$

To make the exponents in the top and bottom of the fractions the same, we'll multiply by 4 inside the parentheses and dividing by 4 outside the parentheses. Then we get

$P = 1 + \frac{1}{4} \times \left(\frac{4}{3} + \frac{4^2}{3^2} + \frac{4^3}{3^3} + \ldots \right)$

In the parentheses we now have an infinite series that looks like one in chapter 1, and one in which A>B, or $\frac{4}{3} > 1$ so the series goes to infinity.

So the perimeter involves a series which is **divergent**.

Here is this snowflake curve, the area forms a convergent series and goes to $1\frac{3}{5}$, while its

perimeter forms a divergent series and goes to infinity. Very interesting!

The Sierpinski curve (the 4th Sierpinski curve is in appendix #4)

$A_1 = \frac{352}{1024} = \frac{11}{32} = \frac{11}{2^5} = .34375$ Again, how should we write this? We'll write it different

ways, then look at the next one to see if there is a pattern.

$A_2 = \frac{408}{1024} = \frac{11}{2^5} + \frac{7}{2^7} = .3984\ldots$

$A_3 = \frac{422}{1024} = \frac{11}{2^5} + \frac{7}{2^7} + \frac{7}{2^9} = .412109\ldots$

$A_4 = \frac{425.5}{1024} = \frac{11}{2^5} + \frac{7}{2^7} + \frac{7}{2^9} + \frac{7}{2^{11}} = .415527344\ldots)$

I assumed this pattern would go on forever; then found the limit of this infinite series.

$A = \frac{11}{2^5} + \frac{7}{2^7} + \frac{7}{2^9} + \frac{7}{2^{11}} + \ldots$ from the second term on I factored out 7 and factored the

inside terms, with a common factor of $\frac{1}{2^7}$

$$A = \frac{11}{2^5} + 7 \times \left(\frac{1}{2^7} \times \frac{1}{2^0} + \frac{1}{2^7} \times \frac{1}{2^2} + \frac{1}{2^7} \times \frac{1}{2^4} + \ldots \right)$$

I then factored out $\frac{1}{2^7}$

$$A = \frac{11}{2^5} + \frac{7}{2^7} \times \left(\frac{1}{2^0} + \frac{1}{2^2} + \frac{1}{2^4} + \ldots \right)$$ and rather than work with even powers of 2, I

saw powers of 4 inside the parentheses

$$A = \frac{11}{2^5} + \frac{7}{2^7} \times \left(1 + \frac{1}{4^1} + \frac{1}{4^2} + \frac{1}{4^3} + \ldots \right)$$ notice now there is an infinite series like

we've done before $\frac{1}{4^1} + \frac{1}{4^2} + \frac{1}{4^3} + \ldots$ which

goes to $\frac{1}{4-1} = \frac{1}{3}$ from chapter 1. So we get

$$A = \frac{11}{2^5} + \frac{7}{2^7} \times \left(1 + \frac{1}{3} \right) = \frac{11}{2^5} + \frac{7}{2^7} \times \frac{4}{3} = \frac{11}{32} + \frac{7}{96} = \frac{40}{96} = \frac{5}{12}$$

So the **area within this Sierpinski curve** approaches $\frac{5}{12}$ of the original square.

There's nothing like some hard work to get results and satisfaction!

We'll now look at the **perimeter of this Sierpinski curve**, using the perimeter of the outside square as 1; I made many mistakes in doing these, mainly because I figured the perimeter was 1024, the area, instead of 128 = 4 × 32:

$$P_1 = \frac{32 + 48\sqrt{2}}{128} \qquad P_2 = \frac{80 + 88\sqrt{2}}{128} \qquad P_3 = \frac{168 + 172\sqrt{2}}{128} \qquad P_4 = \frac{340 + 342\sqrt{2}}{128}$$

Dan, one of my editors, found a recursive rule for the perimeters (you can get from the nth perimeter to the n+1st perimeter:

$$P_{n+1} = 2 \times P_n + \left(\frac{1}{2} \right)^{n+2} \times \left(1 - \frac{\sqrt{2}}{2} \right)$$ which is based on the idea that in going from one figure to

the next it is shrunk by $\frac{1}{2}$, but then you have to do the new reduced shape three times less some pieces, plus other pieces. In the rule, since we end up doubling the previous perimeter and then some, the sequence of perimeters increases without bound, and is divergent (which Martin Gardner in "Penrose Tiles To Trapdoor Ciphers" says it should be doing).

The snowflake curve and the Sierpinski curve act alike in that in both cases the area converges and the perimeter diverges. The snowflake curve is sometimes called one of the "pathological" curves, compared to straight lines, parabolas, circles, ellipses, hyperbolas and sine waves, which Kasner and Newman describe as "healthy and normal".

In fact today the snowflake curve, one of the Koch curves, is in the realm of Fractal Geometry and part of chaos theory. Mandlebrot, the leading force in this new way of looking at geometry, talks about coastlines, turbulence, clouds, and galaxies. He tries to describe the irregular and fragmented in Nature, with applications in economics as well as many other fields. Imbedded in his work is the idea of self-similarity. You can see the same shapes in the first snowflake as in the fourth one.

Question worksheets for **chapter 5**
"The Harmonic Series"

Take a look at this infinite series: $\frac{1}{2} + \frac{1}{3} + \frac{1}{4} + \frac{1}{5} + \frac{1}{6} + \dots$, which is called the Harmonic series.

See what you can find out about it. Does it converge or diverge? If it converges, what is its limit?

Write a program to get the partial sums.

Answer worksheets for **chapter 5**
"The Harmonic Series"

The harmonic series looks innocent enough. My students started to use their calculators and even wrote computer programs on the FX7000G to look at the sums. One day some youngsters must have gotten the sum of the first 10,000 terms, and it didn't reach 10! They were ready to say the infinite sum went to 10 as the limit. Karl T. Cooper wrote from Providence, R.I., that using his computer, he found the sum of the first 1,000,000 terms is 13.3573617935, not 14.392726788474, as I reported in the earlier printing. He showed this graphically as well. This series tends to infinity, diverges, but **very slowly**.

In about 1350 Oresme proved this series to be divergent. The proof goes something like this: we'll compare the harmonic series

$$\frac{1}{2} + \frac{1}{3} + \frac{1}{4} + \frac{1}{5} + \frac{1}{6} + \dots$$

to the series $\quad \frac{1}{2} + \frac{1}{2} + \frac{1}{2} + \frac{1}{2} + \frac{1}{2} + \dots$

which gets bigger and bigger and is divergent. We'll show that the terms of the harmonic series, looked at in a certain way, will be bigger than the terms of the series $\frac{1}{2} + \frac{1}{2} + \frac{1}{2} + \frac{1}{2} + \frac{1}{2} + \dots$ and is therefore divergent also.

The first terms, $\frac{1}{2}$, are the same.

Since $\frac{1}{4} + \frac{1}{4} = \frac{1}{2}$, and $\frac{1}{3} > \frac{1}{4}$, then $\frac{1}{3} + \frac{1}{4} > \frac{1}{2}$. The next 2 terms of the harmonic series add up to a number bigger than $\frac{1}{2}$.

Now $\frac{1}{8} + \frac{1}{8} + \frac{1}{8} + \frac{1}{8} = \frac{4}{8} = \frac{1}{2}$, but $\frac{1}{5} > \frac{1}{8}$, $\frac{1}{6} > \frac{1}{8}$, and $\frac{1}{7} > \frac{1}{8}$. So the sum of the next 4 terms of the harmonic series $\left(\frac{1}{5} + \frac{1}{6} + \frac{1}{7} + \frac{1}{8}\right) > \frac{1}{2}$ also.

The next 8 terms will be bigger than $\frac{1}{2}$ and so on. Since this is an infinite sum, we can go on and on and the harmonic series will be bigger than the $\frac{1}{2} + \frac{1}{2} + \frac{1}{2} + \frac{1}{2} + \frac{1}{2} + \dots$ and is therefore divergent as well.

A program to get the partial sums of the harmonic series, in Basic is

```
10 S = 0
20 For N = 2 to 20
30 S = S + 1/N
40 Print S
50 Next N
```

Question worksheets for **chapter 6**
"On Thin Spaghetti and Nocturnal Animals"

A group of teachers at an National Association of Independent Schools workshop in 1975, spent time on guessing functions and graphing functions and came out with some interesting results, including an infinite sequence.

1. Guess my rule: We'll digress here to look at the guessing functions or guess my rule and graphing functions.

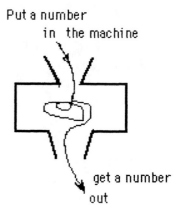

Put a number in the machine

get a number out

I'm thinking of a machine or rule. You give me a number (input), I put your number in my machine or use my rule on your number, then I give you a number back (output). I always do the same thing to the number you give me. Your job is to figure out how my machine works or what my rule is doing to your number.

So if you give me 1, I tell you 5. If you tell me 2, my machine gives out 7 and so on. We'll put the numbers in a table like that at the right .

Can you guess my rule? Guessing the rule also means finding the out put for an input of any number, say 100. Can you find the number I would tell you back if you gave me 100? _____

| input | output |
x	y
1	5
2	7
3	9
4	
10	23

x	y
1	5
2	7
3	9
4	11
10	23

(differences of 2 between successive y values)

There are many ways to say what the rule is. If your description of my rule gets the same pairs of numbers, that's fine. Some people say I added your number twice, then added 3. Others say the y-number goes up 2 each time the x-number goes up 1. Others say I doubled your number then add 3. One way to write the rule is $x + x + 3 = y$, another way is $2 \cdot x + 3 = y$. This is another case of look for patterns, they abound here. Some people look at the differences 1 to 5, 2 to 7, and so on, these go up 4, then 5.. you can write 1+4=5, 2+5=7 .. or 1 + 3+1=5, 2+3+2=7, ...so $x + 3 + x = y$, which amounts to the same rule.

Now you make up a rule for me. Use a 3x5 card, put your table of numbers and name on one side then write your rule on the other side. Have a friend make up one for you. You make up one for a friend. You'll probably make up hard ones to begin with, but try to control your fiendishness and use times and add or subtract to start with.

Here are some rules you can figure out with a friend:

1.

x	y
0	-2
1	5
2	12
3	19
4	26
100	698

2.

x	y
0	5
3	11
10	25
4	13
7	19
20	45

3.

x	y
0	0
1	1
2	3
3	6
4	10
10	55

4.

x	y
0	0
1	1
2	4
3	9
4	16
10	100

For rule 2., as you've undoubtedly noticed, I purposely didn't put the numbers in order. People usually do that when starting work on these rules. You might want to put them in order to help find the rule.

rule 1. _____   rule 2. _____

rule 3. _____   rule 4. _____

Make up some rules for a friend. Don't make them up too hard at first. The idea here is to learn about functions, not try to stump your friend.

2. Graphing equations: We will get back to the guessing functions in a minute, but first let's look at another important idea, graphing of these functions and equations.

We'll start with the equation $x + y = 7$. Find two numbers that add up to 7. We'll make a table to keep track of the pairs of numbers that make this true.

x	y
1	6
5	2
7	0

Like $1 + 6 = 7$, so the pair of numbers 1,6 will go in the table. 5,2 will work and 7,0 will also work. Find some other pairs of numbers that make this sentence or equation true.

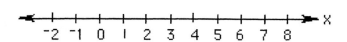

Think of the graph as two number lines, a horizontal one, called the x-axis and a vertical one called the y-axis. Then put them together at (0,0).

This gives our graphing board, called the cartesian plane, after Descartes (pronounced day-cart), circa 1630. Each pair of numbers corresponds to a point on the graph. To plot the point (1,6), you go over 1 and up 6.

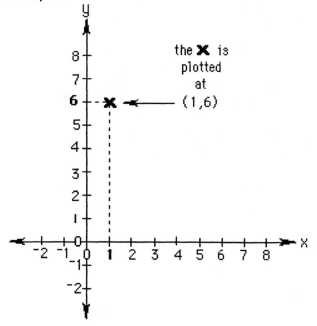

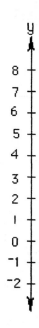

For each pair of numbers which make the sentence true, like (1,6), we'll plot a point on the graph below. The first number is counted along the horizontal or x-axis. The second number is counted along the vertical or y-axis. Plot an x on the graph for each pair of numbers you've found, then look for a pattern. Predict where other x's will go.

$$x + y = 7$$

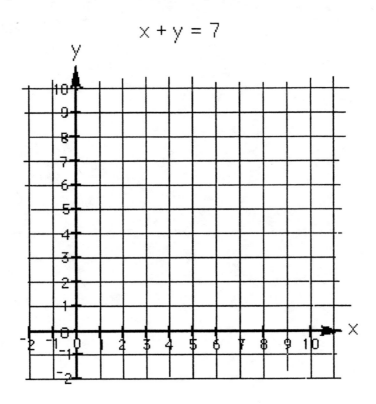

Notice, the numbers are on the lines, not in the spaces when you make a graph.

The points (1,6), (5,2), and (7,0) are shown plotted below.

$$x + y = 7$$

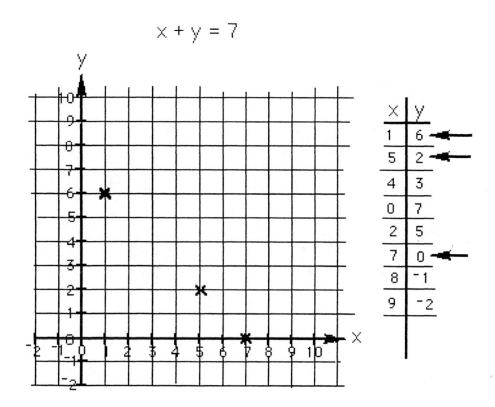

Plot the other points on the graph. Look for a pattern to the x's. You can go beyond the axes also! ..what pairs of numbers can you find there that will work? You can plot points between the lines...what pairs of numbers can you find there that will work? Share your graph with friends.

How can you change the open sentence or equation? What happens to the graph? Try different things, share your discoveries with a friend. Copy some of the $\frac{1}{2}$" graph paper in appendix 4.

Copy some of the $\frac{1}{4}$" graph paper in appendix #4 for the following graphs.

Now we'll graph equations that look like the guess my rule function at the beginning of this chapter: $2 \cdot x + 3 = y$. Use the table of pairs of numbers that make this true and plot the points that go with them. Again look for patterns. There are lots of patterns in the numbers, find them on the graph.

Using a different color for each equation, make a table of numbers and graph these on the same graph paper as $2 \cdot x + 3 = y$. Write the equation, its table of numbers and make the graph, all in the same color, and each equation a different color: $2 \cdot x + 7 = y$ and $2 \cdot x + 1 = y$. What's happening? What's changing and what's staying the same? Where does the adding number show up on the graph?

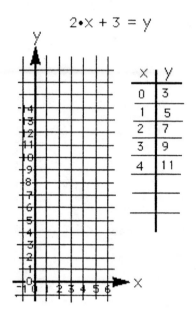

$2 \cdot x + 3 = y$

x	y
0	3
1	5
2	7
3	9
4	11

On another piece of graph paper, graph these 3 equations and color-code them as before: $2 \cdot x + 3 = y$; $5 \cdot x + 3 = y$; and $^-4 \cdot x + 3 = y$

What's changing? What's staying the same? What happens on the graph? What pattern do the points have? How does the graph relate to the rule or equation?

How does the multiplying number show up on the graph?

How does the adding number show up on the graph?

You make up some equations like these for a friend to graph and let them make up some for you to graph. Talk with them about what you find.

Write the equations for two graphs whose lines are parallel (never meet).

Write the equations for two graphs whose lines are perpendicular (at right angles to each other).

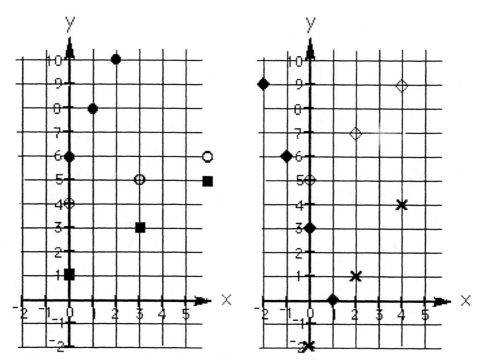

Find the equations for the graphs above by filling in the multiplying number and the adding number below.

● _ • X + __ = y   ◆ _ • X + __ = y

○ _ • X + __ = y   ◇ __ • X + __ = y

■ _ • X + __ = y   ✕ __ • X + __ = y

Check your equations by putting in at least two pairs of numbers from the points on the graph to see if they make the equation true.

3. Functions from experience:
Now we'll get some functions from different things, the first of these is
The shuttle puzzle

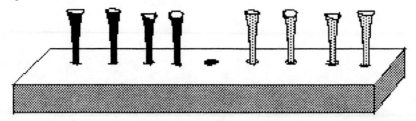

The object of this puzzle is to interchange the blue and the red pegs. The rules are 1) you can move to a hole that's next to a peg; 2) you can jump, but only one peg and it must be of the other color, and 3) you can't move backwards. You must start with the empty space in the middle and end that way. You can use golf tees, as I do, or you can use two different kinds of coins or bottle caps or pieces of colored paper as the pieces.

Try it. It's not easy.

Sometimes if a problem is hard, make up an easier one, do that, then go back to the harder one. In this case, try 2 pairs of pegs with the hole in the middle, instead of 4 pairs.

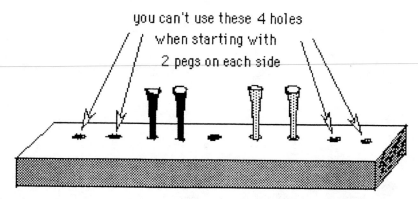

you can't use these 4 holes
when starting with
2 pegs on each side

After each move, how many possible new moves can you make? When do you get stuck? What do you need to do so as not to be in this situation?

When you can interchange 1, 2, 3, and 4 pairs make a guess my rule table, with the x being the number of pairs of pegs and the y being the number of moves.

Write down the number of moves you get, the y numbers, then see if you can find a rule that will get the number of moves if I give you any number of pairs of pegs (like 100). Look for patterns. What do you see about the differences?

Graph these pairs of numbers that you have in the table. What do you see in the graph? Put in negative numbers for x. Even though you can't have a negative number of pegs, you can still study the total situation mathematically.

No. of pairs of pegs	No. of moves to interchange the pegs
X	y
1	
2	
3	
4	

The tower puzzle

The object of this ancient puzzle is to move the disc tower (4 shown here) from any one of the three pegs to either of the other two pegs, ending up in the same order you started with, from smallest to largest. The rules are: you can only move one disc at a time, and you cannot put a larger disc on top of a smaller one. If this is too easy, try it with 5 or 6 discs. Look for patterns.

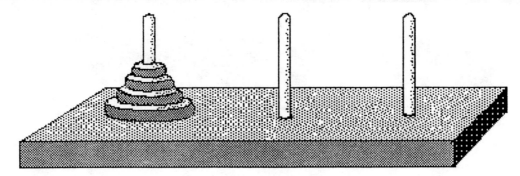

When you have reached a point of being able to move 6 discs, you can the try to move the discs in the minimum number of moves and again look for patterns.

Now make a table, keeping track of the number of discs vs the minimum number of moves.

Look at the differences, what patterns do you see? What kinds of numbers are these? How are the y-numbers related to the differences?

Find a rule which relates the no. of discs to the number of moves.

Make a graph of these pairs of numbers.

The Tower Puzzle

No. of discs X	Minimum No. of moves y
1	1
2	3
3	
4	
5	
6	

Hinged mirrors

Tape two mirrors together as shown in the diagram at the right. Put an object, such as a white rod between the mirrors. As you change the angle between the mirrors, what happens to the number of images you see?

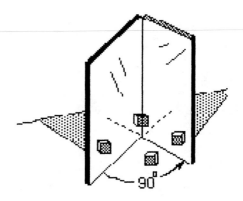

A technique which may help, if I can make it clear, is this: You'll see the bottom edges of the mirrors reflected in the mirrors. When there are 4 sections, 3 in the reflection, plus the 1 section out front, the angle between the mirrors is 90° (the total angle about the axes of the mirrors at the bottom is 360°, and 360°÷ 4=90°). Another way to do it is to measure the angle between the mirrors and count the number of images. I think things like this take time..you really have to look at what is happening.

Change the angle between the mirrors and fill in the the table for 30°, 45°, 60°, 120° and 180°. Then find the relationship. Check with someone else.

Graph the pairs of numbers you get. Have you seen a graph like this before?

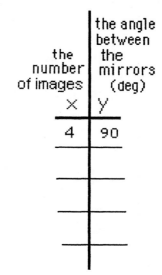

the number of images	the angle between the mirrors (deg)
x	y
4	90

The hinged mirrors at the right are shown 90° apart. The diagram shows with the dark arrows, how the light rays start from the rod, bounce off the mirrors, then arrive at the eye of the observer. One image is the result of reflections off both mirrors. A little physics is involved here in that the angle the light ray hits the mirror equals the angle the ray reflects off the mirror. The equally dashed lines show the "apparent" light path from the images to the eye. Notice that the images are symmetrically opposite the rod or other image in the mirror lines. When Mark, 10 years old, and I worked on these diagrams we found that all the images, the original rod, and the eye all lie on one circle!

Try to make a diagram like this when the mirrors are 60° apart.

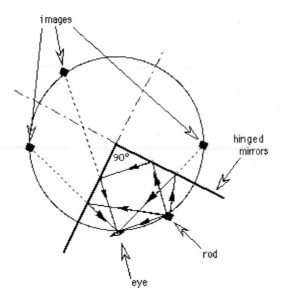

4. How lengths, squares, and cubes grow

Back to the teachers' work mentioned earlier. We looked at the problem: given a certain volume, like 8 cubic centimeters, find their surface area. We used blocks from the set of *Cuisenaire* ® rods, which are 1x1x1 to 1x1x10 cm. in size. Arrange the 8 - 1x1x1 cm. blocks different ways. Two of these arrangements are shown below. Which arrangement will give the smallest skin area (or surface area)? the largest?

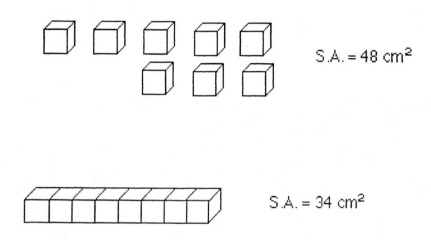

S.A. = 48 cm²

S.A. = 34 cm²

5. We talked about the Nautilus shell, and we'll work on that in a moment. But this led to the study of how lengths, squares and cubes grow. Again we used the rods.

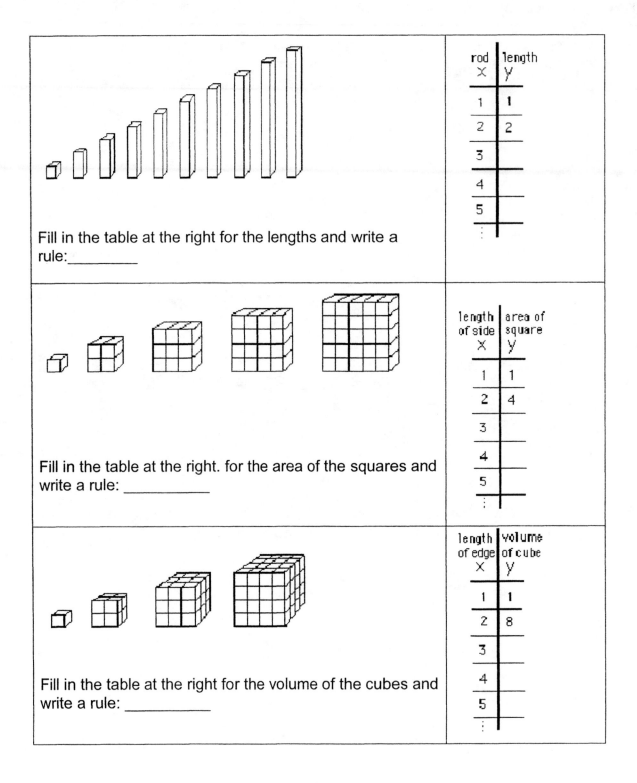

Fill in the table at the right for the lengths and write a rule:_____

rod x	length y
1	1
2	2
3	
4	
5	
⋮	

Fill in the table at the right. for the area of the squares and write a rule: _____

length of side x	area of square y
1	1
2	4
3	
4	
5	
⋮	

Fill in the table at the right for the volume of the cubes and write a rule: _____

length of edge x	volume of cube y
1	1
2	8
3	
4	
5	
⋮	

On the same graph on the right, graph the growth of the length, area and volume
 from the tables above.

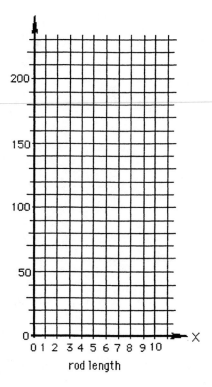

rod length

One of the teachers suggested looking at the surface area of the cubes, not the single rods, because they have the same cross section of 1 cm^2. The surface area just 8amounts to using the face of a white rod as a stamp; how many stamps would it take to cover each cube in the picture of the four cubes above?

Find a rule for the surface area vs. the length: _____

So how does the surface area go up compared to the the length?

How does the volume go up compared to the edge?

length of edge X	surface area of cube y
1	6
2	24
3	
4	
5	
⋮	

6. Now we'll look at the surface area to volume ratios of the rods and see how this is related to why rodents run around at night. Fill in the table below for all the rods lengths 1 to 10, then find the same information for rods of 100 and 1000 cm. long, then generalize for a length X.

Length	Surface area	Volume	Surface area / Volume
1	6	1	$\frac{6}{1} = 6$
2	10	2	$\frac{10}{2} = 5$
3			
4			
5			
6			
7			
8			
9			
10			
:	:	:	:
100			
:	:	:	:
1000			
:	:	:	:
X			

Look at the sequence of $\frac{SA}{Vol}$ ratios; what's happening? Is it a converging sequence? What do you think is the limit of the sequence?

What does the surface area of an animal do for the animal?

What is its volume have to do with heat production?

What does it mean for the smaller animal to have a larger $\frac{SA}{Vol}$ ratio?

The figure above came from a rubbing of half of a chambered Nautilus shell.
Some of my students ask me why I have the chambered Nautilus shell around-- pictures of
it, articles about it, a world map on one, a whole one, a half one, my original watercolor
painting of it, a copy of my painting on the cover of my books, on my stationary... Well, I
say, it is very beautiful, it is one of the oldest living things we know, and of course, it is an
example of a mathematical curve (a spiral) in nature, that has special mathematical
properties of growth. And since we've been studying how length, area and volume grow, we
could look at how the shell grows. You will want to make a few copies of this shell rubbing
first. Look at the shell now and make up some questions you could ask about how it grows,
by measuring different things. Go to it.

OA is a radius vector, a line segment from the
center O of the spiral to the point A on the curve.
OB is also a radius vector 360° from OA.
Measure OA and OB at various places around
the curve. Find the ratios of $\frac{OA}{OB}$.
What do you notice?

CD is a tangent to the curve
at point A on the spiral. Angle A is
the one to be measured. Do this
at various places around the
curve. What do you notice?

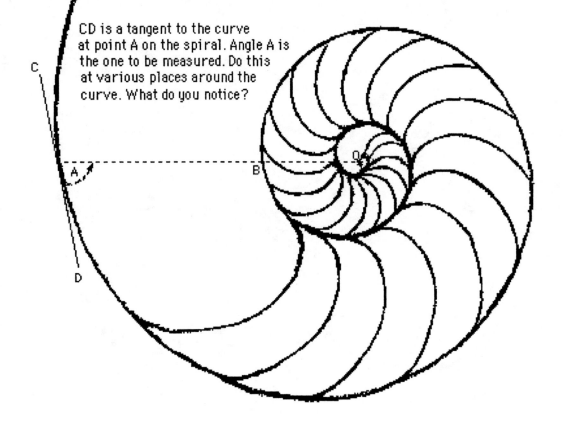

Vickie did three studies on the Nautilus shell; you might want to try these.
1.   She confirmed that the individual chambers (as well as "chunks" of the shell) are the same shape. Cut out pieces of the shell and try the eye test.

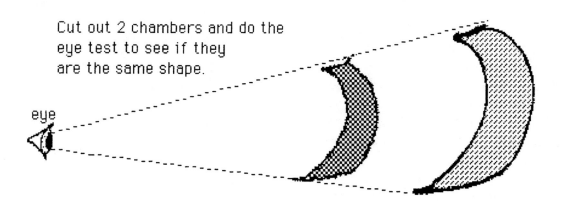

Cut out 2 chambers and do the eye test to see if they are the same shape.

eye

2. Using a real half-shell (see bibliography, under materials), she found the % increase in **volume** of the chambers.

3. Vickie then showed that the **area** of the chambers are proportional to the "length" squared
($A = k \cdot l^2$). She did this by measuring the area and length of some chambers, then calculating k and showing it is the same for each chamber.

Try these yourself.

Other functions to try:

The sum of the interior angles of a polygon vs. #sides

The interior angle of a regular polygon vs. #sides

On a circle, the central angle vs. the length of its chord

#squares on a 4x4 square array of dots; 3x3, 5x5,..array of dots.

The triangular numbers, square numbers, pentagonal numbers, ..

The side of square vs. perimeter

The side of square vs. area

Rectangles of constant perimeter of 20; l vs w   (see ch.14)

Rectangles of constant perimeter of 20; l vs A   (see ch.14)

Rectangles of constant area of 36; l vs w

Rectangles of constant area of 36; l vs perimeter

Triangles of the same shape- double its sides, what happens to area?

Weight vs. stretch of a spring

Length of wire vs. its resistance

Length of a pendulum vs. time for 10 swings

Celsius vs. Fahrenheit temperature

Height of an object vs. length of its shadow

Weight vs. volume of different size pieces of the same solid material

8. Other graphs you might work on:

Graph $x^2 = y$. Look for a pattern as you go up from (0,0) to (1,1) and so on. What's happening? Do all parabolas have this same pattern?

On the same graph paper, graph $y = x$, $y = x^2$, and $y = x^3$ between $x = 0$ and $x = 1$, going up by tenths. What do you notice?

On the same graph paper do the following sequence: graph $y = x^2$, a parabola. What is the equation of the graph which is the same as the first one, but shifted 3 units up? What is the equation of the graph which is the same as the first one, but shifted 2 units to the right? shifted 2 units to the right and 3 units up? What is the equation of the graph which is the same as the first one, but wider? What is the equation of the graph which is the same as the first one, but opens down?

On the same graph paper, graph $x^2 + k \cdot y^2 = 25$. Using $k = 1$ you get one graph; a point on this graph would be (3,4) because $3^2 + 1 \cdot 4^2 = 25$ or $9 + 16 = 25$ is true; find more pairs of numbers to make this true (use a calculator to approximate numbers) and graph them.

Then when $k = 4$ you'll get another graph; then use $k = 0$; $k = \frac{1}{2}$; $k = \text{-}1$; $k = \text{-}4$; $k = \frac{\text{-}1}{2}$.

What do you notice?

Make up other functions, other questions from this chapter.

Answer worksheets for **chapter 6**
"On Thin Spaghetti and Nocturnal Animals"

1. Guess my rule

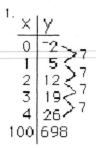

1.

x	y
0	¯2
1	5
2	12
3	19
4	26
100	698

For rule #1, notice the differences are 7, and the rule can be written

$$7 \cdot x - 2 = y \quad \text{or} \quad 7 \cdot x + {}^-2 = y$$

2.

x	y
0	5
3	11
10	25
4	13
7	19
20	45

From 3 to 4, the y-number goes up from 11 to 13, or 2. So I try 2•3 + what = 11? 5. Does this work as the rule: 2•x+ 5 = y ?

2•7+ 5 = 19 that's true, and 2•4+ 5 = 13 that's true, so this rule must work.

3.

x	y
0	0
1	1
2	3
3	6
4	10
10	55

There are many patterns here in rule 3. The differences in the y-numbers are not the same. And the difference of the differences are 1. A pattern I see is is on the right, so the rule could be written $x \cdot \frac{x+1}{2} = y$. Some people see that $\frac{2 \cdot 3}{2} = 3$ and $\frac{3 \cdot 4}{2} = 6$ or written as

$$\frac{3 \cdot (3+1)}{2} \text{ and } \frac{x \cdot (x+1)}{2} = y .$$ **If you write a number so you can see where it comes from**, like 3+1 instead of 4, or the 4-3 instead of 1, above, it often helps to generalize a rule.

These numbers are called the triangular numbers (see ch.1). And they are also the sum of the consecutive numbers: 1+2=3, 1+2+3=6, etc.

x			y
0			0
1 • 1		=	1
2 • 1½	= 2 • 3/2	=	3
3 • 2	= 3 • 4/2	=	6
4 • 2½	= 4 • 5/2	=	10
10 • 5½	= 10 • 11/2	=	55

2. Graphing

In graphing $x + y = 7$, between the lines you can get points like $(4\frac{1}{2}, 2\frac{1}{2})$ because $4\frac{1}{2} + 2\frac{1}{2} = 7$ is true and beyond the axes we get points like $(^-2, 9)$ because $^-2 + 9 = 7$ is true and $(8, ^-1)$ works because $8 + ^-1 = 7$ is true. And these points follow the same pattern!

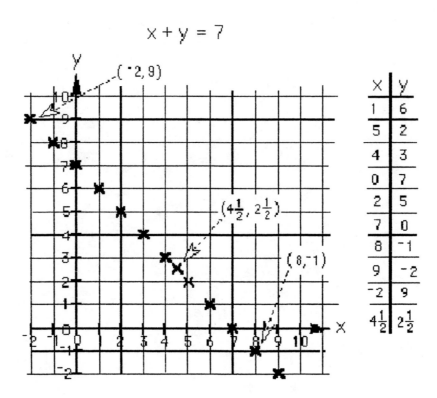

Often young people don't know there is a number between 4 and 5. This takes a little discussion, usually about money, a half dollar, or sharing cookies as in chapter 2. Not complicated though!

How can you change the equations, the graphs? A word of caution, as soon as the learner is asked to make up the problem, in this case, to change the equation, expect the unexpected! The learner is liable to make up something very difficult, very unusual, but very exciting. Even if we have to admit we don't know what will happen, if we try it, we might learn something new. Some possibilities follow:

If you change the equation to x - y = 2 we get a graph like that below. Notice that if we use the point (1, ¯1) which follows the pattern, and plug the numbers into the equation, we get 1 - ¯1 = 2 which is true. And from (0, ¯2) we get 0 - ¯2 = 2, which is also true. How about that.

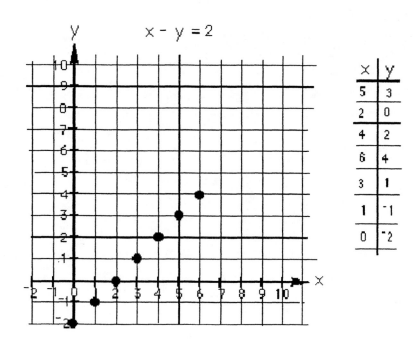

x	y
5	3
2	0
4	2
6	4
3	1
1	¯1
0	¯2

Below is the graph of $x \cdot y = 12$. For those concerned about young people doing arithmetic, this is an opportunity for them to practice their multiplication facts for 12; I never say that to my students, however. Notice $9 \cdot 1\frac{1}{3} = 12$ (you could say we are sharing 12 cookies with 9 people, how much do we each get?). We could also use negative numbers, (⁻2, ⁻6) would work because ⁻2 ⋅ ⁻6= 12. Where would that point be on the graph? Notice also, this is not a straight line, but a curve called an hyperbola. What happens if we change the equation to $x \cdot y = 6$? Make up more questions.

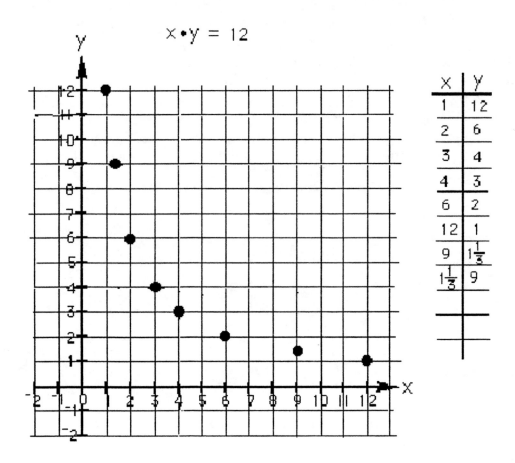

$$x \cdot y = 12$$

x	y
1	12
2	6
3	4
4	3
6	2
12	1
9	$1\frac{1}{3}$
$1\frac{1}{3}$	9

The graph of $\frac{x}{y}$ = 2 is shown below. Lots of interesting avenues to investigate here.

(⁻2, ⁻1) would work because $\frac{⁻2}{⁻1}$ = 2. What about (0,0), would that point work?

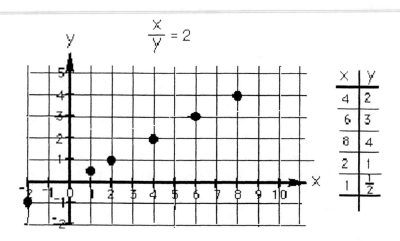

Notice, I'm writing the equation in the form 2•x + 3 = y not y = 2•x + 3 because in the table of numbers, the x - number is on the left also.

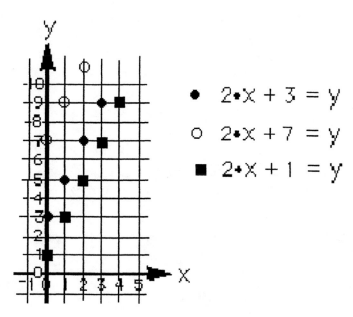

In the equations and graphs above, the multiplying number 2, is the same in each case. The pattern in the graph, the points, go over 1 and up 2 in each case. The adding number, 3, 7, and 1 is changing. That's where they each cross the y - axis, when x = 0; at (0,3), (0,7) and (0,1) respectively.

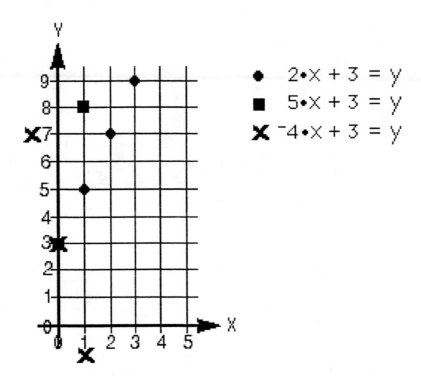

In the equations and graphs above, the multiplying number is changing. The adding number, 3, is staying the same and the three graphs meet at the point (0,3) on the graph. That's where they each cross the y - axis, when x = 0. On the dot graph, the points go over 1 and up 2 spaces. On the diamond graph, the points go over 1 and up 5 spaces. On the x graph, the points go over 1 and down 4 spaces. For the diamond graph, the ratio over 1 and up 2, or $\frac{2}{1}$ = 2 , this 2 is called the slope of the line.

Two equations whose graphs are parallel might be 6•x + 3 = y and 6•x + 1 = y .

Two equations whose graphs are perpendicular might be 4•x + 3 = y and $\frac{^-1}{4}$ •x + 1 = y .

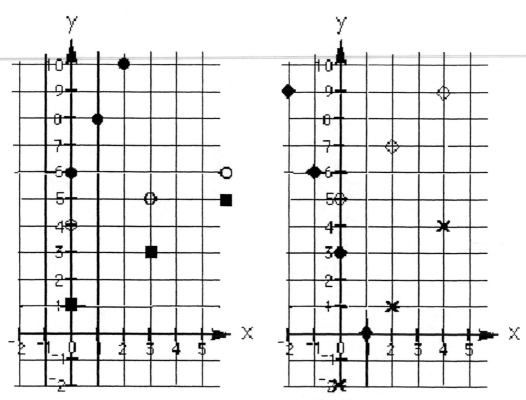

The equations for the graphs above are:

● $2 \cdot x + 6 = y$ ◆ $^-3 \cdot x + 3 = y$

○ $\frac{1}{3} \cdot x + 4 = y$ ◇ $1 \cdot x + 5 = y$

■ $\frac{2}{3} \cdot x + 1 = y$ ✗ $\frac{3}{2} \cdot x + ^-2 = y$

The shuttle puzzle

Quite a while ago, a teacher made the following pattern of the hole as the pegs moved to complete the puzzle. This left an impression on me for many years because it is looking at the movement of the pegs from an entirely different viewpoint. Look at the pattern!

```
start □ □ □ □ ■ □ □ □ □
  1   □ □ □ □ □ ■ □ □ □
  2   □ □ □ ■ □ □ □ □ □
  3   □ □ ■ □ □ □ □ □ □
  4   □ □ □ □ ■ □ □ □ □
  5   □ □ □ □ □ □ ■ □ □
  6   □ □ □ □ □ □ □ ■ □
  7   □ □ □ □ □ ■ □ □ □
  8   □ □ □ ■ □ □ □ □ □
  9   □ ■ □ □ □ □ □ □ □
 10   ■ □ □ □ □ □ □ □ □
 11   □ □ ■ □ □ □ □ □ □
 12   □ □ □ □ ■ □ □ □ □
 13   □ □ □ □ □ □ ■ □ □
 14   □ □ □ □ □ □ □ □ ■
 15   □ □ □ □ □ □ □ ■ □
 16   □ □ □ □ □ ■ □ □ □
 17   □ □ □ ■ □ □ □ □ □
 18   □ ■ □ □ □ □ □ □ □
 19   □ □ ■ □ □ □ □ □ □
 20   □ □ □ □ ■ □ □ □ □
 21   □ □ □ □ □ □ ■ □ □
 22   □ □ □ □ □ ■ □ □ □
 23   □ □ □ ■ □ □ □ □ □
 24   □ □ □ □ ■ □ □ □ □
```

Jonathan, age 8, saw the pattern that the number of pairs of pegs, times 2 more than the number of pairs of pegs, will equal the number of moves. He wrote the rule,

$m = p(p+2) = p^2 + 2p$

No. of pairs of pegs x	No. of moves to interchange the pegs y
1	3
2	8
3	15
4	24

Other people look at the differences, the first differences are the odd numbers.The second differences being constant tells us that the function is a quadratic (has x^2 as the highest power of the function). Another pair of numbers would be (0,0) because we could go back 3 from 3. That tells us that the adding number is 0.

At the right Jonathan graphed the pairs of numbers from the shuttle puzzle.

Then he graphed the function in Derive after I asked him to change the equation to $y = x^2 + 2x$. The graph came out like that below. This was exciting because although I worked with the shuttle puzzle for 30 years, I never had had a student at this point--in a computer program which would allow him to explore the graphs this way.

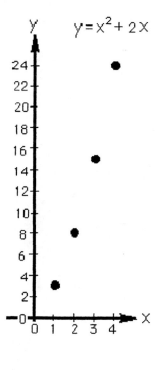

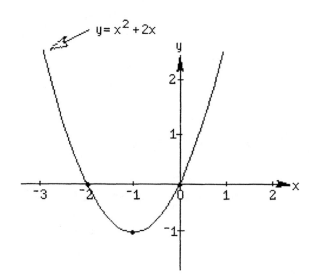

I thought of two things he could explore on the computer: one, move the graph and get the equation for this new graph, and two, have him find out where the graph crosses the x-axis and find the coordinates of the vertex (the low point of this parabola). I asked him what the equation would be if he moved the graph up, or up and over.

At this point Jonathan made up a new equation $y = 3x^2 + 5x$ and graphed that, the dashed one at the right. I then went in the second direction. I asked him if he could find the points where the graph intersected the X - axis and find the coordinates of the vertex. Since the parabolas are symmetrical, he agreed that the X - coordinate of the vertex is halfway between the points where the curve crosses the X - axis (halfway between any 2 points at the same height or have the same y - coordinates). So halfway between ⁻2 and 0 is ⁻1.

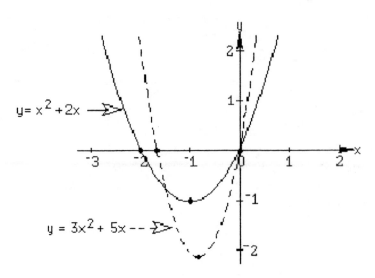

Now how do we find the y - coordinate of the vertex? Just plug in the X - coordinate, ⁻1, into the equation and solve for y.. easy!
He did this:
$y = x^2 + 2x$
$y = (^-1)^2 + 2 \cdot {}^-1$
$y = {}^-1 + {}^-2 = {}^-1$, so the coordinates of the vertex are (⁻1, ⁻1). In *Derive* we are able to move a cross, at the same time have its coordinates show on the screen. To locate the point where the curve $y = 3x^2 + 5x$ crosses the X - axis, besides at 0, we moved the cross to get ⁻1.6666 which he said was $\frac{^-5}{3}$. Now he saw a pattern. Look at the numbers in the equation, 3 and 5, and look at the $\frac{^-5}{3}$. Wow! .. and he saw how to get the X - coordinate of the vertex from the crossing point. I then gave him the equation $y = 5x^2 + 7x$ and he was able to fill in the table below by himself, can you?

Equation	where it crosses the x- axis	the coordinates of the vertex
$y = x^2 + 2x$	$^-2$ and 0	$(^-1, ^-1)$
$y = 3x^2 + 5x$	$\frac{^-5}{3}$ and 0	$(\frac{^-5}{6}, \frac{^-25}{12})$
$y = 5x^2 + 7x$		

The Tower Puzzle

No. of discs X	Minimum No. of moves y

$$1 \quad 1$$
$$2 = 2^1$$
$$2 \quad 3 \quad 3 = 4-1 = 2^2 - 1$$
$$4 = 2^2$$
$$3 \quad 7 \quad 7 = 8-1 = 2^3 - 1$$
$$8 = 2^3$$
$$4 \quad 15 \quad 15 = 16-1 = 2^4 - 1$$
$$16 = 2^4$$
$$5 \quad 31 \quad 31 = 32-1 = 2^5 - 1$$
$$32 = 2^5$$
$$6 \quad 63$$

The tower puzzle

In looking at the table for the tower puzzle at the left, there are many patterns. The y - numbers are odd. The first differences are 2, 4, 8, 16, ... as are the second differences, which are all powers of 2. And these are 1 more than the y-numbers. So we can write the y-number 15, as the next difference, 16, minus 1. But $16 = 2^4$. We can then write $15 = 16 - 1 = 2^4 - 1$. Notice that the exponent is the same as the x-number. This is another clear case where we don't want to write the answer as one number. The tower puzzle rule therefore can be written

$$2^x - 1 = y$$

I think it's important to graph everything.

Jonathan graphed the tower puzzle pairs of numbers on the same graph paper as the shuttle puzzle. He looked at them and said they looked alike. He connected the dots with straight line segments (not a thing I would have done). A couple of questions arose. Will these curves ever meet besides at (0,0)? Yes, at (5.319, 38.938). What happens when we put in negative numbers for x in $2^x - 1 = y$? How would the graph of $2^x = y$ be different from the one above?

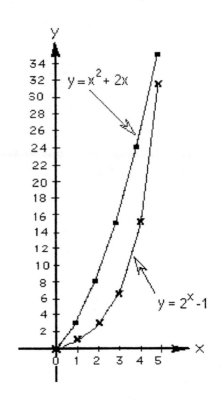

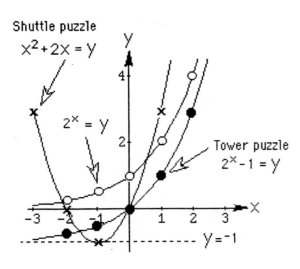

I suggested that Jonathan graph $2^x = y$ on this same graph paper and go into the negatives. We talked about negative exponents again. We looked at the pattern in the powers of 2 (see chapter 1) and he came up with, again, $2^{-1} = \frac{1}{2}$ and $2^{-2} = \frac{1}{4}$, so he was able to graph the points with x-coordinates negative.

He saw that the graph of $2^x = y$, as x gets smaller (goes to the left), approaches the x- axis, y=0, but never crosses it (the x- axis is an asymptote). The graph of $2^x - 1 = y$, as x gets smaller (goes to the left), approaches the line $y = {}^-1$, but never crosses it.

When Jonathan went back to *Derive* to graph the above, he made the mistake (fortuitous, for the teacher), of switching the x and the 2 and graphed $y = x^2 - 1$ instead of $2^x - 1 = y$ with $y = x^2 + 2x$. This lead to a nice discussion of how we move the graphs and how the equation changes.

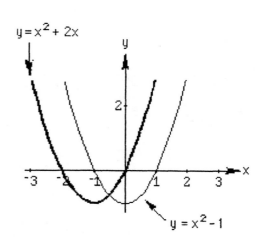

The hinged mirrors

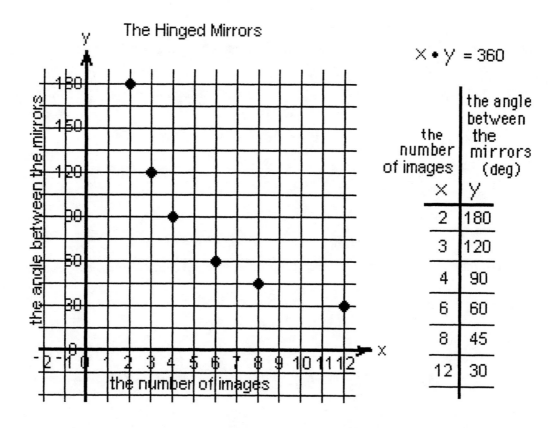

The Hinged Mirrors

$$x \cdot y = 360$$

the number of images	the angle between the mirrors (deg)
X	Y
2	180
3	120
4	90
6	60
8	45
12	30

Amanda wrote the rule as $y = \dfrac{360}{x}$, which is an hyperbola.

4. How lengths, squares and cubes grow
We found the following arrangements of the 1x1x1 cm. cubes

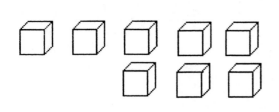

S.A. = 48 cm^3

S.A. = 28 cm^3

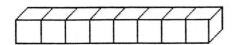

S.A. = 34 cm^3

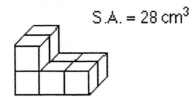

S.A. = 28 cm^3

S.A. = 24 cm^3

We noticed that the smallest surface area, for a given volume, occurred when we built a cube! This same idea occurs in spherical soap bubbles.

rod X	length y
1	1
2	2
3	3
4	4
5	5
⋮	

$x = y$

length of side X	area of square y
1	1
2	4
3	9
4	16
5	25
⋮	

$x^2 = y$

length of edge X	volume of cube y
1	1
2	8
3	27
4	64
5	125
⋮	

$x^3 = y$

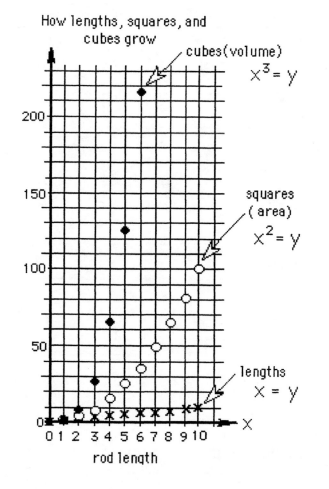

How lengths, squares, and cubes grow

cubes (volume) $x^3 = y$

squares (area) $x^2 = y$

lengths $x = y$

rod length

From the data above, the surface area goes up as the square of the length and the volume goes up as the cube of the length.

6. For the $\frac{SA}{Vol}$ ratio we get an infinite sequence 6, 5, 4.67, 4.5 4.4, 4.33.., 4.28..,

..4.0002,.. which decreases, gets closer and closer to 4 and never gets below 4. So this sequence converges to 4.

Length	Surface area	Volume	$\dfrac{\text{Surface area}}{\text{Volume}}$
1	6	1	$\frac{6}{1} = 6$
2	10	2	$\frac{10}{2} = 5$
3	14	3	$\frac{14}{3} = 4.67$
4	18	4	$\frac{18}{4} = 4.5$
5	22	5	$\frac{22}{5} = 4.4$
6	26	6	$\frac{26}{6} = 4.33$
7	30	7	$\frac{30}{7} = 4.28$
8	34	8	$\frac{34}{8} = 4.25$
9	38	9	$\frac{38}{9} = 4.22$
10	42	10	$\frac{42}{10} = 4.2$
:	:	:	:
100	402	100	$\frac{402}{100} = 4.02$
:	:	:	:
1000	4002	1000	$\frac{4002}{1000} = 4.002$
:	:	:	:
X	$4 \bullet X + 2$	X	$\frac{4 \bullet x + 2}{x} = \frac{4 \bullet x}{x} + \frac{2}{x} = 4 + \frac{2}{x}$

If the white rod (1x1) is a mouse, and the orange rod (1x1x10) a human, the mouse has a greater surface area to volume ratio. The skin acts to rid the body of perspiration and the mass (proportional to the volume) is a measure of heat production. If the mouse ran around during a sunny day, it would lead to "excessive transpiration". That's why rodents are nocturnal animals. A visitor came in on this discussion to say "that's why mice eat more for their weight than elephants and why my son likes thin spaghetti because there is more surface area to be surrounded by sauce than thick spaghetti!" And why we grate cheese before putting it on the spaghetti.

7. The Nautilus Shell

Guan's work on the shell

Guan, 10 years old, measured the following angles between the radius vector and the tangent at various points on the curve: 85°, 80°, 81°, 77°, 79° and averaged them f(85+80+81+77+79,5) = 80.4°. In the process of finding the average, Guan made a mistake in dividing 402 by 5, which he corrected. This helped him understand division better. I think it's important to realize, that if we start young people working on important mathematics, they have time to make mistakes. Frank Land in "The Language of Mathematics" comes out with 79.5°. Guan's measurement error was only about 1%, which I thought was very good . These angles are essentially equal and thus one name for this spiral is the "equiangular spiral".

Guan measured the radius vectors 360° apart got the following ratios:
$\frac{OA}{OB} = \frac{65}{20} = 3.25$, $\frac{50}{15} = 3.33$, $\frac{35}{10} = 3.5$, and averaged them $\frac{3.25+3.33+3.5}{3} = 3.36$. Frank Land in "The Language of Mathematics" comes out with 3.2 . This means the shell lengths from the center, multiply by about 3 each time it goes around 360°.

Vickie's (a 9th grader) work on the shell:
"My first attempt to measure the volume of each chamber was a flop. I failed to have exact and correct equipment, thus I had results that were not accurate. I started from scratch. My second try was more successful. Using a drinking water and a home-made graduated cylinder made from a drinking straw, clay, wax, tape, and a funnel. I discovered the volume of each of the chambers in a measurement system I invented myself and dubbed "Vickies".

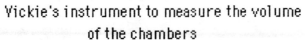

Vickie's instrument to measure the volume
of the chambers

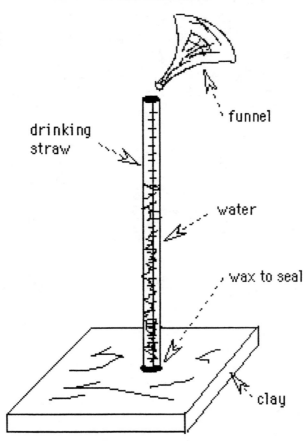

The average percentage of increase from one chamber to another is 6.3%, the figure given in 'On Size and Life', a Scientific American Library book.

     Vol. of Chamber #5 (gray)   = 38.8 Vickies
     Vol. of Chamber #6 (hatched) = 41.5 Vickies

I used the formula:
     Percent increase x original volume = increase of volume
     n% increase x 38.8 Vickies = (41.5 - 38.8) Vickies
     n% increase x 38.8 Vickies = 2.7 Vickies
     n% increase = 6.9%

The next problem was the percentage of increase in the area of the top of the chambers. With the help of the rubbing of the shell and translucent graph paper, I found the approximate area by the tedious method of counting square by square (on mm graph paper).

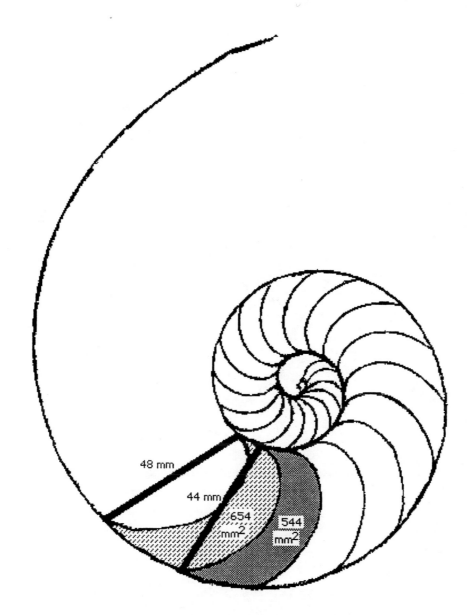

48 mm

44 mm

654 mm^2

544 mm^2

Then I measured one length on some part of the individual chamber (heavy lines above).
Area of chamber #5 = 544 mms^2 Length of chamber #5 = 44 mm
Area of chamber #6 = 654 mms^2 Length of chamber #6 = 48 mm

Then by using the formula: Area = length^2 • k   [This is what we found above, that the area of an object is proportional to the square of a length].
Example of chamber #6
654 = 48^2 • k
k = 0.28
I discovered that k was a constant of approximately 0.3." I did not use all of Vickie's data here, but have since done this with other students and come up with similar results.

8. Other graphs

The graph of $x^2 = y$ from
x= 0 to 4, and its pattern

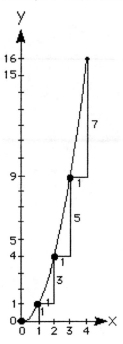

All parabolas (see the graph on the left) have the pattern over 1 up 1, over 1 up 3, over 1 up 5 and so on, because the the odd numbers add up to square numbers. $1+3=4=2^2$, $1+3+5=9=3^2$...If you graph $3x^2 = y$, the pattern would go up 3**x**1, 3**x**3, 3**x**5, ...

On the graph of $x = y$, $x^2 = y$ and $x^3 = y$, if x is say .4, $.4^2$ = .16 < .4 and $.4^3$= .064 < .4, so the points on the curves $x^2 = y$ and $x^3 = y$ are below the graph $x = y$. When x>1, these other graphs will be above the graph $x = y$.

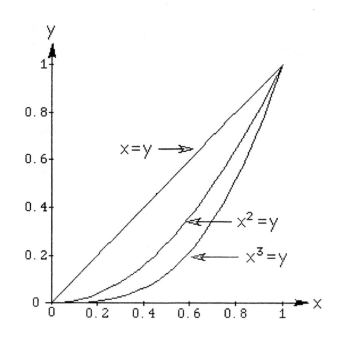

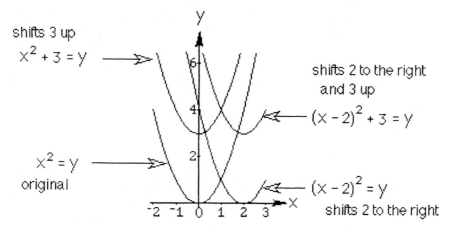

shifts 3 up
$x^2 + 3 = y$ →

shifts 2 to the right
and 3 up
$(x - 2)^2 + 3 = y$

$x^2 = y$ →
original

$(x - 2)^2 = y$
shifts 2 to the right

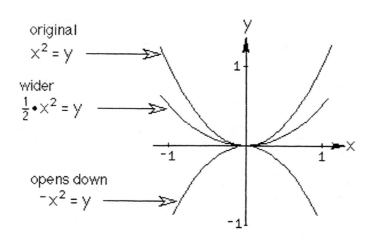

original
$x^2 = y$ →

wider
$\frac{1}{2} \cdot x^2 = y$ →

opens down
$^{-}x^2 = y$ →

Are there any other positions of the parabola that you can find and get an equation for?

Below is the graph of $x^2 + k \cdot y^2 = 25$. Using k = 1 we get a circle with radius 5 or $\sqrt{25}$; when k = 4 we get an ellipse whose highest point is 2.5 or $\sqrt{\frac{25}{4}}$; when k = $\frac{1}{2}$ we get an ellipse whose highest point is 10 or $2 \cdot \sqrt{25}$; when k = 0 we get 2 vertical lines; when k = ⁻1 and k = ⁻4 we get an hyperbola (notice the 2 pieces to each hyperbola).

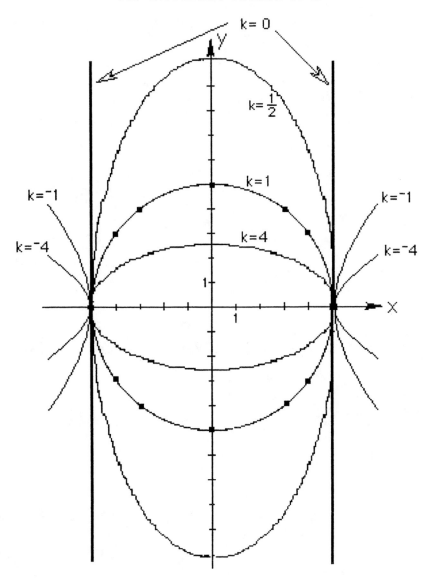

Graph of $x^2 + k \cdot y^2 = 25$
for different values of k

Where do parabolas, circles, ellipses and hyperbolas show up in our world? These are very important shapes.
Lots of things to do here! Make up other questions.

Question worksheets for **chapter 7**
"The Fibonacci Numbers, Pineapples, Sunflowers and The Golden Mean"

1. **Some of the Fibonacci numbers** are found in the "whorling" leaf arrangements (the botanical name is phyllotaxis) of many plants. It took me a year or so to find these patterns, and then the numbers. You really have to look carefully, because these patterns are not in every plant. We'll start with a pineapple.

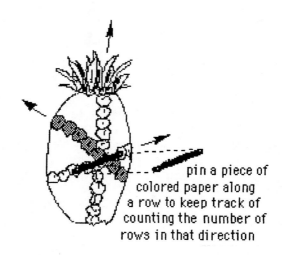

pin a piece of colored paper along a row to keep track of counting the number of rows in that direction

There are rows of nearly-hexagonal cells. Look for them as they whorl or spiral around the pineapple. There are three directions these rows take. Find them on your pineapple. Have someone else work with you.

The leaves of a sunflower
grow helically around the stalk.

Start from any leaf (#0 below) and go to the next leaf that
comes out of the stalk directly above the starting one (#8 below).
There are 2 things to count here:

1 Count the number of times the leaves go around the stalk (3 in this case).

2 Count the number of leaves from the starting one to the one above it (8 in this case).

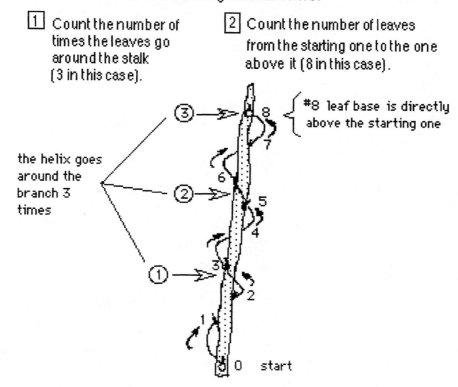

the helix goes around the branch 3 times

#8 leaf base is directly above the starting one

This is called a 3,8 pattern. I found the bush in front of my house has a similar pattern. See if you can find some of these patterns of leaf growth near your house, in your garden, at the plant store.

The numbers we come out with from the pineapple, the number of rows, are

8, **13**, and **21**; the numbers from the sunflower stalk are

3 and **8**

If you look carefully at the 8, 13, 21, what's happening? How do we get the next number in the sequence? 5+8 =13 and 8+13 = 21, so the next number will be 13+21=34; the number before 8 is 5 and we have

1, 1, 2, 3, 5, 8, 13, 21, 34, ...

You add the last 2 numbers to get the next number. This infinite sequence (divergent) is called the Fibonacci numbers. It has very interesting properties and has been studied for many years.

Write down the next 6 numbers in the sequence.

2. Write a computer program that will print out these Fibonacci numbers.

3. Now let's look at the ratios of successive Fibonacci numbers, so we need to divide each number by the previous number. Write the ratios as mixed numbers and decimals. Do the 3 ratios after the ones below by hand, then use a calculator and write as many decimal places as your calculator shows for the decimal.

$\frac{1}{1} = 1$	$\frac{13}{8} =$	
$\frac{2}{1} = 2$		
$\frac{3}{2} = 1\frac{1}{2} = 1.5$		
$\frac{5}{3} = 1\frac{2}{3} = 1.6666...$		$\frac{610}{377} =$
$\frac{8}{5} =$		

Look for patterns in this sequence of mixed numbers. What's happening to the numbers? Are they increasing or decreasing? Can you predict the first 4 decimal places in the next ratio?

Graph the ratios on the paper below, starting with 3rd one (the first 2 are shown below).

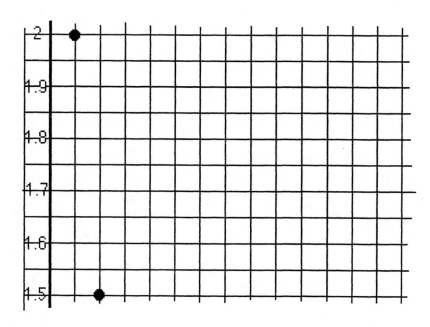

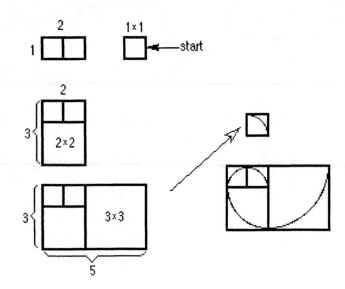

4. Using the Fibonacci numbers we can make a spiral and approach the golden rectangle: On a piece of $\frac{1}{4}$" graph paper, about 10 units from the wide top side and short left side, start a 1x1 square. Then build on this one more of the Fibonacci squares, 1x1, 2x2, 3x3, 5x5, and so on. In the process we obtain rectangles 1x1, 2x1, 3x2, 5x3, and so on; the ratio of length to width of these rectangles approaches the golden mean. Then use a compass to draw an arc of a circle using the corner of the square as the center. Make the rectangle and spiral as large as you can.

In the process of doing this for about the 10th time, I discovered something about the sum of the squares of the Fibonacci numbers and the area of the rectangles. Can you find a pattern?

5. Ratios of other Fibonacci-type numbers

Instead of 1 and 1 for the first two numbers, as in the Fibonacci sequence, what happens to the sequence and their ratios if we start with two different numbers? Use your calculator or computer to investigate this.

What happens if, instead of adding the last two numbers, we change the rule and add the last three numbers?

Make up some other questions to investigate.

4. The golden angle was obtained by a group of teachers examining the sunflower leaves, then finding fractions of 360° using ratios of **alternate** Fibonacci numbers :
1, 1, 2, 3, 5, 8, 13, 21, 34, 55, 89, ...

$\frac{1}{2}$ x 360° = 180°

$\frac{1}{3}$ x 360° = 120°

$\frac{2}{5}$ x 360° = 144°

Keep going and see what happens to this infinite sequence.

What is the golden angle?

Another way to use the sunflower is to count the spirals of seeds on the head of the plant. There are two sets of whorling seeds; the number of these in each in each set varies upon the size of the sunflower, but each number is a Fibonacci number (or close to it). We have gotten 55 and 89. Counting these spiralling seed rows is tricky; we put small colored pins in each row, then counted the pins. Since nothing in nature is perfect, the rows are difficult to count. Whoever said counting is simple, obviously never tried to count sunflower seed rows on a pineapple!

An example of a plant whose leaves whorl at an angle of 144°.

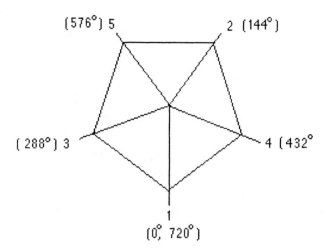

7. Cutting a line segment

One of the more common methods of getting the golden mean or golden section is to cut a line segment AB at point C, such that the following proportion works:

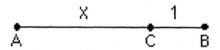

$$\frac{\text{the whole segment AB}}{\text{the larger segment AC}} = \frac{\text{the larger segment AC}}{\text{the smaller segment CB}}$$

If we call the larger segment x, the smaller segment, 1, the whole segment is x + 1. Now write an equation in x using the proportion, then solve it (you might want to see chapter 8 to solve it).

8. The pentagon:
Copy the pentagon sheet in appendix 4. At the
right is a regular (all sides and angles equal)
pentagon ABCDE, with one diagonal, AC, drawn.
With a straight edge, draw in all the diagonals of
the pentagon. Label the points of intersection.

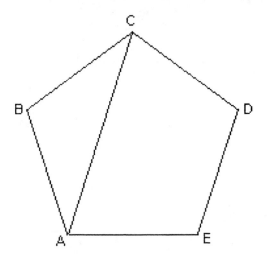

What do you see?

How many different shape triangles are formed?

How many different size angles are formed?
Knowing that the sum of the angles of a triangle
is $180°$ can you figure out the number of degrees
in the different angles?
What do they measure?

How many different length segments are
formed?
Measure all the lengths of the segments formed
(in mm.).

Compare your measurements with those of other
people.

Find the ratio of bigger to smaller length
segments. What do you notice?

Make up other questions to investigate.

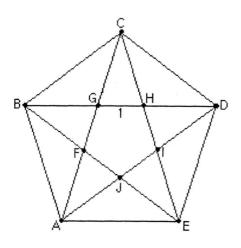

If we say the length of GH = 1, what would be the length of CH? What did you get for the ratio of CH to GH, or $\frac{CH}{GH}$? Whatever this ratio is, it will be the length of CH, if GH is 1.

Remember the golden mean is about 1.6 . Do you see that anywhere in these ratios? If GH = 1 what is CD? BH?

If we let ø = CH and GH = 1. Find the other lengths in terms of ø.

9. Solve this quadratic equation $ø^2 - ø - 1 = 0$ using the quadratic formula:

$$X_1 = \frac{^-b + \sqrt{b^2 - 4ac}}{2a} \quad \text{and} \quad X_2 = \frac{^-b - \sqrt{b^2 - 4ac}}{2a}$$ where a =1, b = ¯1 and c = ¯1

This figure shows 4
arcs of the
golden spiral like
Barbara and Jenny,
both 9th graders,
made.
You make one
starting with a
pentagon.

the first arc has
its center
at point 1

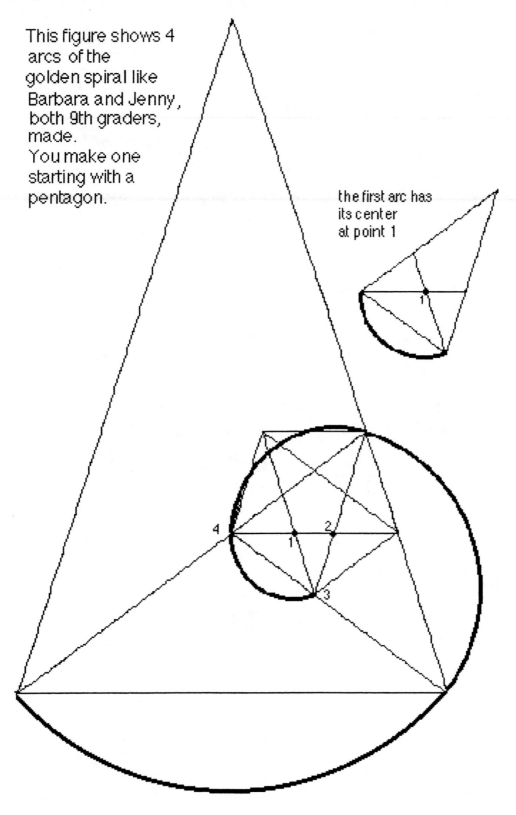

Answer worksheets for **chapter 7**
"The Fibonacci Numbers, Pineapples, Sunflowers and The Golden Mean"

1. Find the first 15 Fibonacci numbers are:

1, 1, 2, 3, 5, 8, 13, 21, 34, 55, 89, 144, 233, 377, 610, ...

	FX 7000G	Basic
2. Computer programs to give the Fibonacci sequence for the FX 7000G (similar to any other programmable calculator) and in Basic are shown at the right:	1-> X: 1->Y: Lbl 7: X+Y->Z Y->X: Z->Y: Goto 7	10 X=1 20 Print X 30 Y=1 40 Print Y 50 Z=X+Y 60 Print Z 70 X=Y 80 Y=Z 90 Goto 50

3. The first 14 **ratios of the successive Fibonacci numbers** are given below:

$\frac{1}{1} = 1$	$\frac{13}{8} = 1\frac{5}{8} = 1.625$	$\frac{144}{89} = 1\frac{55}{89} = 1.61797...$
$\frac{2}{1} = 2$	$\frac{21}{13} = 1\frac{8}{13} = 1.61538...$	$\frac{233}{144} = 1\frac{89}{144} = 1.61805...$
$\frac{3}{2} = 1\frac{1}{2} = 1.5$	$\frac{34}{21} = 1\frac{13}{21} = 1.61904...$	$\frac{377}{233} = 1\frac{144}{233} = 1.61802...$
$\frac{5}{3} = 1\frac{2}{3} = 1.6666...$	$\frac{55}{34} = 1\frac{21}{34} = 1.61764...$	$\frac{610}{377} = 1\frac{233}{377} = 1.61803...$
$\frac{8}{5} = 1\frac{3}{5} = 1.6$	$\frac{89}{55} = 1\frac{34}{55} = 1.61818...$	

This infinite sequence of ratios of Fibonacci numbers

$1, 2, 1\frac{1}{2}, 1\frac{2}{3}, 1\frac{3}{5}, 1\frac{5}{8}, 1\frac{8}{13}, 1\frac{13}{21}, 1\frac{21}{34}, 1\frac{34}{55}, 1\frac{55}{89}, 1\frac{89}{144}, 1\frac{144}{233}, 1\frac{233}{610}$, ... or as decimals,

1, 2, 1.5, 1.66..., 1.6, 1.625, 1.61538..., 1.61904..., 1.61764..., 1.61818..., 1.61797..., 1.61805..., 1.61802..., 1.61803..., ...

does have a limit. This number, to 19 decimal places, 1.6180339887498948482... is called The Golden Mean or The Divine Proportion. It's the irrational number $\frac{1+\sqrt{5}}{2}$.

The graph the ratios of the Fibonacci numbers is shown below.

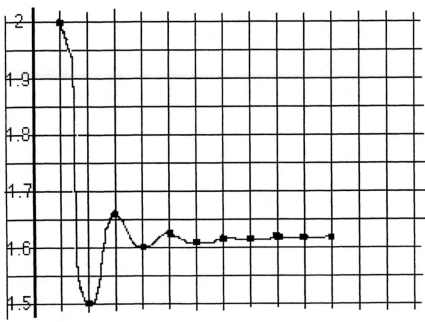

4. The spiral of rectangles

In the process of making the spiral once more, using the Fibonacci numbers as squares and approaching the golden rectangle, I saw that the sum of the squares of the Fibonacci numbers is equal to the area of the rectangle they form (the product of the length by the width):

$$1^2 = 1 \times 1$$
$$1^2 + 1^2 = 2 \times 1$$
$$1^2 + 1^2 + 2^2 = 3 \times 2$$
$$1^2 + 1^2 + 2^2 + 3^2 = 5 \times 3$$

$$1^2 + 1^2 + 2^2 + 3^2 + 5^2 = 8 \times 5$$
$$1^2 + 1^2 + 2^2 + 3^2 + 5^2 + 8^2 = 13 \times 8$$

and generalizing,

$$F_1^2 + F_2^2 + F_3^2 + .. + F_n^2 = F_{n+1} \cdot F_n$$

5. The ratio of other numbers

Instead of 1 and 1 for the first two numbers, as in the Fibonacci sequence, if we start with 1 and 4 we get the sequence 1,4 5, 9, 14, 23, 37, 60, 97, 157,... and the ratios form a convergent sequence with the same limit, the golden mean! Have you found any sequences that don't go to the golden mean? Let us know, OK.

What happens if, instead of adding the last two numbers, we change the rule and add the last three numbers? I have only done 3 cases.

1, 2, 7, 10, 19, 36, 65, 120, ... and 1, 1, 2, 4, 7, 13, 24, 44, 81, ... and -2, 1, 4, 3, 8, 15, 26, 49, ...

The ratios in each case form a convergent sequence which goes to 1.839286755... I wonder what that number is ?? It turns out this is one root of the cubic equation

$$x^3 - x^2 - x - 1 = 0.$$

6. The golden angle was obtained by a group of teachers examining the sunflower leaves, then finding fractions of 360° using ratios of alternate Fibonacci numbers :
1, 1, 2, 3, 5, 8, 13, 21, 34, 55, 89, ...

$\frac{1}{2}$ **x** 360° = 180°

$\frac{1}{3}$ **x** 360° = 120°

$\frac{2}{5}$ **x** 360° = 144°

$\frac{3}{8}$ **x** 360° = 135°

$\frac{5}{13}$ **x** 360° = 138.46...°

$\frac{8}{21}$ **x** 360° = 137.14...°

$\frac{13}{34}$ **x** 360° = 137.64...°

$\frac{21}{55}$ **x** 360° = 137.46...°

$\frac{34}{89}$ **x** 360° = 137.52...°

$\frac{15}{144}$ **x** 360° = 137.50°

This gives us an infinite alternating sequence whose limit is the golden angle, about 137.5° or 137°30'28". This is the angle that allows each leaf to be closest to the leaf below it in the previous whorl and farthest from the youngest previous leaf above it; in other words, it allows the leaf to get maximum sunlight. This number can be written as

$(.618034...)^2$ **x** 360 = $\frac{3-\sqrt{5}}{2}$ **x** 360 and is also $\left(\dfrac{1}{\frac{1+\sqrt{5}}{2}}\right)^2$ **x** 360.

7. The cutting of the segment AB at C

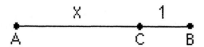

such that $\dfrac{\text{the whole segment AB}}{\text{the larger segment AC}} = \dfrac{\text{the larger segment AC}}{\text{the smaller segment CB}}$

If we call the larger segment x, the smaller segment, 1, then the whole segment is x + 1. We can write this equation in x using the proportion above:

1. $\frac{x+1}{x} = \frac{x}{1}$ or equivalently,

2. $x = \frac{x+1}{x}$

         ÷ by **x** on the right side

3. $x = 1 + \frac{1}{x}$

Mult. both sides by x

4. $x^2 = x + 1$

-1 from both sides

5. $x = x^2 - 1$

- **x** from both sides

6. $x^2 - x - 1 = 0$

We solve this equation in various ways in Ch. 8. Barbara and Jenny used the quadratic formula to solve version #6 later on.

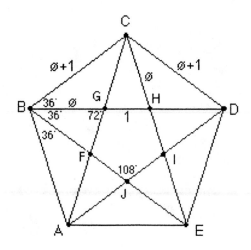

8. The pentagon
There will be other things you find, but here are some things Barbara and Jenny, 9th graders at the time, found:

A smaller pentagon FGHIJ is formed inside, but points in the opposite direction.

The sum of the interior angles of a regular polygon is (n-2) **X** 180°
One angle of a regular pentagon is
$$\frac{(5-2) \times 180°}{5} = 108°.$$

There are only 3 different angles in the pentagon, 36°, 72° (2 **X** 36°), and 108° (3 **X**36°) in the figure.

There are only 2 different shape triangles. The obtuse isosceles triangles like HCD, of only two sizes, and similar. The other shape triangles are the acute isosceles triangles of three sizes, and these are similar triangles also.

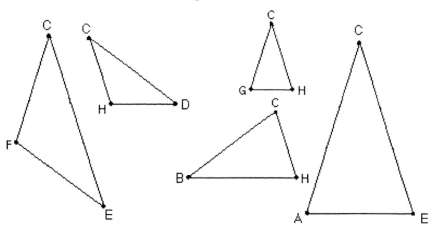

We found also that $\frac{\sin 72°}{\sin 36°} = \text{\o} = 1.6...;$ $\frac{\sin 108°}{\sin 36°} = \text{\o};$ and $\frac{\sin 108°}{\sin 72°} = 1$

The acute triangles at the right taken out of the pentagon, all have the same angles 36°, 72°, and 72°, therefore are similar triangles (do the eye test). They are isosceles triangles (2 sides equal). It turns out they are **golden triangles** because the ratio of the longest side to the shortest side $\frac{CH}{GH}$ = the golden mean ≈ 1.6. We used the symbol ø (the Greek letter phi) to represent it. So we let ø = CH and GH = 1.

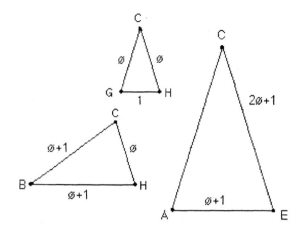

Since triangle HBC is similar to triangle GCH, the sides are proportional, therefore they said the following proportion must be true: $\frac{CH}{GH} = \frac{BC}{HC}$ and $\frac{ø}{1} = \frac{ø+1}{ø}$. From that, $ø^2 = ø+1$. ø+1 is also the length of the side of the pentagon. Triangle ACE is also similar to triangle GCH so the following proportion is true: $\frac{ø}{1} = \frac{2ø+1}{ø+1} = \frac{2ø+1}{ø^2}$ and therefore $ø^3 = 2ø+1$.

Extending the lines, Barbara and Jenny found $ø^4 = 3ø+2$ and $ø^5 = 5ø+3$.

They saw a pattern in the powers of ø and wrote a computer program which printed out:

$$ø^{-5} = 5 \cdot ø + {}^-8 \qquad ø^{-2} = {}^-1 \cdot ø + 2 \qquad ø^1 = 1 \cdot ø + 0 \qquad ø^4 = 3 \cdot ø + 2$$

$$ø^{-4} = {}^-3 \cdot ø + 5 \qquad ø^{-1} = 1 \cdot ø + {}^-1 \qquad ø^2 = 1 \cdot ø + 1 \qquad ø^5 = 5 \cdot ø + 3$$

$$ø^{-3} = 2 \cdot ø + {}^-3 \qquad ø^0 = 0 \cdot ø + 1 \qquad ø^3 = 2 \cdot ø + 1 \qquad ø^6 = 8 \cdot ø + 5$$

... AND YOU SHALL MEET A HORRIBLE FATE... YOU SHALL SPEND ALL ETERNITY FINDING POWERS OF PHI...

9. Barbara and Jenny solved this quadratic equation $ø^2 - ø - 1 = 0$ they got above, using the quadratic formula:

$$x_1 = \frac{{}^-b + \sqrt{b^2 - 4ac}}{2a} \quad \text{and} \quad x_2 = \frac{{}^-b - \sqrt{b^2 - 4ac}}{2a}$$

where a = 1, b = ⁻1 and c = ⁻1. They got $ø_1 = \frac{1+\sqrt{5}}{2} = 1.61803...$ and $ø_2 = \frac{1-\sqrt{5}}{2} = {}^-0.61803...$ They realised that $ø_1 \cdot ø_2 = {}^-1$ and $ø_1 + ø_2 = 1$

Linus and I wrote a program on the FX7000G to solve any quadratic equation $ax^2 + bx + c = 0$ if we put in a, b, and c, using the quadratic formula. Try that.

What happens if you draw the diagonals of this smaller pentagon? Make up other questions.

Question worksheets for **chapter 8**
"Solving Equations, Infinite Continued Fractions and Iteration "
See also Don's videotape "Iteration to Infinite Sequences with 6 to 11 year-olds"

1. Make this equation or open sentence true, by guessing:

$$2 \cdot x + 3 = 17$$

What does this mean? We're looking for a number to put in for x so that when we multiply it by 2, then add 3, we should get 17. Notice that the x is not a times sign, it's a variable, holding the place for a number. The dot (·) here means multiply.

Let's try 5 in for x, $2 \cdot 5 + 3 \overset{?}{=} 17$ is 2·5 + 3 equal to 17? 2·5 = 10

$$10 + 3 \overset{?}{=} 17 \quad \text{is 10 + 3 equal to 17?}$$

$$13 \overset{?}{=} 17 \quad \text{is 13 equal to 17 ? No. 13 = 17 is false.}$$

So 5 doesn't work. Is 5 too big or too small? 5 is too small because we get 13 on the left side of the equation, and that's smaller than 17. What shall we try next? 7. OK.

$$2 \cdot 7 + 3 \overset{?}{=} 17$$

$$14 + 3 \overset{?}{=} 17$$

$$17 \overset{?}{=} 17 \text{ and this is true.}$$

So 7 is the number that works, it makes a true statement, 7 is the answer to
$2 \cdot x + 3 = 17$.

Guessing is very important, for at least 5 reasons:
1) you start off right away.
2) it gets you into the problem, you don't have to think "I haven't been taught this, so I can't do it " attitude and then feel you have to wait for someone to tell you how to solve it.
3) you can solve many equations this way, not a trivial few. Don't be discouraged if you guess wrong the first few times; keep trying, you can do it.
4) you'll also get better at guessing. And
5) you might even come up with different ways to solve the same problem, which would be very good.

Now solve these equations, make these open sentences true:
  2) $2 \cdot x + 3 = 18$
  3) $3 \cdot x + 5 = 11$
  4) $3 \cdot x + 5 = 12$
What could you change if you made up an equation like these?
Make up some equations like these for a friend and have a friend make up some for you. You might want to change one thing at a time to see what happens. See if you can find some patterns. Stay with one variable, in chapter 6 we dealt with graphing equations with 2 variables.

If you make up these equations which have a pattern

$$7 \cdot x + 5 = 11$$
$$8 \cdot x + 5 = 11$$
$$9 \cdot x + 5 = 11$$
$$10 \cdot x + 5 = 11$$

is there a pattern in the answers?

You make up some equations which have a pattern in them, and find a pattern in the answers.

Generalize to get the answer to all equations of this form: $a \cdot x + b = c$

_____

Generalize to get the answer to all equations of this form: $a \cdot x - b = c$

_____

Make up an equation that has more than one answer. Stay with one variable.

2. Make up an equation such that all numbers will make it true.

An example of an equation that all numbers will make it true, is
$2 \cdot x = x + x$ (remember the rule for substituting--in any one open sentence, you must put the same number in for each of the same variables).

$$2 \cdot x = x + x \qquad \text{we'll put } 3 \to x$$
$$2 \cdot 3 = 3 + 3 \qquad \text{and that's true, so 3 works}$$

$$2 \cdot 4 = 4 + 4 \qquad \text{and 4 works}$$
$$2 \cdot 5 = 5 + 5 \qquad \text{and 5 works}$$

$$\vdots$$

...**every** number will make this **open sentence** $2 \cdot x = x + x$ true. This is a special open sentence or equation, called an **identity**.

Make up lots of identities! See how many your friends can make up.

Are all of these identities? Which are not identities? Why?

[1] $x + x + x = 3 \cdot x$

[2] $3 \cdot (x + 5) = 3 \cdot x + 15$

[3] $x \cdot x = 2 \cdot x$

[4] $x + x - x = x$

[5] $2 \cdot 3 = 3 \cdot 2$

[6] $x - y = x + {}^{-}y$

[7] $2^x \cdot 2^y = 2^{x+y}$

[8] $x \div y = x \cdot \dfrac{1}{y}$

[9] $x + 0 = x$

[10] $x \cdot 1 = x$

[11] $(x + 0) \cdot 1 = x$

[12] $3 - 5 = 5 - 3$

[13] $\sqrt{x^2 + y^2} = x + y$

[14] $ab = ba$

[15] $3 \cdot x + 0 = 3 \cdot x$

[16] ${}^{-}({}^{-}x) = x$

[17] $3 \div 2 = 3 \cdot \dfrac{1}{2}$

[18] $A^x \cdot A^y = A^{x+y}$

[19] $x - y = y - x$

[20] $3(x + 4) + 2 = 5x + 12$

[21] $(x + y)^2 = x^2 + y^2$

[22] $3 \cdot x + 2 \cdot x = 5 \cdot x$

[23] $8 \div x = x \div 8$

[24] $3 \cdot x + 2 = 5 \cdot x$

[25] $a + b = c$

[26] ${}^{-}(x - y) = x + y$

[27] $(x - y)^2 = x^2 - 2xy + y^2$

[28] ${}^{-}2 + {}^{-}({}^{-}x - 2 + x) = 0$

Make up an equation that has no answer!

3. Solve this equation with X's on both sides, by guessing:

(Remember the **rule for substituting**... whatever number you put in for one X , you must put in for all the X 's in any one equation).

Look for a pattern in how far apart the left and right sides are after you substitute numbers in for X.

    5). $5 \cdot X + 3 = 2 \cdot X + 27$

                Your answer for 5). _____

Let's try some numbers in for X in equation 5).

$$5 \cdot x + 3 = 2 \cdot x + 27$$

Suppose we try 4 -> X, to see if this makes it true

$$5 \cdot 4 + 3 \overset{?}{=} 2 \cdot 4 + 27$$

$$20 + 3 \overset{?}{=} 8 + 27$$

$$23 \overset{?}{=} 35 \quad \text{this is false and the two sides are 12 apart} \ (35-23=12)$$

Suppose we try 5 -> X,

$$5 \cdot 5 + 3 \overset{?}{=} 2 \cdot 5 + 27$$

$$25 + 3 \overset{?}{=} 10 + 27$$

$$28 \overset{?}{=} 37 \qquad \text{is this true or false? False, but the two sides are only 9 apart}$$

(37-28=9) now. We're getting closer. Try to find a pattern to how much the two sides are apart as we go up 1 for our guess number.

Go get it!

Now solve these:

6) $6 \cdot x + 5 = 5 \cdot x + 7$
7) $4 \cdot x + 3 = 2 \cdot x + 14$
8) $5 \cdot x + 23 = 2 \cdot x + 29$

Make up some equations like these for a friend and have a friend make up some for you.

Make up an equation like this where the answer will be a negative number.
Make up an equation like this where the answer will be a fraction.

Generalize to get the answer to all equations of this form: $a \cdot x + b = c \cdot x + d$

4. Solving quadratic equations, by guessing

There are 2 numbers that will make this one true: $x^2 - 5 \cdot x + 6 = 0$. Let's try a small number, say 4

We'll put 4 in for x: $x^2 - 5 \cdot x + 6 = 0$

$$4^2 - 5 \cdot 4 + 6 \overset{?}{=} 0 \quad \text{is this true or false? } 4^2 = 16, \ 5 \cdot 4 = 20, \text{ so}$$

$$16 - 20 + 6 \overset{?}{=} 0 \quad \text{and} \quad 20 - 16 = 4, \text{ so } 16 - 20 = {}^-4, \text{ so}$$

$${}^-4 \ + \ 6 \overset{?}{=} 0 \quad \text{this statement is False, because } {}^-4 + 6 = {}^-2, \text{ not } 0$$

So 4 does not work, does not make this open sentence true. It's not far away though!

Let's try 2-> x

$$x^2 - 5 \cdot x + 6 = 0$$
$$2^2 - 5 \cdot 2 + 6 \overset{?}{=} 0$$

$$4 - 10 + 6 \overset{?}{=} 0 \quad \text{is this true or false? Let's see, } 4 - 10 = {}^-6 \text{ and}$$

$${}^-6 \ + 6 \overset{?}{=} 0 \quad \text{which is True.}$$

So 2 works, 2 makes our equation true, 2 is one solution of our equation.

It turns out that there is another number that works. See if you can find it. Once you know the 2 numbers, there is a secret way of solving equations like this.

The other number that makes $x^2 - 5 \cdot x + 6 = 0$ true is _____

So... look at the equation and the two answers, the two solutions, the two numbers that make it true. This is the point where looking for patterns becomes important because it can make our work easy.

$$x^2 - 5 \cdot x + 6 = 0 \quad \{\, 2, 3 \,\}$$

How are the 2 and 3 related to the 5 ? How can we get 5 from the two answers, 2 and 3? How can we get the 6 from the answers 2 and 3 ?

See if you can solve these equations, quickly and easily. Do you think you know both secrets? Don't tell, if you do. Check the numbers in each case just to make sure:

$$x^2 - 8 \cdot x + 15 = 0 \quad \{\ ,\ \}$$
$$x^2 - 7 \cdot x + 10 = 0 \quad \{\ ,\ \}$$

Watch out, there are really 2 secrets!

$$x^2 - 10 \cdot x + 24 = 0 \quad \{\ ,\ \}$$
$$x^2 - 11 \cdot x + 24 = 0 \quad \{\ ,\ \}$$
$$x^2 - 25 \cdot x + 24 = 0 \quad \{\ ,\ \}$$

Make up some like these for a friend. You might want to choose your two answers first, then make the equation from those numbers. Don't try to make them too hard right away.

Have your friend make some for you to do.

This one has one answer that is a whole number. Try it.

$$x^2 - 6\tfrac{1}{2} \cdot x + 9 = 0 \quad \{\ ,\ \}$$

5. Using a balance scale model and transform operations to solve

$$5 \cdot x + 3 = 2 \cdot x + 18$$

An equation like this can be modelled using a balance scale. Think of the x 's as bags of washers (flat disks with a hole in the middle). For this equation 5 bags (5·x) of washers and 3 loose ones, balance (=), 2 bags of washers (2·x) and 18 loose ones. Make the equation simpler by taking the same amount of things off both sides, thus keeping the scale balanced, and find how many washers are in each bag (solve for x).

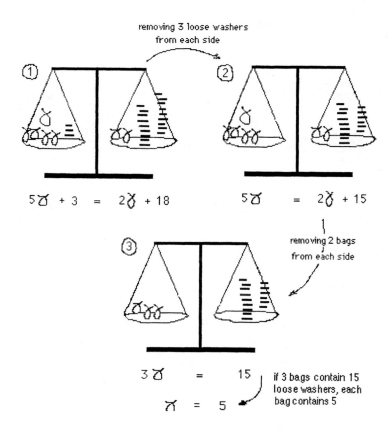

$5x + 3 \;=\; 2x + 18$ $5x \;=\; 2x + 15$

$3x \;=\; 15$

$x \;=\; 5$ if 3 bags contain 15 loose washers, each bag contains 5

There must be 5 washers in each bag then. So x = 5. 5 is the solution of this equation 5·x + 3 = 2·x + 18. To check our answer, put 5 in for x, 5·5 + 3 = 2·5 +18, 28=28, so 5 works. The nice thing about these equations is that you can check yourself and you can tell if you are right or not.

Make up some balance pictures to solve these equations

$$6 \cdot x + 7 = 4 \cdot x + 15$$
$$8 \cdot x + 12 = 2 \cdot x + 24$$

The equations 5·x + 3 = 2·x + 18 , 5·x = 2·x + 15 and 3·x = 15 all have the same answer and are **equivalent** equations. What things can you do to make equations equivalent (besides subtracting the same thing from both sides)?

6. Iteration or Feedback

This is an idea that was new to me just a few years ago. It's important in such studies as chaos theory and fractal geometry. It's interesting and surprising, and fun.

We'll start with the function $3 \cdot x$. Put a number in for x, get the answer, then put that number back in for x again. Continue that procedure, forever. What happens?

> $3 \cdot x$ we'll start by putting $2 \to x$
> $3 \cdot 2 = 6$, then take this 6 and put it back in for x
> $3 \cdot 6 = 18$

Listing our numbers... 2,   6,   18,   54,   162, ...   What's happening?

If we write these   2, $2 \cdot 3$, $2 \cdot 3 \cdot 3$, $2 \cdot 3 \cdot 3 \cdot 3$, $2 \cdot 3 \cdot 3 \cdot 3 \cdot 3$, ...

or with exponents $2 \cdot 3^0$, $2 \cdot 3^1$, $2 \cdot 3^2$, $2 \cdot 3^3$, $2 \cdot 3^4$, .. , $2 \cdot 3^n$ (the nth term),....

This is an infinite sequence which has no limit, it just gets bigger and bigger. **Notice that if you don't write the answer with a single number, you can see patterns and generalize easier.**

Now you try iterating the function $10 \cdot x$ and start by putting $4 \to x$. Write the first 5 terms, and generalize using exponents for the nth term.

Now we'll investigate an application of this iteration or feedback process: If the population of a town increases 10% each year, starting 1000 people, what would the population be after 3 years? n years? (Compound interest can be done similarly, see chapter 11).

A teacher made up this interesting function to iterate: $5 + \dfrac{x}{2}$. Start with 0 and do 10 iterations; see what happens. Make a graph of the sequence you get.

If we start iterating

$5 + \dfrac{x}{2}$ with 0 in for x, for example, we get

$5 + \dfrac{0}{2} = 5 + 0 = \mathbf{5}$, then put **5** back in for x

$5 + \dfrac{5}{2} = 5 + 2\dfrac{1}{2} = 7\dfrac{1}{2}$, then put $7\dfrac{1}{2}$ back in for x

$5 + \dfrac{7\frac{1}{2}}{2} = 5 + 3\dfrac{3}{4} = 8\dfrac{3}{4}$, $\left(\dfrac{7\frac{1}{2}}{2} = \dfrac{1}{2} \text{ of } 7 + \dfrac{1}{2} \text{ of } \dfrac{1}{2} = 3\dfrac{1}{2} + \dfrac{1}{4} = 3\dfrac{3}{4}\right)$. Now put $8\dfrac{3}{4}$ back in for x

$5 + \dfrac{8\frac{3}{4}}{2} = 5 + 4\dfrac{3}{8} = 9\dfrac{3}{8}$, now put $9\dfrac{3}{8}$ back in for x

$5 + \dfrac{9\frac{3}{8}}{2} = 5 + 4\dfrac{11}{16} = 9\dfrac{11}{16}$, now put $9\dfrac{11}{16}$ back in for x, and so on

Let's look at our sequence of numbers:

$0, \ 5, \ 7\dfrac{1}{2}, \ 8\dfrac{3}{4}, \ 9\dfrac{3}{8}, \ 9\dfrac{11}{16}, \ ...$

or as decimals, 0, 5, 7.5, 8.75, 9.375, 9.6875, 9.84375, 9.921875, 9.9609375, 9.98046875, ...

We have an infinite sequence. What's happening? What is it going to?
Graph the number of iterations vs. the number in the sequence, starting with 0.

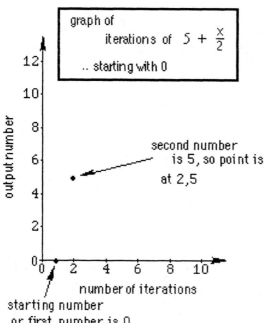

The graph at the left is the beginning of the graph of this sequence that we just obtained by iterating $5 + \dfrac{x}{2}$ and starting with 0. Complete 10 points on the graph.

Use a calculator and try other numbers to start--negative numbers, big numbers..see what happens. Graph the sequences.

Iterate $\dfrac{6}{x}$, then graph the input number vs the output numbers.

Starting with 1->x we get $\dfrac{6}{1}$ = 6, then $\dfrac{6}{6}$ = 1, then we get 6, 1, 6, ...

Start with other numbers, see what happens.

If we graph the input x's vs. the output x's by plotting the points (1,1) and (1,6) because starting with 1 we get 1 and 6 as output numbers, then (2,2), and (2,3). These are plotted on the graph at the right. Plot other points and look closely at the graph to see what we have. It's very interesting.

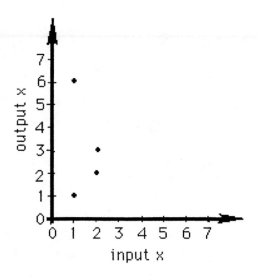

What would happen if we iterate $\dfrac{9}{x}$? Try that and see what happens. Graph the input x's vs. the output x's. Any surprises? Where do the graphs intersect?

7. Continued fractions:

My interest in infinite continued fractions came from looking for different methods to solve quadratic equations, which we will do shortly. Then I found I could write $\sqrt{2}$, the golden mean (ø) and π as infinite continued fractions . Also there are so many patterns within them. The infinite continued fraction gives one the ability to find an infinite sequence of approximations that converges and we can program the computer to do this. First we'll look at finite continued fractions; any ordinary fraction can be written as a finite continued fraction.

Change $\dfrac{43}{29}$ to a finite continued fraction:

$$\frac{43}{29} = 1 + \frac{14}{29} = 1 + \cfrac{1}{\cfrac{29}{14}} = 1 + \cfrac{1}{2 + \cfrac{1}{14}},\ \text{the answer. You continue until the remainder of}$$

the reciprocal of the last fraction is zero, so $\dfrac{14}{1}$ = 14 with remainder 0.

Change $\dfrac{52}{23}$ to a finite continued fraction:

$$\frac{52}{23} = 2 + \frac{6}{23} = 2 + \cfrac{1}{\cfrac{23}{6}} = 2 + \cfrac{1}{3 + \cfrac{5}{6}} = 2 + \cfrac{1}{3 + \cfrac{1}{\cfrac{6}{5}}} = 2 + \cfrac{1}{3 + \cfrac{1}{1 + \cfrac{1}{5}}},\ \text{the answer.}$$

Now you try changing each of these to a continued fraction: a) $\dfrac{13}{9}$ b) $2\dfrac{7}{9}$ c) $\dfrac{163}{48}$

To change this continued fraction $3 + \cfrac{1}{5 + \cfrac{1}{2}}$ to a simple fraction, start at the bottom. $5 + \dfrac{1}{2} = \dfrac{11}{2}$

we get $3 + \cfrac{1}{\frac{11}{2}}$, and since $\cfrac{1}{\frac{11}{2}} = \dfrac{2}{11}$

($\cfrac{1}{\frac{11}{2}}$ means the reciprocal of $\dfrac{11}{2}$ which is $\dfrac{2}{11}$. $\cfrac{1}{\frac{11}{2}}$ also means "? $\cdot \dfrac{11}{2} = 1$". The ?

can be replaced by $\dfrac{2}{11}$, since $\dfrac{2}{11} \cdot \dfrac{11}{2} = 1$)

so we get $3 + \dfrac{2}{11} = 3\dfrac{2}{11} = \dfrac{35}{11}$, all correct names for the answer.

Change these continued fractions to simple fractions:

a.) $1 + \cfrac{1}{2 + \cfrac{1}{5}}$; b.) $3 + \cfrac{1}{1 + \cfrac{1}{2 + \cfrac{1}{4}}}$; c.) $1 + \cfrac{1}{1 + \cfrac{1}{1 + \cfrac{1}{1 + \cfrac{1}{2}}}}$

8. We're going to solve the quadratic equation $x^2 - 5x + 6 = 0$ **in many different ways.**
In doing these different ways, I learned about, what was for me, a whole new area of mathematics -- iteration. When my students do new and different things, it can be very exciting.

Method 1. By guessing -- you did that above and hopefully figured out the 2 secrets and that the two solutions, the two roots of the equation $x^2 - 5x + 6 = 0$ are 3 and 2 .

Now we're going to solve $x^2 - 5x + 6 = 0$ for x using some algebra (transform operations-- by adding, subtracting, dividing, etc., like we did using the balance pictures).

Start with $x^2 - 5x + 6 = 0$

End up with x = something   (Note: this something could have an x in it!)

Try it by yourself, try it with a friend, see what you come up with.

Method 2a. You probably came up with a fine solution see how yours compares with Jonathan's solution (he also does it on the videotape "Iteration to Infinite Sequences with 6 to 11 year-olds"):

Jonathan, age 7 at the time, solved $x^2 - 5x + 6 = 0$ using some algebra this way

$$x^2 - 5x + 6 = 0$$

subtract 6 from both sides

$$x^2 - 5x = {}^-6$$

add $5x$ to both sides

$$x^2 = 5x - 6$$

divide both sides by x

$$x = 5 - \frac{6}{x} \qquad \text{Eq. 1}$$

That's terrific! Now comes an interesting part, the iteration. Since a name for x is $5 - \dfrac{6}{x}$

by Eq. 1, we can then substitute $5 - \dfrac{6}{x}$ back in for x, on the right side. We get

Eq. 2: $x = 5 - \dfrac{6}{5 - \dfrac{6}{x}}$ and then just continue this feedback or iteration process.

Eq. 3: $x = 5 - \dfrac{6}{5 - \dfrac{6}{5 - \dfrac{6}{x}}}$

Eq. 4: $x = 5 - \dfrac{6}{5 - \dfrac{6}{5 - \dfrac{6}{5 - \dfrac{6}{x}}}}$

and so on. This then, if we continued forever, is an infinite continued fraction, unusual, interesting. What would the next continued fraction, Eq. 5, look like? And what would you get for x if you put 1 in for x on the right side of each of these equations 1- 4?

What are we doing? We're looking to solve the quadratic equation $x^2 - 5x + 6 = 0$. This infinite continued fraction represents a solution...how? There are a couple of ways to work with these. One way is to guess a number, say 1, put in for x on the right side in Eq. 1. We get the first approximation, ¯1. Then we again put our first guess, 1, in for for x on the right side in Eq. 2., and so on. This gives us an infinite sequence of rational numbers 1, ¯1, 11, 4.454, .., 3.653, 3.358, ... that converges to 3. The other, and simpler way, is to just use $5 - \dfrac{6}{x}$ in the following way:

Method 2b: Let's iterate $5 - \dfrac{6}{x}$. If we start with 1, we get $5 - \dfrac{6}{1} = {}^-1$; then put ¯1 back in for x, and get $5 - \dfrac{6}{^-1} = 11$; then put 11 back in for x, $5 - \dfrac{6}{11} = \dfrac{49}{11} = 4.455$; if we continue this process forever we get the same infinite sequence of rational numbers (out to 3 places; I use the common fractions, which are exact, to do the calculations, then write the decimal approximations, otherwise I wouldn't get as accurate results):

¯1, 11, 4.455 or $\dfrac{49}{11}$, 3.653 or $\dfrac{179}{49}$, 3.358, 3.213, 3.133, 3.085, 3.055, 3.036, 3.024, 3.016, 3.010, 3.007, 3.005, and it gets closer and closer to 3.

Use your calculator, or **write a computer program** to put in different starting numbers and get the sequences and their limits.

At the right we've plotted two starting numbers and the limit of the sequence it goes to. So for point (**1**,3), **1** is the starting number which upon iteration of $5 - \dfrac{6}{x}$ forms a sequence whose limit is 3. (2,2) is on the graph because 2 goes to 2. Graph other points on this graph.

Are there any numbers which will not form a sequence and go to a number?

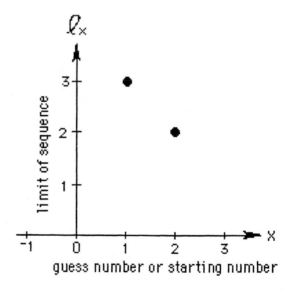

Method 2c: On $\frac{1}{4}$" graph paper, graph $y = 5 - \frac{6}{x}$ (from $x = {}^-10$ to $x = 12$). Then plot the points whose coordinates are the successive numbers in the sequence starting with 1 above -- (1, $^-$1), ($^-$1,11), (11, 4.455), and so on and connect these points with straight lines. An interesting thing happens.

Method 2d: Graph these three equations $y = 5 - \frac{6}{x}$ and $y = 5 - \dfrac{6}{5 - \frac{6}{x}}$

and $y = 5 - \dfrac{6}{5 - \dfrac{6}{5 - \frac{6}{x}}}$ (from $x = 1$ to $x = 3.5$). Where do they intersect?

Method 3: Solve $x^2 - 5x + 6 = 0$ to get $x = \dfrac{x^2 + 6}{5}$. Write a program to iterate the right side and see what happens. Graph the limits of the sequences as we did above and make an infinite continued fraction.

Method 4: Solve $x^2 - 5x + 6 = 0$ to get $x = \dfrac{^-6}{x - 5}$. Write a program to iterate the right side and see what happens. Graph the limits of the sequences as we did above and make an infinite continued fraction.

Method 5: Solve $x^2 - 5x + 6 = 0$ to get $x = \sqrt{5x - 6}$. Write a program to iterate the right side and see what happens. Graph the limits of the sequences as we did above and make an infinite continued radical.

Method 6: Jeff, a 5th grader and Greg, a 4th grader used a calculator in solving $x^2 - x - 1 = 0$. Try it. What are the two roots?

Using **Method 2a:** Solve $x^2 - x - 1 = 0$ for an infinite continued fraction.

We got the infinite continued fraction for ø from the equation $x^2 - x - 1 = 0$. We added x and 1 to both sides to get $x^2 = x + 1$. Then we divided both sides by x to get $x = 1 + \frac{1}{x}$. We then put $1 + \frac{1}{x}$ in for x again, to get $1 + \cfrac{1}{1 + \cfrac{1}{x}}$ and

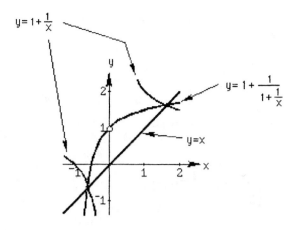

continued this process. On the way we graphed $y = 1 + \frac{1}{x}$, $y = 1 + \cfrac{1}{1 + \cfrac{1}{x}}$ and $y = x$ as

shown on the right. These two hyperbolas and the straight line, all intersect at the two points (1.618, 1.618) and (¯.618, ¯.618) which are the two solutions of the equation $x^2 - x - 1 = 0$ and are ø and ø' (see chapter 7). The infinite continued fraction for ø is:

$$\text{ø} = 1 + \cfrac{1}{1 + \cfrac{1}{1 + \cfrac{1}{1 + \cfrac{1}{1 + \cfrac{1}{1 + \cfrac{1}{\cdots}}}}}}$$

The normal school ways of solving $x^2 - 5x + 6 = 0$ are **Method 7** factoring, **Method 8** completing the square, and **Method 9** using the quadratic formula, as Barbara and Jenny did in chapter 7; we will not go into using methods 7 and 8 here; they are in most algebra 1 texts.

Method 10: Graph $x^2 - 5x + 6 = y$ from x=0 to x=4. Where does the graph intersect the x-axis? What do you notice?

Method 11: Bill Walton when at Webster (in the '60's) had used this method. Then David Fielker from London recently, after "browsing" in my book, told me about this method of spiralling in on the intersection of these two graphs and one solution of $x^2 - x - 1 = 0$. You start one graph and "bounce off" the other. . Each time you get a closer approximation to the intersection point. David said, " You can use the same method for solving simultaneous equations, though you get an awkward case when the lines are at equal but opposite angles! One of the nice things is that all these iterative methods, which are eminently suited for calculators or computers, can be used for practically any type of equation, and I always resented the formula for quadratics, which never generalized to anything else. Some of the iterations have a lovely effect on the calculator. As you press the same sequence of keys again and again, more and more rapidly as you get used to them, you really get the FEEL what iteration is!"

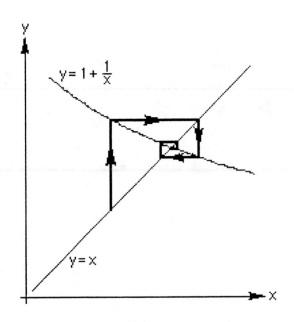

Try this yourself. Start with the example shown above with $x = 1.1$ and $y = 1.1$. You might even write a program to do this, which I have not been able to do yet. Ian did a version on *Mathamatica*.

9. Using iteration to solve a linear equation
One of the most interesting ideas came up when I was working with Sean, 8 years old at the time. I made up this equation off the top of my head (one like you may have made up earlier). He solved it this way:

$$6x + 5 = 2x + 25$$

add ⁻5

$$6x = 2x + 20$$

÷6 (unexpected)

$$x = \frac{2x + 20}{6} \text{ and}$$

Eq. 8: $x = \frac{1}{3}x + 3\frac{1}{3}$

He then said since $x = \frac{1}{3}x + \frac{2}{3}x$, $(\frac{1}{3}x + \frac{2}{3}x = \frac{3}{3}x = 1x)$ then

$$\frac{2}{3}x = 3\frac{1}{3}$$ and multiplying both sides by $\frac{3}{2}$, he got

$$x = 5 \text{ Terrific.}$$

I then looked at Eq. 8 and saw x's on both sides and thought, hmmmmm, could we iterate this like the quadratics above. Try it. Put the right side of Eq. 8 in for x on the right side and keep doing that forever (don't do any arithmetic).

The first iteration of Eq. 8 look like this:

$$x = \tfrac{1}{3}\left(\tfrac{1}{3}x + 3\tfrac{1}{3}\right) + 3\tfrac{1}{3}$$

See if you get an infinite series (don't do any arithmetic).

10. Using iteration to solve a cubic equation

Another Jenny, finished 5th grade, had done many of the ways above of using iteration to get the solutions of the quadratic equation $x^2 - 5x + 6 = 0$. When I gave her the cubic equation, $x^3 = 8$ to solve, what do you think she did? Try it yourself.

11. Infinite continued fractions to get π and e:

An infinite continued fraction for $\tfrac{4}{\pi}$, by Lord Brouncker, circa 1658 -- see Olds:

$$\frac{4}{\pi} = 1 + \cfrac{1}{2 + \cfrac{9}{2 + \cfrac{25}{2 + \cfrac{49}{2 + \cfrac{81}{\cdots}}}}}$$

An infinite continued fraction for e (see ch. 11), by Euler, circa 1737-- see Olds

$$e = 2 + \cfrac{1}{1 + \cfrac{1}{2 + \cfrac{2}{3 + \cfrac{3}{4 + \cfrac{4}{\cdots}}}}}$$

Answer worksheets for **chapter 8**
"Solving Equations, Infinite Continued Fractions and Iteration"
See also Don's videotape "Iteration to Infinite Sequences with 6 to 11 year-olds"

Equation solving, infinite continued fractions and iteration are very much intertwined ideas and I am trying to sort them out for myself and for you. Unlike my original book, I'm starting out to solve equations as I would do with 6 year-olds and up. Then I introduce the idea of iteration, then infinite continued fractions, then the solution of quadratic equations many ways, using iteration and graphs, then get to the solution of a linear and a cubic equation using iteration.

1. Solving equations by guessing
Solve these equations --that is, make these true:

$\qquad$ 2) $2 \cdot x + 3 = 18$

7 is too small, and 8 is too big. Let's try $7\frac{1}{2}$

$2 \cdot 7\frac{1}{2} + 3 \overset{?}{=} 18$ Let's see $2 \cdot 7\frac{1}{2}$ is $14\frac{1}{2}$ ..**oh no**, $2 \cdot 7\frac{1}{2} = 15$ because $7\frac{1}{2} + 7\frac{1}{2} = 7 + 7 +$

$\frac{1}{2} + \frac{1}{2} = 14 + 1 = 15$

So $2 \cdot 7\frac{1}{2} + 3 = 18$

$\qquad$ $15 + 3 = 18$ and this is true, so the answer is $7\frac{1}{2}$

3) $3 \cdot x + 5 = 11$ $\{2\}$ the answer is 2, which we'll put in the wiggly brackets.
4) $3 \cdot x + 5 = 12$ $\{2\frac{1}{3}\}$

Make up some equations like these for a friend !

What can you change in the equation?
The + to a -, like $3 \cdot x - 4 = 19$
The • to a ÷, like $\frac{3}{x} + 2 = 8$ Notice, it's probably better to write $3 \div x$ as $\frac{3}{x}$ because it's more commonly used that way.

Look at the patterns in the answers:
$7 \cdot x + 5 = 11$ $\{\frac{6}{7}\}$; $8 \cdot x + 5 = 11$ $\{\frac{6}{8}\}$; $9 \cdot x + 5 = 11$ $\{\frac{6}{9}\}$; $10 \cdot x + 5 = 11$ $\{\frac{6}{10}\}$

Generalizing for all equations of this form: $a \cdot x + b = c$ $\{\frac{c-b}{a}\}$ or $x = \frac{c-b}{a}$

So if we put 7 in for a, 5 in for b and 11 in for c, we get $x = \frac{c-b}{a} = \frac{11-5}{7} = \frac{6}{7}$, which is the same answer as for one of those equations above.

Generalizing for all equations of this form: $a \cdot x - b = c$ $\{\frac{c+b}{a}\}$ or $x = \frac{c+b}{a}$

This equation that has more than one answer: $x^2 = 16$, the answers are 4 and sup5(-)4 because $^-4 \cdot {}^-4 = {}^+16 = 16$. If you have a question about this, look at the pattern in the problems below

$$1 \cdot {}^-4 = {}^-4 \text{ (because 1 times any number is that number)}$$

$$0 \cdot {}^-4 = 0 \text{ (because 0 times any number is 0)}$$

As the number on the left comes **down 1**, the answer on the right goes **up 4.** Keep that pattern going for the next one

$${}^-1 \cdot {}^-4 = {}^+4 = 4. \text{ and eventually,}$$

$${}^-4 \cdot {}^-4 = {}^+16 = 16.$$

2. Identities: An equation for which **every** number will make it true like $2 \cdot x = x + x$, is called an **identity.**

$2 \cdot x = x + x$	because 3 works
$2 \cdot 3 = 3 + 3$	and 4 works
$2 \cdot 4 = 4 + 4$	and 5 works
$2 \cdot 5 = 5 + 5$	

       :
       .

Which of these are identities?

[1] $x + x + x = 3 \cdot x$ yes

[2] $3 \cdot (x + 5) = 3 \cdot x + 15$ yes

[3] $x \cdot x = 2 \cdot x$ no

[4] $x + x - x = x$ yes

[5] $2 \cdot 3 = 3 \cdot 2$ no

[6] $x - y = x + {}^- y$ yes

[7] $2^x \cdot 2^y = 2^{x+y}$ yes

[8] $x \div y = x \cdot \dfrac{1}{y}$ yes

[9] $x + 0 = x$ yes

[10] $x \cdot 1 = x$ yes

[11] $(x + 0) \cdot 1 = x$ yes

[12] $3 - 5 = 5 - 3$ no

[13] $\sqrt{x^2 + y^2} = x + y$ no

[14] $ab = ba$ yes

[15] $3 \cdot x + 0 = 3 \cdot x$ yes

[16] ${}^-({}^-x) = x$ yes

[17] $3 \div 2 = 3 \cdot f(1,2)$ no

[18] $A^x \cdot A^y = A^{x+y}$ yes

[19] $x - y = y - x$ no

[20] $3(x + 4) + 2 = 5x + 12$ no

[21] $(x + y)^2 = x^2 + y^2$ no

[22] $3 \cdot x + 2 \cdot x = 5 \cdot x$ yes

[23] $8 \div x = x \div 8$ no

[24] $3 \cdot x + 2 = 5 \cdot x$ no

[25] $a + b = c$ no

[26] ${}^-(x - y) = x + y$ no

[27] $(x - y)^2 = x^2 - 2xy + y^2$ yes

[28] ${}^-2 + {}^-(x - 2 + x) = 0$ yes

If you use 2 variables, like $2 \cdot x + 3 = y$ you can find an infinite number of pairs of numbers that will make this true, as we saw in chapter 6. But not every pair of numbers will make this true, like 2->x and 100->y will not make a true statement.

This is an equation that has **no answer**: $x + 1 = x$

6) $6 \cdot x + 5 = 5 \cdot x + 7$ {2}; 7) $4 \cdot x + 3 = 2 \cdot x + 14$ $\{5\frac{1}{2}\}$; 8) $5 \cdot x + 23 = 2 \cdot x + 32$ {3}

An equation like this in which the answer is a negative number would be:

$6 \cdot x + 15 = 5 \cdot x + 7$ { ${}^-8$}

For the general equation $ax + b = cx + d$ the solution is $x = \dfrac{d-b}{a-c}$

4. Quadratic equations by guessing

$$x^2 - 8 \cdot x + 15 = 0 \quad \{3,5\}$$

$$x^2 - 7 \cdot x + 10 = 0 \quad \{2,5\}$$

Watch out, there are really 2 secrets!

$$x^2 - 10 \cdot x + 24 = 0 \quad \{6,4\}$$

$$x^2 - 11 \cdot x + 24 = 0 \quad \{3,8\}$$

$$x^2 - 25 \cdot x + 24 = 0 \quad \{1,24\}$$

This one has one answer that is a fraction. Try it: $x^2 - 6\frac{1}{2} \cdot x + 9 = 0$

5. Using a balance scale model and transform operations to solve
$6 \cdot x + 7 = 4 \cdot x + 15 \quad \{4\}$

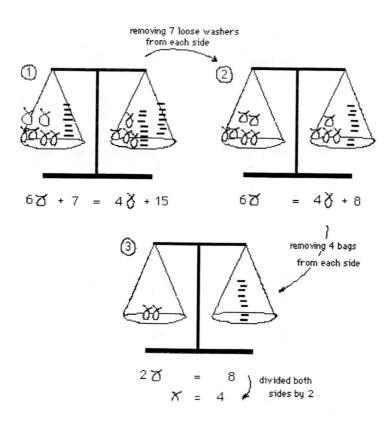

removing 7 loose washers from each side

① $6\text{Ö} + 7 = 4\text{Ö} + 15$ ② $6\text{Ö} = 4\text{Ö} + 8$

③

removing 4 bags from each side

$2\text{Ö} = 8$ divided both
$x = 4$ sides by 2

The solution for $8 \cdot x + 12 = 2 \cdot x + 24$ is {2}, the balance pictures below.

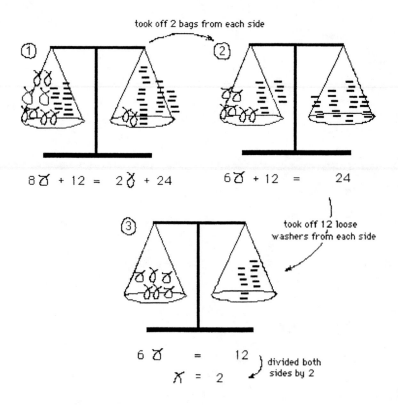

took off 2 bags from each side

$8 \cancel{\circ} + 12 = 2 \cancel{\circ} + 24$ $6 \cancel{\circ} + 12 = 24$

took off 12 loose
washers from each side

$6 \cancel{\circ} = 12$ } divided both
$x = 2$ sides by 2

The equations $5 \cdot x + 3 = 2 \cdot x + 18$, $5 \cdot x = 2 \cdot x + 15$ and $3 \cdot x = 15$ all have the same answer and are **equivalent** equations. These things you can do to make equations equivalent :

Subtract the same thing from both sides
Add the same thing from both sides
Divide both sides by the same thing (as long as you don't divide by 0)
Multiply both sides by the same thing
Take the square root of both sides

6. Iteration or Feedback

If we iterate the function 10•**x** and put 4 -> **x** . The first 5 terms, and generalize using exponents for the nth term is arrived at like this:

10•**x** we'll start by putting 4-> **x**

10•4 = 40 , then take this 40 and put it back in for **x**

10•40= 400

10•400= 4000

Listing our numbers... 4,   40,   400,   4000,   What's happening?

If we write these   4,   4•10,   4•10•10,   4•10•10•10,   ...

or with exponents $4 \cdot 10^0$, $4 \cdot 10^1$, $4 \cdot 10^2$, $4 \cdot 10^3$, .. , $4 \cdot 10^n$ (the nth term),...

If the population of a town increases 10% each year, starting with, a population of 1000, what would be the population after 3 years? n years?
Start with 1000 people. 10% of 1000 = 100, which is the increase. So after the first year the population is $1000 + .1 \cdot 1000 = 1000 + 100 = 1100 = 1000 \cdot 1.1$, because 100% + 10% = 1 + .1 = 1.1. **Again, being able to write the answer different ways will help us find a pattern.**
After the first year the population is
$1000 + 1000 \cdot .1 = 1000 + 100 = 1100 =$ **$1000 \cdot (1.1)$**
After the second year the population is
$1100 + 1100 \cdot .1 = 1100 + 110 = 1210 =$ **$1000 \cdot (1.1)^2$**
After the third year the population is
$1210 + 1210 \cdot .1 = 1210 + 121 = 1331 =$ **$1000 \cdot (1.1)^3$**
After the nth year the population is .... = **$1000 \cdot (1.1)^n$**
So we have a problem exactly the same as the iteration of the function $1.1x$, starting with 1000 for x
(See chapter 11 to see how the compound interest can be done similarly).

Iterating $5 + \frac{x}{2}$: Starting with 10 -> 10; starting with 8 we get the infinite sequence 8, 9, $7\frac{1}{2}$, $8\frac{3}{4}$, $9\frac{7}{8}$, $9\frac{15}{16}$, ... which goes to 10 as the limit. Seen these fractions before?

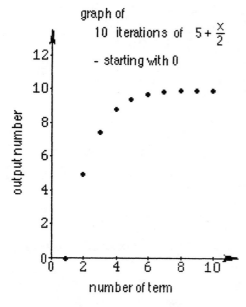

graph of
10 iterations of $5 + \frac{x}{2}$
- starting with 0

Let's look at the numbers we get starting with
$0, 5, 7\frac{1}{2}, 8\frac{3}{4}, 9\frac{3}{8}, 9\frac{11}{16}$, ... or as decimals,
0, 5, 7.5, 8.75, 9.375, 9.6875, 9.84375, 9.921875, 9.9609375, 9.98046875, ...

Something Alison and I noticed, look at the differences! They start with 5, then they are halved each time. So the differences get smaller and smaller and approach 10

Starting the iteration of $5 + \dfrac{x}{2}$ with ⁻17, ⁻3.5, 3.25, 6.625, 8.3125, 9.15625, 9.578125, 9.7890625, 9.89453125, ... ->10

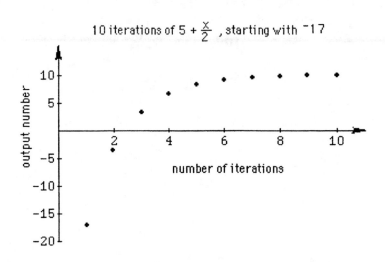

10 iterations of $5 + \frac{x}{2}$, starting with ⁻17

Starting with 156, 83, 46.5, 28.25, 19.125, 14.5625, 12.28125, 11.140625, 10.5703125, ... ->10. At this point, I 'm willing to say that in iterating $5 + \dfrac{x}{2}$, every starting number forms a sequence that goes to 10.

Iterate $\dfrac{6}{x}$

Starting with 2, we get $\dfrac{6}{2}$ = 3, then 2, 3, 2, 3,...

Starting with 4 we get $1\frac{1}{2}$, 4, $1\frac{1}{2}$,4, ...

Starting with 1 we get 1, 6, 1, 6, ...

Starting with 3 we get 2, 3, 2,...

The graph of the iteration of $\frac{6}{x}$

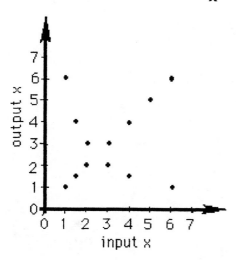

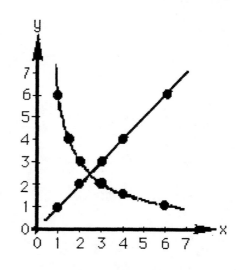

Learning new things always gives me a surprise and is enjoyable. I had never seen a graph like this before! If the the points are connected, this turns out to be 2 graphs, the graphs of $y = \frac{6}{x}$ and $y = x$. The point of intersection is $(\sqrt{6}, \sqrt{6})$!

Iterating $\frac{9}{x}$ would be similar to the one above. The graphs would intersect at the point (3,3)

7. Change each of these to a continued fraction:

a.) $\frac{13}{9} = 1 + \frac{4}{9} = 1 + \frac{1}{\frac{9}{4}} = 1 + \frac{1}{2 + \frac{1}{4}}$

b.) $2\frac{7}{9} = 2 + \frac{7}{9} = 2 + \frac{1}{\frac{9}{7}} = 2 + \frac{1}{1 + \frac{2}{7}} = 2 + \frac{1}{1 + \frac{1}{\frac{7}{2}}} = 2 + \frac{1}{1 + \frac{1}{3 + \frac{1}{2}}}$

c.) $\frac{163}{48} = 3 + \frac{19}{48} = 3 + \frac{1}{\frac{48}{19}} = 3 + \frac{1}{2 + \frac{10}{19}} = 3 + \frac{1}{2 + \frac{1}{\frac{19}{10}}} =$

$= 3 + \frac{1}{2 + \frac{1}{1 + \frac{9}{10}}} = 3 + \frac{1}{2 + \frac{1}{1 + \frac{1}{\frac{10}{9}}}} = 3 + \frac{1}{2 + \frac{1}{1 + \frac{1}{1 + \frac{1}{9}}}}$

Change these continued fractions to simple fractions:

a.) $1 + \cfrac{1}{2+\cfrac{1}{5}} = 1\frac{5}{11} = \frac{16}{11}$

b.) $3 + \cfrac{1}{1+\cfrac{1}{2+\cfrac{1}{4}}} = 3\frac{9}{13} = \frac{48}{13}$

c.) $1 + \cfrac{1}{1+\cfrac{1}{1+\cfrac{1}{1+\cfrac{1}{2}}}} = 1\frac{5}{8} = \frac{13}{8}$ Does this last one look familiar? It is an

approximation to the golden mean. What continued fraction would be a better approximation?

8. Solving quadratic equations 11 ways!

I don't think any student should be forced to go through all of the 11 methods. Encourage questions, new ways to do the same problem. See Linus' and Grant's work below.

Method 2a.

Eq. 5: $X = 5 - \cfrac{6}{5-\cfrac{6}{5-\cfrac{6}{5-\cfrac{6}{5-\cfrac{6}{X}}}}}$ and if you put 1 in for x you'd get 3.358...

Computer programs to iterate the function $5 - \frac{6}{X}$ on the FX7000G, in Mathematica and in BASIC	FX 7000G	Mathematica	Basic
	?-> x: Lbl 5: 5-6÷ x -> x Δ Goto 5 (press EXE to get the next approximation)	g[x_]:=5-6/x N[NestList[g,1,20],10] (you define the function, it starts with 1-> x, iterates 20 times and gives 10 digits for each number)	10 INPUT X 20 for N=0 to 20 30 X=5-6/X 40 Print X 50 Next N 70 end

Jonathan then used the program above on the FX7000G to iterate

$5 - \frac{6}{X}$. Starting with 1 he gets an infinite sequence 1, ⁻1, 11, 4.4545..., 3.6530, 3.358,...that

converges to 3. It turns out that an infinite number of starting numbers go to 3. Only 2 goes to 2.

Starting with ⁻17, we get ⁻17, 5.35294, 3.87912, 3.45326, 3.26251, 3.16093, 3.10182, 3.06565, 3.04283, 3.02815, 3.01859, ... which converges to 3

Starting with 420, 4.98571, 3.79656, 3.41962, 3.24542, 3.15124, 3.09599, 3.06201, 3.0405, 3.02664, 3.0176, ... which converges to 3.

Starting with 2.0003, 2.00045, 2.00067, 2.00101, 2.00152, 2.00227, 2.00341, 2.0051, 2.00763, 2.0114, 2.01701, 2.0253, 2.03748, 2.05518, 2.08055, 2.11615, 2.16466, 2.2282, 2.30724, 2.39949, 2.49947, 2.59949, 2.69185, 2.77105, 2.83476, 2.88342, 2.91914, 2.9446, 2.96237, 2.97459, 2.98292, ... which surprisingly still converges to 3. I went out 30 iterations before I would really believe that starting with a number so very close to 2, like 2.0003, still formed a sequence that converges to 3. Amazing!

If we start with 0->x in $5 - \frac{6}{x}$, we get $5 - \frac{6}{0}$ and $\frac{6}{0}$ has no answer since no number times 0 will give 6. We also say "it blows up", because as the denominator of a fraction goes to zero, the fraction gets bigger and bigger and goes to infinity.

For a while I thought 0 was the only number that gave no answer, then I found $\frac{6}{5}$ which goes to zero on the second iteration and Jerry made me realize there must be other numbers like $\frac{30}{19}$. Since $5 - \frac{6}{\frac{30}{19}} = 5 - \frac{19}{5} = \frac{6}{5}$ and I knew $\frac{6}{5}$ made it blow up. Now the question stuck in my head, how could I find these numbers that made the function blow up? By just saying what number will make $5 - \frac{6}{x} = 0$, I was able to calculate $\frac{6}{5}$. Then I asked what would make $5 - \frac{6}{x} = \frac{6}{5}$? This gave $\frac{30}{19}$. Then I wrote each of these fractions in terms of the 5 and 6 in the original equation, and there were patterns, but it was getting unwieldy and tedious. I thought there should be another, easier way. I thought about it this way: I would let $5 - \frac{6}{x} = a$, then solve this equation for x in terms of a, getting $x = \frac{6}{5-a}$. What I did then was to iterate this function $\frac{6}{5-a}$ starting with a=0.

	FX7000G	in Basic
That did it! I wrote a program on the FX7000G and in Basic to do the iteration:	0->A:	10 for n=0 to 20
	Lbl 7:	20 A=0
	6÷ (5-A) -> A△	30 A=6/(5-A)
	Goto 7	40 print A
		50 Next n

Now here is another surprise... these numbers that make $5 - \frac{6}{x}$ blow up, form a sequence themselves, that converges to 2. Wow! Here are the first 20: 0., 1.2 $\left(\frac{6}{5}\right)$, 1.5789 $\left(\frac{30}{19}\right)$, 1.7538 $\left(\frac{114}{65}\right)$, 1.8483, 1.9037, 1.9378, 1.9594, 1.9732, 1.9823, 1.9883, 1.9922, 1.9948, 1.9965, 1.9977, 1.9984, 1.9989, 1.9993, 1.9995, 1.9997, ...

The graph of the guess numbers or starting numbers to iterate $5 - \dfrac{6}{x}$ vs the limit of the sequence formed is shown at the right. Notice that there are an infinite number of numbers that converge to 3, 2 goes to 2, and there are an infinite number of numbers (the holes) that make the function blow up.

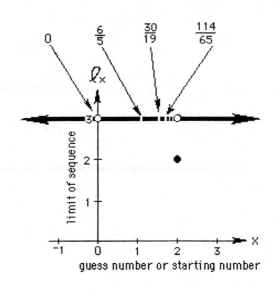

Method 2c: When you plot the successive pairs of numbers in the sequence 1, ¯1, 11, 4.4545,... obtained from iterating $5 - \dfrac{6}{x}$ starting with 1, which goes to 3, it looks like this on the graph...The points move along the curve approaching (3,3). Another way of looking at the situation.

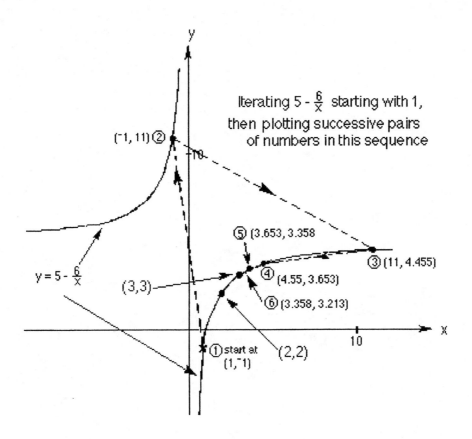

Iterating $5 - \frac{6}{x}$ starting with 1, then plotting successive pairs of numbers in this sequence

(¯1, 11) ②

⑤ (3.653, 3.358

③ (11, 4.455)

$y = 5 - \frac{6}{x}$

(3,3)

④ (4.55, 3.653)

⑥ (3.358, 3.213)

① start at (1,¯1)

(2,2)

Method 2d. The graphs of $y = 5 - \dfrac{6}{x}$, $y = 5 - \dfrac{6}{5 - \dfrac{6}{x}}$ and $y = 5 - \dfrac{6}{5 - \dfrac{6}{5 - \dfrac{6}{x}}}$

are shown below. We get 3 hyperbolas (just one of the two pieces is shown for each) and much to our amazement, they intersect at (2,2) and (3,3), the two solutions of the quadratic equation
$x^2 - 5x + 6 = 0$.

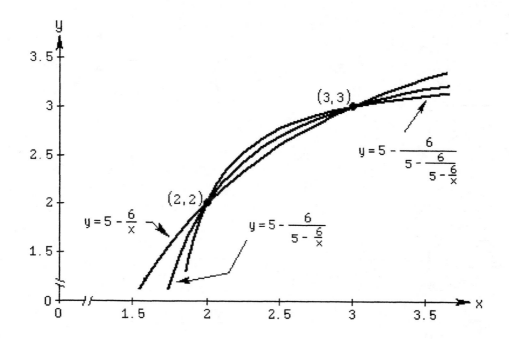

Grant's study, age 12

Grant changed the iterating function from $\dfrac{-6}{x} + 5$ to $\dfrac{-5}{x} + 4$. He decided to take 1 from each number, which was great. He put 4 in for x and did the 20 iterations, asking for 10 digits of accuracy in *Mathematica* and got this sequence:

4., 2.75, 2.181818182, 1.708333333, 1.073170732, ⁻0.6590909091, 11.5862069, 3.568452381, 2.59883236, 2.07605905, 1.591590663, 0.8584887335, ⁻1.824188257, 6.740945175, 3.258264254, 2.465440612, 1.97196494, 1.464457963, 0.5857674807, ⁻4.535810137, 5.102338909.

We looked at this sequence. It didn't look like it was converging, so we decided to graph the numbers, doing 500 iterations. The following was the result. Very interesting!

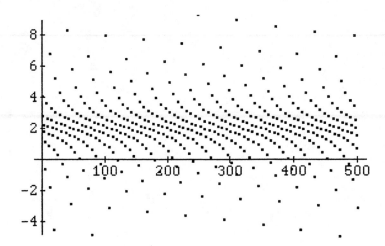

We then decided to connect the points on the above graph and this was the result:

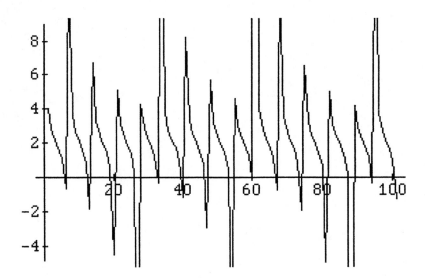

After working on 5 - $\frac{6}{x}$, Linus, age 11, made an investigation of 5 - $\frac{a}{x}$. He decided to try different numbers instead of the 6. He tried factors of 6, multiples of 6, numbers that add to 5, prime numbers... he worked for a week on this. Try some things like this and see what starting numbers go to what numbers. Do they always go to whole numbers as in the case above? Can you always tell what the second root will be if you know the first one?

Method 3:

$x^2 - 5x + 6 = 0$

add 5x to both sides

$x^2 + 6 = 5x$

divide both sides by 5

$x = \dfrac{x^2 + 6}{5}$

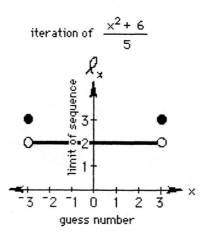

iteration of $\dfrac{x^2 + 6}{5}$

guess number

The graph of the guess numbers or starting numbers to iterate $\dfrac{x^2 + 6}{5}$ vs the limit of the sequence formed is shown at the right. Notice, here every number between ⁻3 and 3 goes to 2. 3 and ⁻3 go to 3 and everything above 3 and below ⁻3 gives a divergent sequence (goes to infinity). Notice that a computer program to iterate the functions in each of methods 3, 4 and 5, would essentially be the same as for that used for method 2. You would just change the iterating function from say,

$5 - \dfrac{6}{\mathbf{x}}$ to $\dfrac{x^2 + 6}{5}$.

Method 4:

$x^2 - 5x + 6 = 0$

add ⁻6 to both sides

$x^2 - 5x = {}^-6$

factor the left side

$x(x - 5) = {}^-6$

$\div (x - 5)$

$x = \dfrac{{}^-6}{\mathbf{x} - 5}$

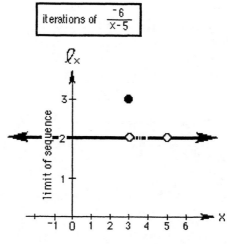

iterations of $\dfrac{{}^-6}{x-5}$

guess number or starting number

The graph of the guess numbers or starting numbers to iterate $\dfrac{{}^-6}{\mathbf{x} - 5}$ vs the limit of the sequence formed is shown at the right. 3 goes to 3, 5 and an infinite sequence of number approaching 3, put a zero in the denominator and there is no solution, and all other numbers go to 2.

Method 5:

$$x^2 - 5x + 6 = 0$$

add 5x and ⁻6 to both sides

$$x^2 = 5x - 6$$

take the $\sqrt{}$ of both sides

$$x = \sqrt{5x - 6}$$

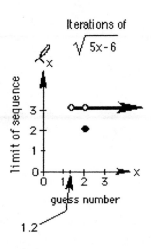

Iterations of $\sqrt{5x-6}$

This is different. It doesn't give an infinite continued fraction, but an infinite continued radical, something like Ian had in chapter 3. Do the iteration the same way, but just put the radical in for x on the right side. The graph of the guess numbers or starting numbers to iterate $\sqrt{5x-6}$ vs the limit of the sequence formed is shown at the right.

Using just the positive radical, numbers >1.2 go to 3, except 2 goes to 2. Every guess number ≤ 1.2 goes to complex numbers. Not only are the answers complex though, but all (?) guess numbers ≤ 1.2 form an <u>infinite sequence of complex numbers which goes to 3 also!</u> That was exciting to find out. In *Mathematica* I started with ⁻37, iterated $\sqrt{5x-6}$, 20 times, then showed the **last 5** numbers: 3.10325 + 0.0304583 **i**, 3.08494 + 0.0246831 **i**, 3.07003 + 0.0201 **i**, 3.05785 + 0.0164331 **i**, 3.04786 + 0.0134792 **i**, ... Notice the real part is going to 3 and the imaginary part is going to zero. Not more than 3 years ago when we got *Mathematica*, I would never have even thought about being able to do this work with complex numbers.

Method 6

Jeff and Greg solved $x^2 - x - 1 = 0$ using a calculator by approximations, keeping track of what is too big and what's too small. They ended up with 1.618034 to give 0. Jeff then said "I suppose there must be another number" from knowing the fact that a quadratic has two answers and he knew the two secrets. I thought that was great and told him so. He thought about what the other number should be and said it should be ⁻.618034. He figured that the coefficient of x was ⁻1, so he subtracted 1 from 1.618034 and made it negative. And of course he was right. I then told him that this number was The Golden Mean and how the ancient Greeks used that ratio to build the Parthenon.

Methods 7, 8 are in most algebra 1 texts; **Methods 9:** see ch. 7 for the solution by the quadratic formula.

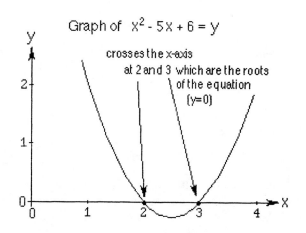

Graph of $x^2 - 5x + 6 = y$

crosses the x-axis
at 2 and 3 which are the roots
of the equation
(y=0)

Method 10. Graphing

$x^2 - 5 \cdot x + 6 = y$. The roots of the

equation $x^2 - 5 \cdot x + 6 = 0$ are
where the graph, in this case a
parabola, crosses the x-axis, at 2
and 3.

9. Using iteration with linear equations:

$$\text{Eq. 8: } x = \frac{1}{3}x + 3\frac{1}{3}$$

The first few iterations of Eq. 8 look like this:

$$x = \frac{1}{3}\left(\frac{1}{3}x + 3\frac{1}{3}\right) + 3\frac{1}{3}$$

$$x = \frac{1}{3}\left(\frac{1}{3}\left(\frac{1}{3}x + 3\frac{1}{3}\right) + 3\frac{1}{3}\right) + 3\frac{1}{3}$$

and we end up with

$$x = \left(\frac{1}{3}\right)^n \cdot x + 3\frac{1}{3} \cdot \left[\left(\frac{1}{3}\right)^0 + \left(\frac{1}{3}\right)^1 + \left(\frac{1}{3}\right)^2 + .. + \left(\frac{1}{3}\right)^{n-1}\right]$$

as $n \to \infty$, $\left(\frac{1}{3}\right)^n$ goes to 0; Sean said "almost 0". Then

$$x = 3\frac{1}{3} \cdot \left[1 + \left(\frac{1}{3}\right)^1 + \left(\frac{1}{3}\right)^2 + \left(\frac{1}{3}\right)^3 \ldots\right] \text{ From solving Eq. 8 the other way,}$$

Sean knew that $x = 3\frac{1}{3} \cdot \frac{3}{2} = 5$

so $\left[1 + \left(\frac{1}{3}\right)^1 + \left(\frac{1}{3}\right)^2 + \left(\frac{1}{3}\right)^3 \ldots\right] = \frac{3}{2} = 1\frac{1}{2}$ and we ended up with

$$\left(\frac{1}{3}\right)^1 + \left(\frac{1}{3}\right)^2 + \left(\frac{1}{3}\right)^3 \ldots = \frac{1}{2}$$

	FX7000G	in Basic
A program to iterate Eq. 8	?->X△	5 c=0
on on the FX7000G and in	Lbl 7:	10 input x
Basic would be:	X ÷3 + 10÷3 -> X △	20 print x
	Goto 7	30 x= x/3 + 10/3
		40 c=c+1
		50 if c >20 then stop
		60 goto 30

Put 17 in for X and we get an infinite sequence which goes, not surprisingly, to 5 : 17, 9, 6.333,.., 5.444, 5.148,.., 5.049,.., 5.016,.., 5.005,... Will this work on all linear equations? So we arrived at the sum of an infinite series from solving a linear equation!

If we now graph $y = \frac{1}{3}x + 3\frac{1}{3}$ and

$y = \frac{1}{3}\left(\frac{1}{3}x + 3\frac{1}{3}\right) + 3\frac{1}{3}$ and

$y = \frac{1}{3}\left(\frac{1}{3}\left(\frac{1}{3}x + 3\frac{1}{3}\right) + 3\frac{1}{3}\right) + 3\frac{1}{3}$

we get three straight lines that intersect at--yes, (5,5)! and 5 is the solution to

$6x + 5 = 2x + 25$ or $x = \frac{1}{3}x + 3\frac{1}{3}$.

So what happened with the quadratic equations also works for some linear equations (not all). Try some others.

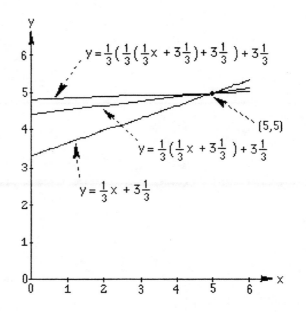

10. Solving a cubic equation using iteration

Needless to say Jenny, after doing about 4 of the iteration methods, solved the equation $x^3 = 8$ by dividing by x^2, to get $x = \frac{8}{x^2}$ and iterated the right side. Try some numbers other than 2 and see what happens. For the three solutions on the computer we got:

Derive gives: $^{-}1 - \sqrt{3}\ \mathbf{i}$, $^{-}1 + \sqrt{3}\ \mathbf{i}$, and 2.

Mathematica gives: $2 \cdot e^{\frac{2i\pi}{3}}$, $2 \cdot e^{\frac{4i\pi}{3}}$, and 2.

This started some nice discussions with Jenny and John, also a 6th grader, about **e** and **i** and $\sqrt{3}\ \mathbf{i}$. Can you predict, as John did, the roots of the equation $x^3 = 125$? See ch. 11 to graph **i** in the Argand plane and the possibility of **e** to imaginary powers.

The iteration of $\mathbf{z^2 + c \rightarrow c}$ with complex numbers leads to fractals. See the great IES java applet at http://www.ies.co.jp/math/java/comp/itoi/itoi.html , taken from chapter 11 below.

Question worksheets for **chapter 9**
"The Binomial Expansion and Infinite Series "

To get to our beginning goal in this chapter, you can start with any (or all) of the 7 problems below. Only the first three are done in detail:
1. The area within squares
2. The people tiles
3. The number of routes between two points on a grid
4. How many ways can you turn 4 light switches on and off?
5. How many ways can 4 coins can come up when tossed?
6. How many ways can you form committees of people with 4 people to choose from?
7. How many ways can you make trains as long as the purple Cuisenaire rod?

1. The area within squares:

What is the area within the square with sides 5 cm.?

What does area mean? The amount of flat space. The question is how many square centimeters fit within the square?

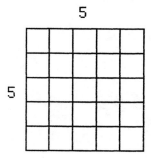

Suppose we break up the square so that the side is still 5, but we break 5 into 2 + 3 and our picture looks like this:

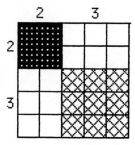

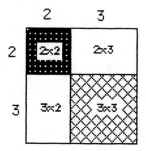

Find the area within each piece.

We get $2^x2 + 2^x3 + 3^x2 + 3^x3 =$
    4 + 6 + 6 + 9 = 25

Again, it is important not to write just the answer, but also where the answer comes from, then we can generalize. Draw the picture and find the area of the square, A+B on a side, in other words, what is $(A+B)^2$? _____Note: we can't write the answer as one number, we need to write it in terms of A and B.

Here's the picture for $(A+B)^2$:

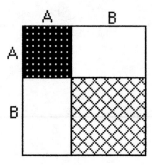

The area of each piece will look like this:

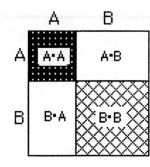

From the picture, to find the area of the square, just add the areas of the pieces:

$(A+B)^2 = (A+B) \cdot (A+B) = A \cdot A + A \cdot B + B \cdot A + B \cdot B$. We could write this other ways, like

$$A^2 + A \cdot B + A \cdot B + B^2$$

or $$A^2 + 2 \cdot A \cdot B + B^2$$

What patterns do you see in:

$$(A+B)^2 = A \cdot A + A \cdot B + B \cdot A + B \cdot B$$

What do you predict for $(A+B)^3$? _____

You should build $(A+B)^3$ using rods. It would be a cube with edges of length A+B.

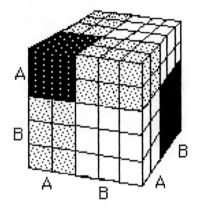

We'll look at 2-D drawings of the 3-D cube and the pieces. What will the volume of each piece be and what will the volume of the whole cube be in terms of A and
B ?

$(A+B)^3$ = Yes, it's (A+B)(A+B)(A+B) = $(A+B)^2$(A+B), multiply them, you get

_____

The whole cube, the 8 pieces and their volumes are shown below:

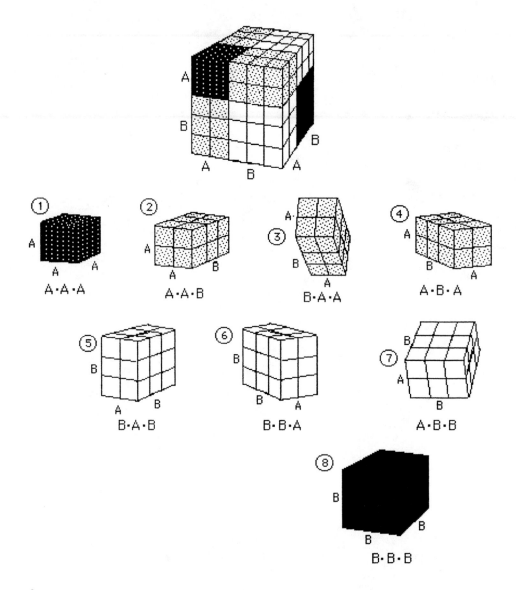

So $(A+B)^3$ = A•A•A + A•A•B + A•B•A + B•A•A + A•B•B + B•A•B + B•B•A + B•B•B or we could write $(A+B)^3$ = $A^3 + 3•A^2•B + 3•A•B^2 + B^3$

What patterns do you see here?

Let's look at what we have so far.. we'll put in the first two, which we haven't talked about yet:

$(A+B)^0 = 1$

$(A+B)^1 = A+B = \mathbf{1} \cdot A + \mathbf{1} \cdot B$

$(A+B)^2 = A \cdot A + A \cdot B + B \cdot A + B \cdot B = \mathbf{1} \cdot A^2 + \mathbf{2} \cdot A \cdot B + \mathbf{1} \cdot B^2$

$(A+B)^3 = A \cdot A \cdot A + A \cdot A \cdot B + A \cdot B \cdot A + B \cdot A \cdot A + A \cdot B \cdot B + B \cdot A \cdot B + B \cdot B \cdot A + B \cdot B \cdot B =$

$$\mathbf{1} \cdot A^3 + \mathbf{3} \cdot A^2 \cdot B + \mathbf{3} \cdot A \cdot B^2 + \mathbf{1} \cdot B^3$$

What patterns do you see?

How many terms are there in each answer?
How many A's, how many B's?

Sean looked at $A \cdot A \cdot A + A \cdot A \cdot B + A \cdot B \cdot A + B \cdot A \cdot A + A \cdot B \cdot B + B \cdot A \cdot B + B \cdot B \cdot A + B \cdot B \cdot B$
and said if you take 2 A's and 1 B, then $A \cdot A \cdot B$, $A \cdot B \cdot A$ and $B \cdot A \cdot A$ would be all the possible ways you could combine them. What do you think?

What do you predict for

$(A+B)^4 = $ _____

$(A+B)^5 = $ _____

_____

Let's put the coefficients in some order:
1
1 1
1 2 1   put these on graph paper, one number in a square

Look for patterns in the numbers and in the sums. Write the next 4 rows.

Sum

1									=	1
1	1								=	2
1	2	1							=	4
1	3	3	1						=	8
1	4	6	4	1					=	16

In the table at the left are the coefficients for the first 5 rows and the sum of the numbers in each row.

Use the sum of the row and all the patterns you can find, to help you fill in the next 3 rows.

2. The People Tiles-- copy this sheet, glue it on cardboard, then cut out the tiles and get an envelope to put them into when you stop working on this activity.

Look at the people tiles. How are they the same? How are they different?

Sort them into **2 piles** so a friend can tell how you did it.

Mix them up, then sort them into 2 piles again, but sort them a different way than the first time.

How many ways can you do this?

In doing the following, we'll use these four sortings only ..
Color-- **freckled** we'll call **red**, **greyish** we'll call **blue**
Sex-- **male** and **female**
Height-- **tall** and **short**
Width -- **wide** and **thin**

Now, pick any one person, say you pick the blue, male, short and wide. In the first column to the right of the one you picked, you are to put all those who are different in exactly 1 way from the one you picked. For example, the person in the 1-different column is female (different) and the same in the other ways-- short, wide and blue. What others go here in the the 1-different column? On the next page I have put one in each column except the 4-different column. Have a couple of friends check your work, because everything you do next depends on these being correct.

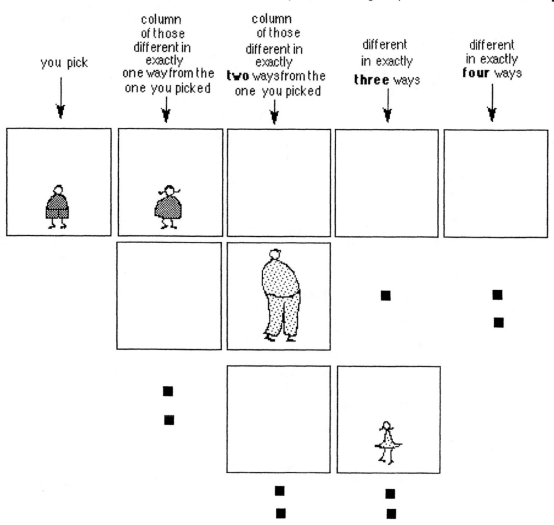

The next page shows the finished arrangement as started above. If you started as I did above, each column should contain the same tiles (the order may be different).

Keep the tile arrangement intact. Somewhere near the center of a piece of graph paper, write in how many tiles are in each column, like this.

		1	4	6	4	1		

Now, from your tile arrangement take out all people with one certain attribute, like all blue tiles. Keep the others in the same columns. If you take out all the blue tiles you should end up with this arrangement:

We'll keep track of the number of tiles in each column and the total of the row on the graph paper at the right.

1	3	3	1						=	8
1	4	6	4	1					=	16

The next question? Take out of the arrangement of tiles, all those with one attribute, like all tall people. Keep the others in the same columns. If you take out all the tall people, What arrangement will you end up with? Write the number of tiles in each column on your graph paper chart and continue this procedure until you have only one tile left.

We've arrived at the triangle of numbers two ways so far:
1. The area within squares leading to multiplying binomials
2. The people tiles
Now we'll do it one more way,
3. The number of routes between two points on a grid

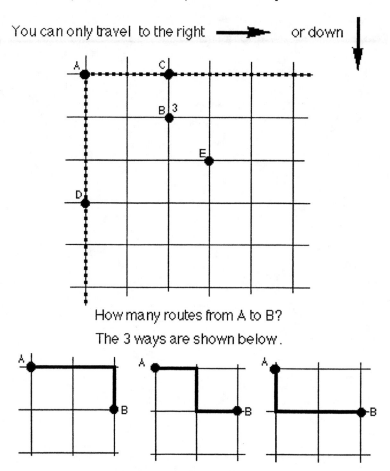

How many routes from A to points to the right or below A ?

You can only travel to the right ➡ or down ↓

How many routes from A to B?

The 3 ways are shown below.

How many routes from A to C? A to E? A to D? Form A to each point? Remember, you can only go to the right or down (no going left or up). Write the number of routes to each point on the grid at that point. Look for patterns.

Below are the beginning questions for four other ways to get the triangle of numbers, which are equivalent to the above:

4. How many ways can you turn 4 light switches on and off?

5. How many ways can 4 coins can come up when tossed?

6. How many ways can you form committees of people with 4 people to choose from?

7. How many trains can you make as long as the purple Cuisenaire rod?

8. Patterns in the triangle & Ian's discovery

Now we can look back and see the binomial expansion, with the coefficients heavy:

$(A+B)^0 = 1$

$(A+B)^1 = \mathbf{1}{\cdot}A + \mathbf{1}{\cdot}B$

$(A+B)^2 = \mathbf{1}{\cdot}A^2 + \mathbf{2}{\cdot}A{\cdot}B + \mathbf{1}{\cdot}B^2$

$(A+B)^3 = \mathbf{1}{\cdot}A^3 + \mathbf{3}{\cdot}A^2{\cdot}B + \mathbf{3}{\cdot}A{\cdot}B^2 + \mathbf{1}{\cdot}B^3$

$(A+B)^4 = \mathbf{1}{\cdot}A^4 + \mathbf{4}{\cdot}A^3{\cdot}B + \mathbf{6}{\cdot}A^2{\cdot}B^2 + \mathbf{4}{\cdot} A{\cdot}B^3 + \mathbf{1}{\cdot}B^4$

$(A+B)^5 = \mathbf{1}{\cdot}A^5 + \mathbf{5}{\cdot}A^4{\cdot}B + \mathbf{10}{\cdot}A^3{\cdot}B^2 + \mathbf{10}{\cdot} A^2{\cdot}B^3 + \mathbf{5}{\cdot} A{\cdot}B^4 + \mathbf{1}{\cdot}B^5$

The whole idea here is to find for example, the 8th number in the 20th row in this triangle of numbers below, and of course without doing a lot of work. That's why we want to find as many patterns to see which one is most helpful. This is sometimes called Pascal's triangle (after Blaise Pascal, 1632-1662, but known by Indian and Chinese thinkers 2000 years before) or Sean's or Ian's triangle. See what other patterns you can find.

	Column #										row sum
Row #	0	1	2	3	4	5	6	7	8		
0	1										1
1	1	1									2
2	1	2	1								4
3	1	3	3	1							8
4	1	4	6	4	1						16
5	1	5	10	10	5	1					32
6	1	6	15	20	15	6	1				64
7	1	7	21	35	35	21	7	1			128
8	1	8	28	56	70	56	28	8	1		256

Looking down a column and down a diagonal, the numbers are the same, as shown at the right. Looking down the column 1, 3, 6, some people want to say 1, 3, 6, 9, but they forget about the 1. Instead there is a pattern of adding 2, then 3, then 4, etc. It sometimes takes a while to see that 4+6 in row 4, adds to 10, the number below the 6 in row 5.

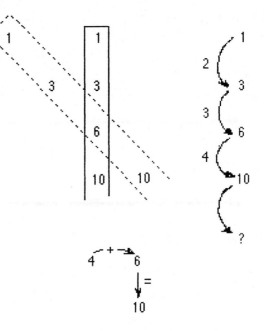

Ian's discovery

For about 35 years my students and I looked at these numbers and we found many patterns in them, but what Ian did was something special. Ian did this when he was 12 years old. Isaac Newton did a very similar thing when he was 19, according to W. W. Sawyer in "Integrated Mathematics Scheme-Book C". In Ian's words: "I was faced with the problem of generating Pascal's triangle. I decided to start looking at patterns until I found one that applied to the entire triangle. After some trail and error, I noticed a pattern in the ratios from one column to the next. In row 4, for example,

$$1 \quad 4 \quad 6 \quad 4 \quad 1$$

the ratios are arrived at by asking, what times 1 = 4? $\frac{4}{1}$. What times 4 = 6? $\frac{6}{4} = \frac{3}{2}$.

Then $\frac{4}{6} = \frac{2}{3}$ and $\frac{1}{4}$. I wrote these ratios

$$\frac{4}{1} \qquad \frac{3}{2} \qquad \frac{2}{3} \qquad \frac{1}{4} \quad \text{and}$$

$$\frac{4-0}{1} \quad \frac{4-1}{2} \quad \frac{4-2}{3} \quad \frac{4-3}{4}$$

So to get the 3rd number in the 4th row, I multiply

$$\frac{4-0}{1} \cdot \frac{4-1}{2} = \frac{4}{1} \cdot \frac{3}{2} = \mathbf{6}$$

To get the 8th number in the 20th row:

$$\frac{20-0}{1} \cdot \frac{20-1}{2} \cdot \frac{20-2}{3} \cdot \frac{20-3}{4} \cdot \frac{20-4}{5} \cdot \frac{20-5}{6} \cdot \frac{20-6}{7} = 77520$$

The number in the x-th column, y-th row = $\dfrac{\frac{y!}{(y-x)!}}{x!}$. "

Ian switched from number in the row to column #. Since the columns start with the 0th column, his x is one less than the number in the row, for example the 3rd number is in column #2 (in other words , just subtract 1 first, from the number in the row and use that as x). Ian's notation is the same as used to write the coefficients in combination form, to which Sean alluded. Ian also introduced the factorial notation (3 factorial = 3! =1•2•3 = 6).

Notice that

$$\frac{20-0}{1} \cdot \frac{20-1}{2} \cdot \frac{20-2}{3} \cdot \frac{20-3}{4} \cdot \frac{20-4}{5} \cdot \frac{20-5}{6} \cdot \frac{20-6}{7} =$$

$$\frac{20}{1} \cdot \frac{19}{2} \cdot \frac{18}{3} \cdot \frac{17}{4} \cdot \frac{16}{5} \cdot \frac{15}{6} \cdot \frac{14}{7} = \frac{20 \bullet 19 \bullet 18 \bullet 17 \bullet 16 \bullet 15 \bullet 14}{1 \bullet 2 \bullet 3 \bullet 4 \bullet 5 \bullet 6 \bullet 7}$$

$1 \bullet 2 \bullet 3 \bullet 4 \bullet 5 \bullet 6 \bullet 7 = 7!$ (read as 7 factorial) and

$$20 \bullet 19 \bullet 18 \bullet 17 \bullet 16 \bullet 15 \bullet 14 = \frac{20 \bullet 19 \bullet 18 \bullet 17 \bullet 16 \bullet 15 \bullet 14 \bullet 13 \bullet 12 \bullet 11 \bullet 10 \bullet 9 \bullet 8 \bullet 7 \bullet 6 \bullet 5 \bullet 4 \bullet 3 \bullet 2 \bullet 1}{13 \bullet 12 \bullet 11 \bullet 10 \bullet 9 \bullet 8 \bullet 7 \bullet 6 \bullet 5 \bullet 4 \bullet 3 \bullet 2 \bullet 1} = \frac{20!}{13!}$$

so $\dfrac{20 \bullet 19 \bullet 18 \bullet 17 \bullet 16 \bullet 15 \bullet 14}{1 \bullet 2 \bullet 3 \bullet 4 \bullet 5 \bullet 6 \bullet 7} = \dfrac{\frac{20!}{13!}}{7!} = \dfrac{\frac{20!}{(20-7)!}}{7!} = \dfrac{20!}{(20-7)! \bullet 7!} = 77520$ ..this is the 8th
number in the 20th row in Pascal's triangle.

You try some:
a.) Find the 10th number in the 15th row.
b.) Find the 5th number in the 18th row

Make up some for your friend.
At this time Ian also worked on extending the triangle to the left with negative numbers. A couple of years earlier when he was in about 4th grade, Ian was graphing factorials (it's important to graph everything!), when he decided since these numbers got so big so fast, he graphed the log of the factorial. I wasn't even aware he knew about logs. And Sterling found a relationship between factorials and logs.

9. The first 5 terms of the binomial expansion
Remember above, the 4th row of the binomial expansion looks like this

$$(A+B)^4 = \mathbf{1} \bullet A^4 + \mathbf{4} \bullet A^3 \bullet B + \mathbf{6} \bullet A^2 \bullet B^2 + \mathbf{4} \bullet A \bullet B^3 + \mathbf{1} \bullet B^4$$

Write the first 5 terms of $(A+B)^n$, using n to denote the row number instead of y (instead of 4 above, use the n).

You might first want to write the **general term** of the binomial expansion, in the x-th column and the **n**-th row;

You'll need   <u>some number (Ian's number) </u>times $A^{\text{(some power)}}$ times $B^{\text{(some other power)}}$

Then you could put 0->x, then 1->x , 2->x, 3->x, and 4->x to get the first 5 terms.

$(A+B)^n =$
How does the exponent of B compare to x ?
What do the exponents of A and B add to ?

Using the general term of the binomial expansion $\frac{n!}{(n-X)! \cdot X!} \cdot A^{n-x} \cdot B^{x}$, write the first 5 terms of the binomial expansion with X going from 0 to 4, (n stays as n). To get the first term substitute 0 for X in

$\frac{n!}{(n-X)! \cdot X!} \cdot A^{n-x} \cdot B^{x}$ we get

$\frac{n!}{(n-0)! \cdot 0!} \cdot A^{n-0} \cdot B^{0} = \frac{n!}{n!} \cdot A^{n} = 1 \cdot A^{n}$ this is the **first** term of the binomial expansion (you knew this!)

To get the 2nd term, substitute 1 in for X in the general term, like this

$\frac{n!}{(n-X)! \cdot X!} \cdot A^{n-x} \cdot B^{x}$ We get

$\frac{n!}{(n-1)! \cdot 1!} \cdot A^{n-1} \cdot B^{1} = \frac{n(n-1)(n-2)(n-3)(n-4)..3 \cdot 2 \cdot 1}{(n-1)(n-2)(n-3)(n-4)..3 \cdot 2 \cdot 1} \cdot A^{n-1} \cdot B^{1} = n \cdot A^{n-1} \cdot B^{1}$ this is the **2nd**

term of the binomial expansion and so on. So far we have

$(A+B)^{n} = 1 \cdot A^{n} + n \cdot A^{n-1} \cdot B^{1} +$
Find the next three terms.

10. What is the connection between the infinite series and the binomial expansion?

Start with

$\frac{A}{B-A} = \frac{A}{B} + \left(\frac{A}{B}\right)^{2} + \left(\frac{A}{B}\right)^{3} + \left(\frac{A}{B}\right)^{4} + \cdots$ and end up with

$(... + ...)^{n}$ = an infinite series with X's in it.

Hint: Put $BX = A$ or $\frac{A}{B} = X$ in the equation above.

Answer worksheets for **chapter 9**
"The Binomial Expansion and Infinite Series "

1. The area within squares:

Algebraically, we can get $(A+B)^2$ this way

$(A+B)^2 = (A+B) \cdot (A+B)$

using the distributive property

$\qquad = (A+B) \cdot A \ + \ (A+B) \cdot B$

using the commutative property twice

$\qquad = A \cdot (A+B) \ + \ B \cdot (A+B)$

using the distributive property twice, we get

$(A+B)^2 = A \cdot A + A \cdot B + B \cdot A + B \cdot B = A^2 + 2 \cdot A \cdot B + B^2$

$(A+B)^3 = (A+B) \cdot (A+B) \cdot (A+B)$

$\qquad = (A+B) \cdot (A^2 + 2 \cdot A \cdot B + B^2)$

$\qquad = A \cdot (A^2 + 2 \cdot A \cdot B + B^2) + B \cdot (A^2 + 2 \cdot A \cdot B + B^2)$ using the distributive property

$\qquad = A^3 + 2 \cdot A^2 \cdot B + A \cdot B^2 + B \cdot A^2 + 2 \cdot A \cdot B^2 + B^3$ using the distributive property twice

$(A+B)^3 = A^3 + 3 \cdot A^2 \cdot B + 3 \cdot A \cdot B^2 + B^3$

$(A+B)^0 = \mathbf{1}$

$(A+B)^1 = A+B = \mathbf{1} \cdot A + \mathbf{1} \cdot B$

$(A+B)^2 = A \cdot A + A \cdot B + B \cdot A + B \cdot B = \mathbf{1} \cdot A^2 + \mathbf{2} \cdot A \cdot B + \mathbf{1} \cdot B^2$

$(A+B)^3 = A \cdot A \cdot A + A \cdot A \cdot B + A \cdot B \cdot A + B \cdot A \cdot A + A \cdot B \cdot B + B \cdot A \cdot B + B \cdot B \cdot A + B \cdot B \cdot B =$

$$\mathbf{1} \cdot A^3 + \mathbf{3} \cdot A^2 \cdot B + \mathbf{3} \cdot A \cdot B^2 + \mathbf{1} \cdot B^3$$

When the exponent is 2, there are 4 terms. When the exponent is 3, there are 8 terms. When the exponent is 4, there are 16 terms. With the exponent n, there are 2^n terms.

Sean looked at $A \cdot A \cdot A + A \cdot A \cdot B + A \cdot B \cdot A + B \cdot A \cdot A + A \cdot B \cdot B + B \cdot A \cdot B + B \cdot B \cdot A + B \cdot B \cdot B$ and said if you take 2-A's and 1-B, then $A \cdot A \cdot B$, $A \cdot B \cdot A$ and $B \cdot A \cdot A$ would be all the possible ways you could combine them. What do you think?

It's interesting, that in *Mathematica* this little code, Table[Expand[(A+B)^n],{n,1,3}] ,will give us as many terms of the expansion as we want (3 in this case):

$$\{A + B, \ A^2 + 2AB + B^2, \ A^3 + 3A^2B + 3AB^2 + B^3\}$$

										sum
1									=	1
1	1								=	2
1	2	1							=	4
1	3	3	1						=	8
1	4	6	4	1					=	16
1	5	10	10	5	1				=	32
1	6	15	20	15	6	1			=	64
1	7	21	35	35	21	7	1		=	128
1	8	28	56	70	56	28	8	1	=	256

2. The People Tiles

After taking away the tall people we have:
121

After taking away the
wide people we have
11

After taking away the
male, we have
1

And again we
have the triangle
of numbers

1				
1	1			
1	2	1		
1	3	3	1	
1	4	6	4	1

3. The number of routes between two points on a grid

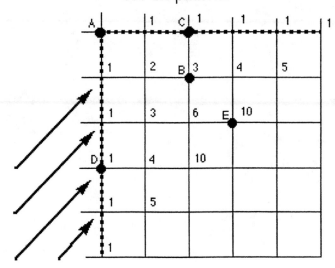

The number of routes from A to other points on the grid. Look along the arrows to see the patterns

Using Ian's pattern

a. the 10th number (x=9) in the 15th row (y =15) =

$$\frac{15!}{(15-9)! \cdot 9!} = \frac{15 \cdot 14 \cdot 13 \cdot 12 \cdot 11 \cdot 10 \cdot 9 \cdot 8 \cdot 7 \cdot 6 \cdot 5 \cdot 4 \cdot 3 \cdot 2 \cdot 1}{(6 \cdot 5 \cdot 4 \cdot 3 \cdot 2 \cdot 1) \cdot (9 \cdot 8 \cdot 7 \cdot 6 \cdot 5 \cdot 4 \cdot 3 \cdot 2 \cdot 1)} = \frac{15 \cdot 14 \cdot 13 \cdot 12 \cdot 11 \cdot 10}{6 \cdot 5 \cdot 4 \cdot 3 \cdot 2 \cdot 1} = 5005$$

b.) the 5th number in the 18th row=

$$\frac{18!}{(18-4)! \cdot 4!} = \frac{18 \cdot 17 \cdot 16 \cdot 15 \cdot 14 \cdot 13 \cdot 12 \cdot 11 \cdot 10 \cdot 9 \cdot 8 \cdot 7 \cdot 6 \cdot 5 \cdot 4 \cdot 3 \cdot 2 \cdot 1}{(14 \cdot 13 \cdot 12 \cdot 11 \cdot 10 \cdot 9 \cdot 8 \cdot 7 \cdot 6 \cdot 5 \cdot 4 \cdot 3 \cdot 2 \cdot 1) \cdot (4 \cdot 3 \cdot 2 \cdot 1)} = \frac{18 \cdot 17 \cdot 16 \cdot 15}{4 \cdot 3 \cdot 2 \cdot 1} = 3060$$

$$(A+B)^5 = 1 \cdot A^5 + 5 \cdot A^4 \cdot B + 10 \cdot A^3 \cdot B^2 + 10 \cdot A^2 \cdot B^3 + 5 \cdot A \cdot B^4 + 1 \cdot B^5$$

$$(A+B)^5 = 1 \cdot A^5 + \frac{5!}{(5-1)! \cdot 1!} \cdot A^4 \cdot B^1 + \frac{5!}{(5-2)! \cdot 2!} \cdot A^3 \cdot B^2 + \frac{5!}{(5-3)! \cdot 3!} \cdot A^2 \cdot B^3 +$$

$$\frac{5!}{(5-4)! \cdot 4!} \cdot A^1 \cdot B^4 + \frac{5!}{(5-5)! \cdot 5!} \cdot B^5 \quad \text{Note } A^0 = 1 \text{ and } 0! = 1$$

How does the exponent of B compare to x ? The exponent of B = x

What do the exponents of A and B add to ? The exponents of A and B add to n. So the exponent of A is n-x.

The general term of the binomial expansion in the x-th column and the n-th row is:

$$\frac{n!}{(n-X)! \cdot X!} \cdot A^{n-x} \cdot B^x$$

9. The first 5 terms of the binomial expansion

The first 5 terms of the binomial expansion would look like this:

$$(A+B)^n = 1 \cdot A^n + n \cdot A^{n-1} \cdot B^1 +$$
$$\frac{n(n-1)}{1 \cdot 2} \cdot A^{n-2} \cdot B^2 + \frac{n(n-1)(n-2)}{1 \cdot 2 \cdot 3} \cdot A^{n-3} \cdot B^3 + \frac{n(n-1)(n-2)(n-3)}{1 \cdot 2 \cdot 3 \cdot 4} \cdot A^{n-4} \cdot B^4 + \dots$$

10. What is the connection between the infinite series and the binomial expansion?

From chapter 1,

$$\frac{A}{B-A} = \frac{A}{B} + \left(\frac{A}{B}\right)^2 + \left(\frac{A}{B}\right)^3 + \left(\frac{A}{B}\right)^4 + \dots$$ Now, putting $Bx = A$ or $\frac{A}{B} = x$, we get

$$\frac{Bx}{B-Bx} = x + x^2 + x^3 + x^4 + x^5 + \dots \text{ reducing the left side}$$

$$\frac{x}{1-x} = x + x^2 + x^3 + x^4 + x^5 + \dots$$

adding 1 to both sides-- on the left side the $1 = f(1-x, 1-x)$ gives

$$\frac{x}{1-x} + \frac{1-x}{1-x} = \frac{1}{1-x} = 1 + x + x^2 + x^3 + x^4 + x^5 + \dots$$

which is the infinite series Ian came up with in Chapter 3. Since $\frac{1}{1-x} = (1-x)^{-1}$

This gives us the important connection between the binomial expansion and the infinite series

$$(1-x)^{-1} = 1 + x + x^2 + x^3 + x^4 + x^5 + \dots$$

because $(1-x)^{-1}$ can be expanded by putting $1 \to A$, $x \to B$ and $-1 \to n$ in $(A+B)^n$.

The binomial expansion and infinite series were important because they made it possible to take roots using $(1+x)^{\frac{1}{2}}$, as we'll see in chapter 10. If a function can be expanded as a series (like **e** and sin x), then one can take the derivative or integral of the pieces, as we'll see in chapters 11, 13 and 14.

Question worksheets for **chapter 10**
"Pi and Square Roots "

1. Kohler follows Archimedes

Kohler, a 5th grader, worked on drawing inscribed regular polygons in a 12-dot circle. This is similar to what Archimedes did (287-212 B.C.). Copy some 12-dot circles from appendix 4.

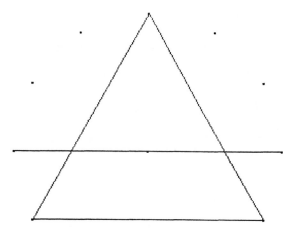

Do these three things as Kohler did:
1) Measure the perimeter of the equilateral triangle at the left ;
2) measure the diameter of the circle and 3) divide the perimeter by the diameter $\frac{p}{d}$. Now do the same three things for an inscribed regular hexagon (6 sides), and a regular dodecagon -- each on a different 12- dot circle.

If you kept this up forever, what would happen to this infinite sequence of ratios? Does it converge? If so, to what number? Try writing a computer program to find these ratios.

2. The Gregory-Leibnitz series

Sean was reading "The History of Pi" and found the Gregory-Leibnitz series below. Write a computer program to find approximations to the following sum and find out how it's related to π:

$$1 - \frac{1}{3} + \frac{1}{5} - \frac{1}{7} + \frac{1}{9} - ...$$

3. Wells: "Tamura and Kanada calculate π to 16 million places, based on Gauss' study of arithmetic-geometric mean of two numbers. The initial values are A = x = 1, B = $\frac{1}{\sqrt{2}}$ and C = $\frac{1}{4}$. The program steps follow:

$$Y = A \; ; A = \frac{(A+B)}{2} \; ; B = \sqrt{B \cdot Y} \; ; C = C - x \cdot (A - Y)^2 \; ; X = 2 \cdot X \; ; PRINT \; \frac{(A+B)^2}{4 \cdot C} \; ; \text{ go back to}$$

the first step.
It has the amazing property that the number of correct digits approximately doubles with each circuit of the loop". Try it on your computer.

From "The Penguin Dictionary of Curious and Interesting Numbers" by David Wells; copyright David Wells, 1986; pp 54, 55 and was reproduced by permission of Penguin Books Ltd., Harmondsworth, Middlesex, England.

4. Iterating the square root of a number

One day one of my students, in a moment of trying to do nothing, started to continuously hit the $\sqrt{}$ of a number on the calculator. If say, we start with 10, find $\sqrt{10}$. Then find $\sqrt{\sqrt{10}}$ and keep doing this, an iteration of $\sqrt{10}$. Graph the sequence. Does it converge? Try other numbers.

5. Finding $\sqrt{2}$ by squaring numbers on a calculator.

Keep track of your work so that you get a number too big and too small to nearest whole number, to the nearest tenth, to the nearest hundredth, etc.

Too big: 2,   1.5,   ,   ,

Too small: 1,   1.4,   ,   ,
Will you ever find such a number which when squared gives 2?
What happens to the two sequences you are getting?
Find the square roots of other numbers this way.

6. Finding $\sqrt{40}$ by iteration of the averaging method

What does $\sqrt{}$ mean? We're trying to find two numbers the same, which when multiplied will give 40. Suppose we guess 5. $\frac{40}{5}$ = 8, which means 5 is too small and 8 is too big and the $\sqrt{40}$ must lie between 5 and 8. We take the average of 5 and 8, or $\frac{40}{5}$. The average is

$$\frac{5 + \frac{40}{5}}{2} = 6.5$$

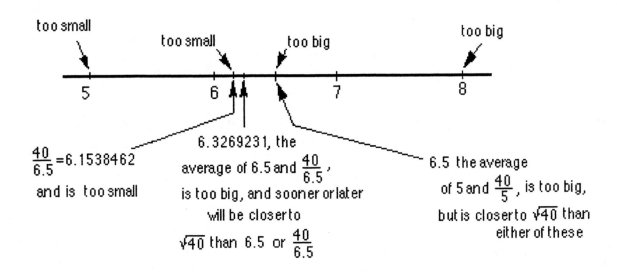

$\frac{40}{6.5} = 6.1538462$

and is too small

6.3269231, the

average of 6.5 and $\frac{40}{6.5}$,

is too big, and sooner or later

will be closer to

$\sqrt{40}$ than 6.5 or $\frac{40}{6.5}$

6.5 the average

of 5 and $\frac{40}{5}$, is too big,

but is closer to $\sqrt{40}$ than

either of these

We then put 6.5 in for the guess number $\dfrac{6.5 + \frac{40}{6.5}}{2}$ = 6.3269231. We have another

iteration problem! The iterating function is $\dfrac{G + \frac{40}{G}}{2}$ where **G** is the first guess

number. Use your calculator or write a program that will get the first 20 approximations to $\sqrt{40}$ by doing this iteration of the average.

Find $\sqrt{76}$ using this method.

7. Using the binomial expansion to find $\sqrt{2}$

Newton knew his binomial expansion could ease the problem of finding the roots of a number. It is just a tricky matter of writing this number as a binomial to some power.

$\sqrt{2} = 2^{\frac{1}{2}} = \left(\frac{1}{2}\right)^{\frac{-1}{2}} = \left(1 - \frac{1}{2}\right)^{\frac{-1}{2}}$ which is now in its binomial form. Now put 1->A, $\frac{-1}{2}$ ->B,

and $\frac{-1}{2}$ -> n , in the binomial expansion, and see what you get for the sum of 5 terms:

$$(A+B)^n = 1 \cdot A^n + n \cdot A^{n-1} \cdot B^1 +$$
$$\frac{n(n-1)}{1 \cdot 2} \cdot A^{n-2} \cdot B^2 + \frac{n(n-1)(n-2)}{1 \cdot 2 \cdot 3} \cdot A^{n-3} \cdot B^3 + \frac{n(n-1)(n-2)(n-3)}{1 \cdot 2 \cdot 3 \cdot 4} \cdot A^{n-4} \cdot B^4 + \dots$$

Try finding $\sqrt[3]{28}$ this way. You want to get something like $\mathbf{x} \cdot (1 + \Delta)^{\frac{1}{3}}$ where Δ is a number less than 1. Hint: 27 is close to 28 and is a perfect cube.

Answer worksheets for **chapter 10**
"Pi and Square Roots "

1. Kohler follows Archimedes

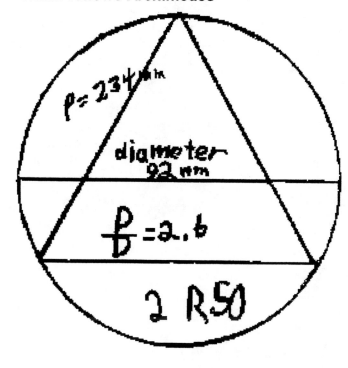

For a diameter of 92 mm, Kohler found the perimeter of the triangle to be 234 mm, and the ratio of $\frac{p}{d} = \frac{234}{92} = 2.6$

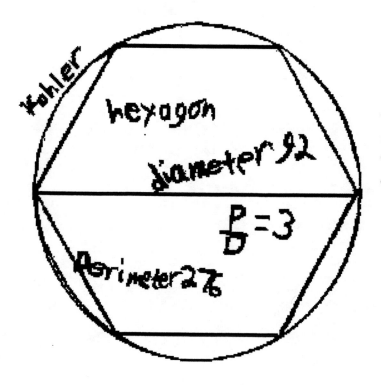

The perimeter of the hexagon he measured 276 mm, the same diameter of 92 mm, and the ratio of $\frac{p}{d} = \frac{276}{92} = 3$

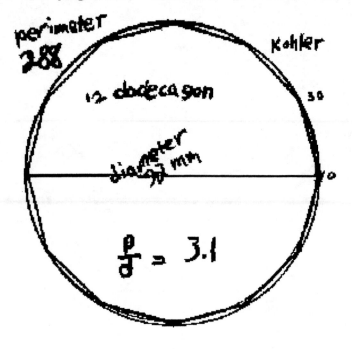

The perimeter of the dodecagon he he found to be 288 mm, the same diameter of 92 mm, and the ratio of $\frac{p}{d} = \frac{288}{92} = 3.1$

From the diagram below,

$$\frac{p}{d} = \frac{N \bullet \sin\left(\frac{180}{N}\right)}{d}$$

If N=# of sides of the polygon (3, 6, 12, 24, ... doubling each time and is $3 \bullet 2^F$, where F is a whole number starting at 0 and goes to ∞), a program to find these ratios

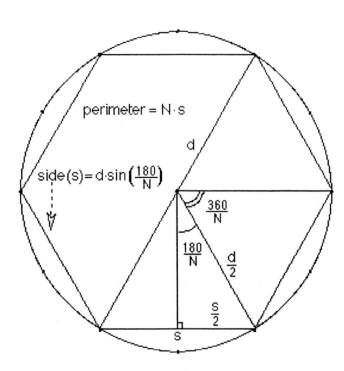

$$\frac{p}{d} = N \bullet \sin\left(\frac{180}{N}\right) = X$$, would look like this for the

FX7000G:
0->F:Lbl 4: 3x2 x^y F -> N:
N x sin(180 ÷ N) ->X Δ:
 F= F+1:Goto 4

In basic this program would look like this:
10 f=0
20 N=3x2^f
30 PRINT N x SIN(3.14159/N)
40 f=f+1
45 IF f>10 THEN STOP
50 GOTO 20

The infinite sequence we get is 2.59807, 3, 3.1058, 3.1326, 3.1393, ... and after 10 loops, we get 3.14159... . Notice the first 3 are very close to what Kohler had.

2. The Gregory-Leibnitz series

It turns out that the limit of this series

$$1 - \frac{1}{3} + \frac{1}{5} - \frac{1}{7} + \frac{1}{9} - ... = \frac{\pi}{4}$$

A program in basic which approximates π using this series is at the right. This is a slowly converging series.

```
10 x=0
20 b=0
30 a=(⁻1)^x • (1/(2•x+1))
40 c=a+b
50 PRINT 4•c
60 b=c
70 x=x+1
80 IF x>20 THEN STOP
GOTO 30
```

4. Iterating the square root of a number.

If you iterate the square root of *any* number you get a sequence whose limit is 1. A graph is shown at the right.

Briggs in 1620 used successive square roots of 10 to calculate logarithms, so this turns out to be an important idea.

A program to do this in <u>basic</u>:

```
10 Input N
20 For c = 1 to 20
30  N = SqrtN
40 PRINT N
50 Next c
```

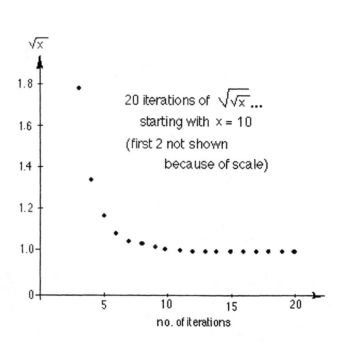

20 iterations of $\sqrt{\sqrt{x}}$ ...
starting with x = 10
(first 2 not shown because of scale)

no. of iterations

5. Finding $\sqrt{2}$ by squaring numbers on a calculator

We get two infinite sequences, one made up of the smallest numbers that are too big, the other sequence made up of the biggest numbers that are too small.

Too big: 2,   1.5, 1.42, 1.415, 1.4143, 1.41422, 1.414214, ...

Too small: 1,   1.4, 1.41, 1.414, 1.4142, 1.41421, 1.414213, ...

Both sequences approach $\sqrt{2}$ as a limit.

6. Finding $\sqrt{76}$ by iteration of the averaging method.

Using the iterating function $\dfrac{G + \frac{76}{G}}{2}$ to find the $\sqrt{76}$, if we guess 2, say, we get $\dfrac{2 + \frac{76}{2}}{2}$

$= 20$. Then $\dfrac{20 + \frac{40}{20}}{2} = 11.9$ and $\dfrac{11.9 + \frac{40}{11.9}}{2} = 9.143277$ and so on.

A program in <u>basic</u> to find $\sqrt{N}$ by iteration of the averaging method is shown below (20 iterations):

```
10 C=0
20 INPUT N
30 INPUT G
40 G=((G + N/G )/2)
50 C = C+1
60 PRINT G
70 IF C<19 THEN GOTO 40
80 END
```

The output of this program to find the $\sqrt{76}$; 2 is the first guess.

```
20
11.9
9.143277
8.727697
8.717804
8.717798
```

This last number doesn't change in the first 6 decimal places. The sequence converges very rapidly.

7. Using the binomial expansion to find $\sqrt{2}$: = $\sqrt{2} = 2^{\frac{1}{2}} = \left(\frac{1}{2}\right)^{\frac{-1}{2}} = \left(1 - \frac{1}{2}\right)^{\frac{-1}{2}}$ which is now in its binomial form. Now put 1->A, $\frac{-1}{2}$ ->B, and $\frac{-1}{2}$ -> n , in the binomial expansion, and with 5 terms we get:

$$(A+B)^n = 1 \cdot A^n + n \cdot A^{n-1} \cdot B^1 +$$
$$\frac{n(n-1)}{1 \cdot 2} \cdot A^{n-2} \cdot B^2 + \frac{n(n-1)(n-2)}{1 \cdot 2 \cdot 3} \cdot A^{n-3} \cdot B^3 + \frac{n(n-1)(n-2)(n-3)}{1 \cdot 2 \cdot 3 \cdot 4} \cdot A^{n-4} \cdot B^4 + \ldots$$

$$\sqrt{2} = \left(1 - \frac{1}{2}\right)^{\frac{-1}{2}} = 1 \cdot 1^{\frac{-1}{2}} + \frac{-1}{2} \cdot 1^{\frac{-1}{2}-1} \cdot \left(\frac{-1}{2}\right)^1 + \frac{\frac{-1}{2} \cdot \left(\frac{-1}{2}-1\right)}{1 \cdot 2} \cdot 1^{\frac{-1}{2}-2} \cdot \left(\frac{-1}{2}\right)^2 +$$

$$\frac{\frac{-1}{2} \cdot \left(\frac{-1}{2}-1\right) \cdot \left(\frac{-1}{2}-2\right)}{1 \cdot 2 \cdot 3} \cdot 1^{\frac{-1}{2}-3} \cdot \left(\frac{-1}{2}\right)^3 + \frac{\frac{-1}{2} \cdot \left(\frac{-1}{2}-1\right) \cdot \left(\frac{-1}{2}-2\right) \cdot \left(\frac{-1}{2}-3\right)}{1 \cdot 2 \cdot 3 \cdot 4} \cdot 1^{\frac{-1}{2}-4} \cdot \left(\frac{-1}{2}\right)^4 + \ldots$$

$\sqrt{2}$ = 1 + 0.25 + 0.09375 + 0.0390625 + 0.017089844 + ...

$\sqrt{2}$ = 1.399902344... using 5 terms as an approximation of this infinite series. Notice this doesn't converge very quickly.

$\sqrt[3]{28} = (27+1)^{\frac{1}{3}} = \left[27\left(1+\frac{1}{27}\right)\right]^{\frac{1}{3}} = 27^{\frac{1}{3}} \cdot \left(1+\frac{1}{27}\right)^{\frac{1}{3}} = 3 \cdot \left(1+\frac{1}{27}\right)^{\frac{1}{3}}$. Now we'll use the binomial expansion, with 1->A, $\frac{1}{27}$ ->B and $\frac{1}{3}$ ->n:

$$\sqrt[3]{28} = 3 \cdot \left(1+\frac{1}{27}\right)^{\frac{1}{3}} = 3 \cdot \left[1 \cdot 1^{\frac{1}{3}} + \frac{1}{3} \cdot 1^{\frac{1}{3}-1} \cdot \left(\frac{1}{27}\right)^1 + \frac{\frac{1}{3} \cdot \left(\frac{1}{3}-1\right)}{1 \cdot 2} \cdot 1^{\frac{1}{3}-2} \cdot \left(\frac{1}{27}\right)^2 + \right.$$

$$\frac{\frac{1}{3} \cdot \left(\frac{1}{3}-1\right) \cdot \left(\frac{1}{3}-2\right)}{1 \cdot 2 \cdot 3} \cdot 1^{\frac{1}{3}-3} \cdot \left(\frac{1}{27}\right)^3 + \frac{\frac{1}{3} \cdot \left(\frac{1}{3}-1\right) \cdot \left(\frac{1}{3}-2\right) \cdot \left(\frac{1}{3}-3\right)}{1 \cdot 2 \cdot 3 \cdot 4} \cdot 1^{\frac{1}{3}-4} \cdot \left(\frac{1}{27}\right)^4 + \ldots \left. \right]$$

$\sqrt[3]{28}$ = 3 + 0.037037... - 0.000457247.. + 0.000009408... - 0.000000116...+ ...

$\sqrt[3]{28}$ = 3. 03658... correct to 5 places. When A = 1 and B is small, the series expansion converges quicker, because raising a small number to larger powers, makes the value very much smaller. This can be seen from these two examples above where B = $\frac{-1}{2}$ in the first case, then $\frac{1}{27}$ in this second case.

Questions worksheets for **chapter 11**
"Compound Interest to **e** and **i**"

The problem of compound interest was brought up by Ian when he was 11 years old because he wanted to know how much his father would have to pay in monthly installments on a house worth $10,000 at 10% interest over 30 years. This got us working on the simpler problem, first, of investing and finding the interest.

1. Simple interest
Suppose you put $1 in the bank at a 6% annual rate of interest. How much interest would you earn and what amount of money would you have after 1 year?
The *interest* = principal $\times$ rate $\times$ time

$$I \quad = \quad \$1 \quad \times \ 6\% \times 1 \ yr. = \$.06$$

So you earn 6 cents interest in a year.
The Amount you have after 1 year = principal + *interest* = $1 + *$.06* = $1.06 .

For 2 years,
The *interest* = principal $\times$ rate $\times$ time

$$I \quad = \quad \$1 \quad \times \ 6\% \ \times \ 2 \ yr. = 1 \times .06 \times 2 \ = \$.12$$

Amount you have after 2 years = principal + *interest*

$$A \quad = \quad \$1 \quad + \quad \$.12 \quad = \$1.12$$

For $\frac{1}{2}$ year
The *interest* = principal $\times$ rate $\times$ time

$$I \quad = \quad \$1 \quad \times 6\% \ \times \frac{1}{2} \ yr. = 1 \times .06 \times \frac{1}{2} = \$.03$$

Amount you have after $\frac{1}{2}$ year = principal + interest = $1 + *$.03* = $1.03

Find the simple interest and amount you will have
a) on a $500 investment at 7% for 1 year ;   a) I _____ A _____

b) on a $500 investment at 7% for 2 years;   b) I _____ A _____

c) on a $500 investment at 7% for $2\frac{1}{2}$ years; c) I _____ A _____

If you have a total amount of $348 at the end of 2 years at an annual rate of 8%, what was your original investment? _____

2. Compound interest (principal $1, compounded annually)
Now we'll look at the problem when the interest is compounded, as is normally done. Compounding means adding the interest to the principal, then figuring the interest on this new principal for the next time period.

How much money will you have after 3 years, with a $1 investment (the principal) at a 6% annual rate of interest, compounded annually (once a year)?

Interest (earned during 1st year) = principal $\times$ rate $\times$ time

$$I \quad = \quad \$1 \quad \times \: 6\% \times 1 \text{ yr.} = \$.06$$

Amount you have after 1 year = principal + *interest*

$$A \quad = \quad \$1 \quad + \quad \$.06 \quad = \$1.06 \text{ , but we will leave it in the form}$$

1 + .06. Very often if we don't write an answer as one number, but show where it came from, it will help find a pattern. Don't be too quick to use a calculator! Notice that this answer is the same as the one we got using the simple interest.

Now things will change. **The \$1.06 now becomes the new principal**.

Interest (earned during 2nd year) = **new principal** $\times$ rate $\times$ time

$$I \qquad\qquad = \qquad \$1.06 \times 6\% \times 1 \text{ yr.}$$
$$= \quad (\,1+.06\,) \times .06 \quad = \$.0636 \text{ which is slightly more}$$
$$\text{than it was for the simple interest.}$$

Amount you have at the end of 2 years = new principal + *interest*

$$A \qquad\qquad = \quad (1+.06) \quad + \quad (1+.06) \times .06 =$$
$$= (1+.06) \times (1+.06) \text{ , by factoring out } (1+.06)$$
$$= \quad 1 + .06 + .06 + .06^2 =$$

Amount you have at the end of **2** years = $(1+.06)^2 \: = \$1.1236$, again a little more than the simple interest case.

Notice we have a binomial expansion problem $(A + B)^2$.

What amount you will have at the end of 3 years? _____

Interest (earned during 3rd year) = **new principal** × rate × time

$$I = \$1.06^2 \times 6\% \times 1 \text{ yr.}$$
$$I = (1 + .06)^2 \times .06 = .067416$$

Amount you have at the end of **3** years = **new principal** + *interest*

$$A = (1 + .06)^2 + (1 + .06)^2 \times .06$$
$$= (1 + .06)^2 \times (1 + .06),$$

by factoring out the $(1 + .06)^2$. So

Amount you have at the end of **3** years = $(1+.06)^3 = \$1.191016$

How much money will you have at the end of 7 years?
Write your answer as one number and as a binomial raised to some power.

_____

How much money will you have at the end of 100 years? _____

How much money will you have at the end of t years? _____

After about how many years will you double your money? _____

In the original problem of compound interest , as in most problems, there are different variables, things that can be changed. So far we have changed **the number of years** we invest the money, without changing **the rate** (6%), **the principal** ($1), **and the number of times per year it is compounded** (annually, 1 time per year).

3. Compound interest (principal $5, compounded annually)
Suppose now we change **the principal**, the amount of our investment, keeping the the same, the number of years, the annual rate of interest and the number of times per year it is compounded.

How much money will you have after 3 years, with a **$5** investment (instead of $1 before), at a 6% annual rate of interest, compounded annually ? Look at what we've done above, can you predict what this will be?

Write your answer as an amount as well as showing how you can get it easily.

_____

See if you agree with this...
How much money will you have after 3 years, with a **$5** investment (the principal) at a 6% annual rate of interest, compounded annually (once a year)?

Interest (earned during 1st year) = principal $^\times$ rate $^\times$ tim

   I = $5 $^\times$ 6% $^\times$ 1 yr. = *$.30*

Amount you have after 1 year = principal + interest

   A = $5   +   *5$^\times$ $.06*   = $5.30 , but we will leave it in the

form $5^\times(1 + .06)$

Interest (earned during 2nd year) = **new principal** $^\times$ rate $^\times$ time

   I = $5^\times(1 + .06)$ $^\times$ 6% $^\times$ 1 yr.

               =   *5$^\times$(1+.06)$^\times$.06* = *$.318*

Amount you have at the end of **2** years = **new principal** + *interest*

   A = $5^\times(1 + .06)$ + *5$^\times$(1+.06)$^\times$.06* =

                       = $5^\times(1 + .06)^\times(1 + .06)$, by factoring out

                          $5^\times(1+.06)$

                       = $5^\times(1 + .06 + .06 + .06s(2))$ =

                       = $5^\times(1 + .06)^2$ = $5.618

Can you predict now what amount you will have at the end of 3 years?

_____

Interest (earned during **3rd** year) = **new principal** × rate × time

I $= 5 \times (1 + .06)^2 \times 6\% \times 1$ yr.

           = 5 × (1 + .06)² × .06   = $.33708

Amount you have at the end of 3 years = **new principal** + *interest*

A $= 5 \times (1 + .06)^2$ + *5 × (1 + .06)² × .06*

by factoring out the $5 \times (1 + .06)^2$ we get

$= 5 \times (1 + .06)^2 \times (1 + .06)$, or

Amount you have at the end of 3 years = $\mathbf{5} \times (1 + .06)^3$ = $5.95508)

Were you right?

Try these problems:

How much money will you have after **8** years, with a $5 investment (the principal) at a 6% annual rate of interest, compounded annually (once a year)? Write your answer as one number <u>and</u> as a binomial raised to some power.

_____

How much money will you have at the end of 200 years?   _____

How much money will you have at the end of t years?   _____

After about how many years will you double your money? _____

How does this compare with what you got with a principal of $1?   _____

What happens if we change the rate of interest?

How much money will you have after 3 years, with a $5 investment (the principal) at a 7% annual rate of interest, compounded annually (once a year)?

_____

How much money will you have after **t** years, with an investment (the principal) of **P** dollars at an annual rate of interest of **r**, compounded annually (once a year)?

_____

4. Leading to a very important infinite sequence
Compound interest, changing the # times per year the interest is compounded
We'll compare compounding the interest 2 times per year, 12 times a year, 365 times per year, a million times per year, and finally an infinite number of times per year. We'll see what difference these make and what new **patterns** we find.
Use your calculator after you find a pattern.

How much money will you have after 1 year, with a $1 investment at an 6% annual rate of interest, **compounded semi-annually (2 times a year)**?

Interest (1st $\frac{1}{2}$ year) = principal $\times$ rate $\times$ time

$$I \quad = \quad \$1 \quad \times 6\% \times \frac{1}{2} \text{ yr.} = \$.03 = \frac{.06}{2} \quad \textit{(3 cents)}$$

Amount (end of $\frac{1}{2}$ year) = principal + *interest*

$$= \quad 1 \quad + \quad \frac{.06}{2} = \$1.03$$

Interest (2nd $\frac{1}{2}$ year) = **new principal** $\times$ rate $\times$ time

$$I \quad = \quad \left(1 + \frac{.06}{2}\right) \times .06 \times \frac{1}{2} = \left(1 + \frac{.06}{2}\right) \times \frac{.06}{2}$$

Amount (end of $\frac{2}{2}$ or 1 year) = **new principal** + interest

$$A \quad = \left(1 + \frac{.06}{2}\right) \quad + \left(1 + \frac{.06}{2}\right) \times \frac{.06}{2}$$

$$= \left(1 + \frac{.06}{2}\right) \times \left(1 + \frac{.06}{2}\right), \text{ by factoring out } \left(1 + \frac{.06}{2}\right)$$

$$= \quad 1 + \frac{.06}{2} + \frac{.06}{2} + \left(\frac{.06}{2}\right)^2 \quad =$$

Amount (end of $\frac{2}{2}$ or 1 year) $= \left(1 + \frac{.06}{2}\right)^2 \quad = \$1.0609$

So after 1 year, with a $1 investment at an 6% annual rate of interest, **compounded semi-annually (2 times a year)** you will have $\left(1 + \frac{.06}{2}\right)^2 \quad = \$1.0609$, a little more than when it was compounded annually.

Can you predict now, what amount you will have at the end of 1 year if you invest $1 at a 6% annual rate of interest, **compounded quarterly (4 times a year)**?

_____

Let's do it. How much money will you have after 1 year, with a $1 investment at a 6% annual rate of interest, **compounded quarterly (4 times a year)**?

Interest (1st $\frac{1}{4}$ year) = principal × rate × time

$$= \quad \$1 \quad \times 6\% \times \frac{1}{4} \text{ yr.} = \$.015 = 1.5 \text{ cents} = \frac{.06}{4}$$

Amount (end of $\frac{1}{4}$ year) = principal + interest

$$= \quad 1 \quad + \frac{.06}{4} = \$1.015$$

Interest (2nd $\frac{1}{4}$ year) = **new principal** × rate × time

$$= \quad \left(1 + \frac{.06}{4}\right) \times .06 \times \frac{1}{4}$$

$$= \quad \left(1 + \frac{.06}{4}\right) \times \frac{.06}{4} = \$.015225$$

Amount (end of $\frac{2}{4}$ or $\frac{1}{2}$ year) = **new principal** + interest

$$= \left(1 + \frac{.06}{4}\right) \quad + \left(1 + \frac{.06}{4}\right) \times \frac{.06}{4} =$$

$$= \left(1 + \frac{.06}{4}\right) \times \left(1 + \frac{.06}{4}\right) \text{, obtained by factoring out}$$

$$\left(1 + \frac{.06}{4}\right) \text{ from the two terms above}$$

$$= \quad 1 + \frac{.06}{4} + \frac{.06}{4} + \left(\frac{.06}{4}\right)^2 =$$

$$= \left(1 + \frac{.06}{4}\right)^2 = \$1.030225$$

What's interest do we earn during the 3rd $\frac{1}{4}$ of the year ?

_____

What amount will we have after the 3rd $\frac{1}{4}$ of the year ?

_____

Do you see a pattern ?

You realize that if you had brought out your calculator too soon, you would never see the pattern!!

Interest (3rd $\frac{1}{4}$ year) = **new principal** $^\times$ rate $^\times$ time

$$= \left(1 + \frac{.06}{4}\right)^2 \times .06 \times \frac{1}{4}$$

$$= \left(1 + \frac{.06}{4}\right)^2 \times \frac{.06}{4} = \$.01545$$

Amount (end of f(3,4) of a year) = **new principal** +   *interest*

$$= \left(1 + \frac{.06}{4}\right)^2 + \left(1 + \frac{.06}{4}\right)^2 \times \frac{.06}{4}$$

$$= \left(1 + \frac{.06}{4}\right)^2 \times \left(1 + \frac{.06}{4}\right) \text{, obtained by factoring out}$$

$$\left(1 + \frac{.06}{4}\right)^2 \text{ from the two terms above}$$

$$= \left[1 + \frac{.06}{4} + \frac{.06}{4} + \left(\frac{.06}{4}\right)^2 \right] \times \left(1 + \frac{.06}{4}\right)$$

$$= \left[1 + 3 \times \frac{.06}{4} + 3 \times \left(\frac{.06}{4}\right)^2 + \left(\frac{.06}{4}\right)^3 \right]$$

$$= \left(1 + \frac{.06}{4}\right)^3 = \$1.045678$$

Interest (4th $\frac{1}{4}$ of the year) = **new principal** $^\times$ rate $^\times$ time

$$= \left(1 + \frac{.06}{4}\right)^3 \times .06 \times \frac{1}{4}$$

$$= \left(1 + \frac{.06}{4}\right)^3 \times \frac{.06}{4} = \$.01568$$

Amount (end of $\frac{4}{4}$ or 1 year) = **new principal** +   *interest*

$$= \left(1 + \frac{.06}{4}\right)^3 + \left(1 + \frac{.06}{4}\right)^3 \times \frac{.06}{4}$$

$$= \left(1 + \frac{.06}{4}\right)^3 \times \left(1 + \frac{.06}{4}\right)$$

Amount (end of $\frac{4}{4}$ or 1 year) $= \left(1 \frac{.06}{4}\right)^4 = \$1.06136$

So far, if we invest $1 for 1 year, at 6%, compounding the interest
1 time per year, we end up with $1.06

2 times per year, we end up with $\left(1 + \frac{.06}{2}\right)^2 = \$ 1.0609$

4 times per year, we end up with $\left(1 + \frac{.06}{4}\right)^4 = \$1.061363551$

Can you find a pattern now?

Write a computer program that will calculate the amount you will have after 1 year, for any
number of compound interest periods, at 6%.

Can you predict the amount we will have if we invest $1 for 1 year, at 6%, compounding the interest monthly (**12** times per year) ?

compounding the interest daily (**365** times per year)?

_____

_____

Can you predict the amount we will have if we invest $1 for 1 year, at 6%, compounding the interest **1,000,000** times per year! Then calculate the number.

_____

Generalize the amount we will have if we invest $1 for 1 year, at an annual interest rate of **r** compounding the interest **n** times per year.

_____

It looks like we have an infinite sequence. We'll put these numbers in a table:

# of times interest is compounded per year	Amount of money we have after 1 year (in $)
1	1.06
2	1.0609
⋮	⋮
4	1.061363551
⋮	⋮
12	1.061677812
⋮	⋮
365	1.061831311
⋮	⋮
1,000,000	1.061836545
⋮	⋮

So, no matter how many times a year the interest is compounded, the amount we have in 1 year at a 6% annual rate of interest, never gets bigger than $1.07 and won't get bigger than 1.06183 out to 5 places. If we compound the interest continuously then, an infinite number of times per year, it turns out that this number $(1+ \frac{.06}{n})^n$ as n goes to infinity, gives us an infinite sequence whose limit is 1.061836547... . We'll write it this way:

$$\lim_{n \to \infty} \left(1+ \frac{.06}{n}\right)^n = 1.061836547... = e^{.06}$$

Ahhh... there is that very special number **e** which is the base of the natural logarithms.

Now some questions...

What would **e** equal? Use the expression above.

_____

Can you predict the amount we will have if we invest $1 for 1 year, at **8%**, compounding the interest <u>continuously</u>! Then calculate the number.

_____

Generalize the amount we will have if we invest $1 for 1 year, at an annual interest rate of **r** compounding the interest **n** times per year.

_____

Can you predict the amount we will have if we invest **$5** for 1 year, at **8%**, compounding the interest 1000 times per year. Then calculate the number.

_____

Can you predict the amount we will have if we invest **$5** for 1 year, at **8%**, compounding the interest <u>continuously</u>! Then calculate the number.

_____

Can you predict the amount we will have if we invest **P** dollars for **1** year, at an annual interest rate **r**, compounding the interest **n** times per year.

Let's try this one:

How much money will you have after **3** years, with a **$5** investment at a **6%** annual rate of interest, **compounded daily**?

Interest (earned during 1st day) = principal $^\times$ rate $^\times$ time

$$= \quad \$5 \quad ^\times 6\% \ ^\times \ \frac{1}{365} \text{ yr.}$$

Amount you have after **1st** day = principal +   *interest*

$$= \quad 5 \quad + \quad (5 \ ^\times .06 \ ^\times \ \frac{1}{365})$$

$$= \ 5 \ ^\times \left(1 \ + \ \frac{.06}{365} \right) \ , \text{ writing } .06 \ ^\times \ \frac{1}{365} \ \text{ as } \ \frac{.06}{365}$$

Interest (earned during **2nd** day) =   principal $^\times$ rate $^\times$ time

$$= \quad 5 \ ^\times \left(1 \ + \ \frac{.06}{365} \right) \ ^\times \quad \frac{.06}{365}$$

Amount you have after **2nd** day =   principal   +   interest

$$= 5 \ ^\times \left(1 \ + \ \frac{.06}{365} \right) \ + \ 5 \ ^\times \left(1 + \frac{.06}{365} \right) \ ^\times \ \frac{.06}{365}$$

$$= 5 \ ^\times \left(1 \ + \ \frac{.06}{365} \right) \ ^\times \left(1 \ + \ \frac{.06}{365} \right)$$

$$= 5 \ ^\times \left(1 \ + \ \frac{.06}{365} \right)^{2}$$

Amount you have after **372nd** day $= 5 \ ^\times \left(1 + \frac{.06}{365} \right)^{372}$

Amount you have after **2 years** $= 5 \ ^\times \left(1 + \frac{.06}{365} \right)^{2 \times 365}$

Amount you have after **3 years** $= 5 \ ^\times \left(1 + \frac{.06}{365} \right)^{3 \times 365} = \$5.986..$

How much money will you have after **7** years, with a **$5** investment at a **6%** annual rate of interest, compounded daily?

_____

Generalizing, how much money will you have after **t** years, with an investment of **P** dollars, at an annual rate of interest **r**, compounded **n** times per year?

_____

5. Naming e^x with an infinite series

$$(A+B)^n = 1 \cdot A^n + n \cdot A^{n-1} \cdot B^1 +$$

$$\frac{n(n-1)}{1 \cdot 2} \cdot A^{n-2} \cdot B^2 + \frac{n(n-1)(n-2)}{1 \cdot 2 \cdot 3} \cdot A^{n-3} \cdot B^3 + \frac{n(n-1)(n-2)(n-3)}{1 \cdot 2 \cdot 3 \cdot 4} \cdot A^{n-4} \cdot B^4 + \ldots$$

Notice that when n = 2 we get 3 terms $(A+B)^2 = A^2 + 2 \cdot A \cdot B + B^2$

Putting 1 in for A and $\frac{.06}{n}$ in for B above, we get the following infinite series:

$$(A+B)^n = 1 \cdot A^n + n \cdot A^{n-1} \cdot B^1 +$$
$$\frac{n(n-1)}{1 \cdot 2} \cdot A^{n-2} \cdot B^2 + \frac{n(n-1)(n-2)}{1 \cdot 2 \cdot 3} \cdot A^{n-3} \cdot B^3 + \frac{n(n-1)(n-2)(n-3)}{1 \cdot 2 \cdot 3 \cdot 4} \cdot A^{n-4} \cdot B^4 + \ldots$$

$$\left(1 + \frac{.06}{n}\right)^n = 1^n + n \cdot 1^{n-1} \cdot \frac{.06}{n} + \frac{n(n-1)}{2!} \cdot 1^{n-2} \cdot \left(\frac{.06}{n}\right)^2 + \frac{n(n-1)(n-2)}{3!} \cdot 1^{n-3} \cdot \left(\frac{.06}{n}\right)^3$$

$$+ \frac{n(n-1)(n-2)(n-3)}{4!} \cdot 1^{n-4} \cdot \left(\frac{.06}{n}\right)^4 + \ldots$$

Simplifying this series, 1 to any power is 1, writing $\left(\frac{.06}{n}\right)^4$ as $\frac{.06^4}{n^4}$, and just switching the factorials and the powers of n, we get

$$\left(1 + \frac{.06}{n}\right)^n = 1 + .06 + \frac{n(n-1)}{n^2} \cdot \frac{.06^2}{2!} + \frac{n(n-1)(n-2)}{n^3} \cdot \frac{.06^3}{3!} +$$

$$\frac{n(n-1)(n-2)(n-3)}{n^4} \cdot \frac{.06^4}{4!} + \ldots$$

We've gone out 5 terms; now let's look at what happens as n -> ∞ . All the fractions with n's in them will go to 1, and we get

$$\lim_{n \to \infty} \left(1 + \frac{.06}{n}\right)^n = 1 + .06 + \frac{.06^2}{2!} + \frac{.06^3}{3!} + \frac{.06^4}{4!} + \frac{.06^5}{5!} + \frac{.06^6}{6!} + \frac{.06^7}{7!} + \ldots =$$

$$e^{.06} = 1.061836547\ldots$$

Write out the first 6 terms of the binomial expansion, then put 1 in for A and $\frac{.08}{n}$ in for B and see what you get.

Write out the first 6 terms of the binomial expansion, then put 1 in for A and $\frac{1}{n}$ in for B and see what you get.

Write the first 6 terms for e^x as an infinite series. In other words find $\underset{n\to\infty}{\text{limit}} \left(1 + \frac{x}{n}\right)^n$ by using the binomial expansion, then let $n \to \infty$.

_____

_____

e is a very important number in mathematics; not only does it show up in the compound interest problem, but in as the base of natural logarithms, as well as in exponential growth and decay and can be written in terms of sines and cosines.

6. Patterns with i.

In solving equations we come across one like $x^2 = {}^-1$.

If we try 1 in for x, 1•1=1, not $^-1$, so 1 doesn't work.

Try $^-1$ in for x, $^-1 \cdot {}^-1 = {}^+1$, not $^-1$, so $^-1$ doesn't work (we have to put the same number in for x, remember.

So there is no "regular" number that works. We'll invent a new number and call it **i** .

Then $\mathbf{i} \cdot \mathbf{i} = \mathbf{i}^2 = {}^-1$. This is how we'll define **i** .

Now look for patterns with **i**

$\mathbf{i} = \mathbf{i}$

$\mathbf{i}^2 = {}^-1$

$\mathbf{i}^3 = \mathbf{i} \cdot \mathbf{i} \cdot \mathbf{i} = {}^-\mathbf{i}$ (because $\mathbf{i} \cdot \mathbf{i} =$

$^-1$ and $^-1 \cdot \mathbf{i} = {}^-\mathbf{i}$)

$\mathbf{i}^4 = \mathbf{i} \cdot \mathbf{i} \cdot \mathbf{i} \cdot \mathbf{i} = 1$ (because $\mathbf{i}^4 = \mathbf{i}^3 \cdot \mathbf{i} = {}^-\mathbf{i}^2$

$=1$ or $\mathbf{i}^4 = \mathbf{i}^2 \cdot \mathbf{i}^2 = {}^-1 \cdot {}^-1 = 1)$

$\mathbf{i}^5 = \mathbf{i} \cdot \mathbf{i} \cdot \mathbf{i} \cdot \mathbf{i} \cdot \mathbf{i} = \mathbf{i}$

$\mathbf{i}^6 = {}^-1$

Now you try these

$\mathbf{i}^7 = $ _____

$\mathbf{i}^8 = $ _____

$\mathbf{i}^9 = $ _____

and without too much work

$\mathbf{i}^{127} = $ _____ , and

$\mathbf{i}^{-2} = $ _____

What patterns do you see?

7. Leading to a very exciting number sentence!

From above:

$$e^x = 1 + x + \frac{x^2}{2!} + \frac{x^3}{3!} + \frac{x^4}{4!} + \frac{x^5}{5!} + \frac{x^6}{6!} + \frac{x^7}{7!} + ...$$

In place of x we will put **ia**, **i** times a, where **i** is our imaginary number and a is any number in radians. We'll need to raise **ia** to successive powers.

What is $(ia)^7$ equal to? Well $(ia)^7 = i^7 \cdot a^7 = {}^-i \cdot a^7 = {}^-ia^7$

Now try the whole thing by yourself, put **ia** in for **x**, through $\frac{x^7}{7!}$ in the infinite series for e^x and write down what you get.

_____

$$e^x = 1 + x + \frac{x^2}{2!} + \frac{x^3}{3!} + \frac{x^4}{4!} + \frac{x^5}{5!} + \frac{x^6}{6!} + \frac{x^7}{7!} + ...,\text{ now put }ia\text{ in for }x$$

$$e^{ia} = 1 + ia + \frac{(ia)^2}{2!} + \frac{(ia)^3}{3!} + \frac{(ia)^4}{4!} + \frac{(ia)^5}{5!} + \frac{(ia)^6}{6!} + \frac{(ia)^7}{7!} + ...,$$

raising ia to the powers-- $(ia)^2 = {}^-a^2$ and $(ia)^3 = {}^-ia^3$ and $(ia)^4 = a^4$ and $(ia)^5 = ia^5$, and so on...
and we get

$$e^{ia} = 1 + ia - \frac{a^2}{2!} - \frac{ia^3}{3!} + \frac{a^4}{4!} + \frac{ia^5}{5!} - \frac{a^6}{6!} - \frac{ia^7}{7!} + ...$$

What patterns do you see? _____

We have some of the terms above that are real, some imaginary; let's separate these:

$$e^{ia} = 1 - \frac{a^2}{2!} + \frac{a^4}{4!} - \frac{a^6}{6!} + ... \ ia - \frac{ia^3}{3!} + \frac{ia^5}{5!} - \frac{ia^7}{7!} + ...$$

factoring out the i's

$$e^{ia} = 1 - \frac{a^2}{2!} + \frac{a^4}{4!} - \frac{a^6}{6!} + ... \ i\bullet\left(a - \frac{a^3}{3!} + \frac{a^5}{5!} - \frac{a^7}{7!} + ...\right)$$

Newton first figured out that the cosine and sine could be written as infinite series

$$\cos a = 1 - \frac{a^2}{2!} + \frac{a^4}{4!} - \frac{a^6}{6!} + ... \text{ and}$$

$$\sin a = a - \frac{a^3}{3!} + \frac{a^5}{5!} - \frac{a^7}{7!} + ... \text{ and later Cotes in 1716 discovered that}$$

one can write e^{ia} in terms of the cos a and sin a. You try it from what we did above.

$$e^{ia} = \text{_____}$$

Since $e^{ia} = 1 - \dfrac{a^2}{2!} + \dfrac{a^4}{4!} - \dfrac{a^6}{6!} + ... \; i \bullet \left(a - \dfrac{a^3}{3!} + \dfrac{a^5}{5!} - \dfrac{a^7}{7!} + ... \right)$

$$e^{ia} = \cos a \; + \; i \bullet \sin a$$

If we now put π radians in for a above, we get

$$e^{i\pi} = \cos \pi + \; i \bullet \sin \pi$$

Since $\cos \pi = {}^-1$ and $\sin \pi = 0$, we get $e^{i\pi} = {}^-1 + 0$. Adding 1 to both sides we get the amazing result

$$e^{i\pi} + 1 = 0$$

This is a true statement that has the five most important numbers in mathematics in it: e, i, π, 1 and 0. Wow! When I first saw this in college I did a watercolor painting with this in the center. Amazing stuff!

On a computer try to find Ln ($^-1$), then change this to an exponential equation. What happens?

8. Using iteration to do the compound interest

Another way of looking at the compound interest is as an iteration function introduced in chapter 8. The iteration function is $P \bullet (1 + .06)$. Iterate this function to find how much money you will have after 7 years (iterate the function 7 times), with a $5 investment (P=5) at a **6%** annual rate of interest, compounded annually?

Iterating the function: $P_{old} \bullet (1+.06) = P_{new}$, then P_{new} will become P_{old} and so forth. To start $5 \bullet (1+.06) = \$5.30$; $5.30(1+.06) = 5.618$; $5.618(1+.06) = 5.955..$ and so on. After 7 years we get $7.518151295 or $7.51 . Another way to look at the problem is $5 \bullet (1+.06)$ after 1 year. Then $5 \bullet (1+.06) \bullet (1+.06)$ after 2 years, then $5 \bullet (1+.06) \bullet (1+.06) \bullet (1+.06)$ after 3 years, and so on.

Try this on the problem: find how much money you will have after 10 years (iterate the function 10 times), with a **$1000** investment (P=1000) at a 8% annual rate of interest, compounded annually?

9. One result of Ian playing with powers of powers.

Ian, in Physics class with his calculator, came up with the following pattern of differences of ratios of powers of powers. Try some numbers. What happens as X goes to infinity?

$$\frac{(\mathbf{x}+1)^{(x+1)}}{\mathbf{x}^x} - \frac{\mathbf{x}^x}{(\mathbf{x}-1)^{(x-1)}}$$

10. Graphing powers of i

Graph the real powers of i on the
Argand plane at the right, real
numbers on the horizontal axis vs
imaginary numbers on the vertical
axis. At the right we've plotted
(1,0) because $i^0 = 1$ or $1 + 0i$ and
(0,1) because $i^1 = i$ or $0 + 1i$
Where is i^2, i^3 and so on...

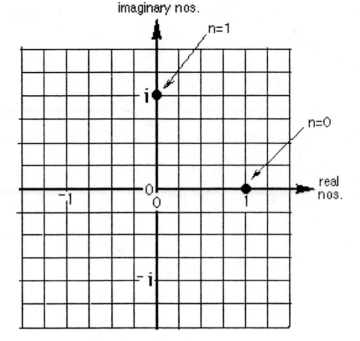

What is $i^{\frac{1}{2}}$? Where would it be
on the graph?

Make up some other questions.

See Abe's work on Don's website at http://www.shout.net/~mathman/html/abe2.html .

11. Graph powers of (1 + i) on the Argand plane.

Since
$(1 + i)^0 = 1$
$(1 + i)^1 = 1 + i$
$(1 + i)^2 = 1 + 2i + i^2 = 1 + 2i + ^-1 = 2i.$

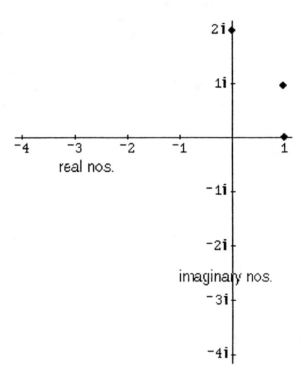

The graph of $(1 + i)^n$ has been started at
the right. Plot some more points.

What's happening?

Make up some questions.

See Ana's work on Don's website at http://www.shout.net/~mathman/html/anae.html .

I never knew anything about i^i before maybe 5 years ago, when I came across it using *Mathematica* ®. Iterate i^n, starting with n = i.

You get i^i , then $i^{(i^i)}$, $i^{\left(i^{(i^i)}\right)}$ and so on. Notice that i^i is not i^2.

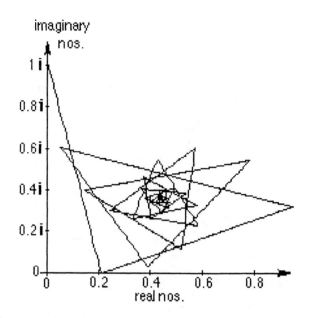

Would you believe that i^i is a real number 0.20788... That's a little hard to believe. The graph of about 100 iterations of i^n is shown at the right. Another spiral!! I still don't know the significance of the point to which this sequence of numbers is converging. The 100th term in this sequence is 0.438283 + 0.360599 i .

See the great IES Java applet at http://www.ies.co.jp/math/java/comp/itoi/itoi.html .

At the right is the curve r = 2^t ; a polar graph. Try to make this yourself. t is the angle in radians, starting at the positive x, around the origin counterclockwise, and r is the distance from the origin to the curve. I originally made the graph on $\frac{1}{4}$" graph paper. Another way to do

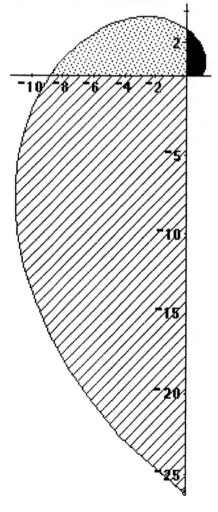

it is to use polar graph paper. A third way is to use parametric equations where **x** = r•cos t and **y** = r•sin t . You might like to try some things that I have done with this graph. Copy the graph, glue it on cardboard, then cut out the 3 different pieces (black, spotted and striped). Do the "eye test"; that is, see if these are the same shape. Put the black (smaller piece) in front of the spotted one, move it and see if the black one "covers" the spotted one.. see the diagram below.

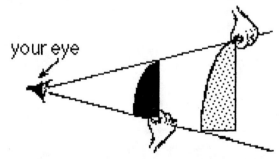

your eye

Another thing you might like to try is compare the area of each of the three pieces. You'll want to outline the cardboard pieces on graph paper first.

12. Getting back to Ian's problem.. What would his Dad pay in monthly installments on a $10,000 home loan at 10% annual interest with a 30-year mortgage? The formula usually given is

$$M = \frac{P \cdot R \cdot (1+R)^n}{(1+R)^n - 1}$$ where M is the monthly installment ($) which is what we are looking for,

P is the amount of the loan ($10,000 in this case), R is the monthly rate (in this case $\frac{10\%}{12}$,

and n is the number of payments (12×30=360 in this case). What do you get for M?

For those who wish to find out how to get this formula -- the bankers don't know how to do this by the way -- just follow along. The calculations are based on the fact that after the end of each month the amount of the loan (P for principal) is decreased by (the monthly payment (M) - the interest you pay). The new principal we shall call the Declining Balance (DB). When the Declining Balance is **0**, you will be through paying off your loan. Most of the algebra involved is using the distributive property (factoring out P's and M's), subtracting and substitution. We're going to get DB in terms of M, P, R, and eventually n. Let's do it!

I_1 = PR (the first month's interest) ...notice $P-(M- I_1) = P- M + I_1$..we'll use this form..

DB_1 = P- M+I_1 = P-M+PR = P+PR-M=P(1+R)-M = first Declining Balance

I_2= $DB_1 \cdot R$=[P(1+R)-M] $\cdot R$=P(R+R^2)-MR = interest for the second month

DB_2= DB_1-M+I_2= P(1+R)-M-M+P(R+R^2)-MR = P(1+2R+R^2)-M(2+R) ..anything familiar?

I_3= $DB_2 \cdot R$ = [P(1+2R+R^2)-M(2+R)] $\cdot R$ = P(R+2R^2+R^3)-M(2R+R^2)

DB_3= DB_2 -M+I_3 =P(1+2R+R^2)-M(2+R)-M+P(R+2R^2+R^3)-M(2R+R^2)

DB_3 = P(1+3R+3R^2+R^3)-M(3+3R+R^2)... aha, if you look at what's in the parentheses! Do you see the binomial expansion there? 1+3R+3R^2+R^3 = (1+R)^3 and the other one is a little tricky, but

$$(3+3R+R^2) \cdot \frac{R}{R} \;=\; \frac{3R+3R^2+R^3}{R} \;=\; \frac{(1+R)^3 - 1}{R}$$

So DB_3 = P$\cdot$(1+R)^3 - M $\cdot \dfrac{(1+R)^3 - 1}{R}$. Now if we go 360 payments,

$$DB_{360}= P\cdot(1+R)^{360} - M \cdot \frac{(1+R)^{360} - 1}{R} = 0 \text{ , Solving for M} = \frac{P\cdot(1+R)^{360}}{\frac{(1+R)^{360} - 1}{R}} = \frac{P\cdot R \cdot(1+R)^{360}}{(1+R)^{360} - 1}$$

Generalizing for n payments, we get $M = \dfrac{P \cdot R \cdot (1+R)^n}{(1+R)^n - 1}$ and our problem is solved.

Answer worksheets for **chapter 11**
"Compound Interest to **e** and **i** "

1. Simple interest
Find the simple interest and amount you will have

a) on a $500 investment at 7% for 1 year: I = $500 ×.07= $35;
A= $500+$35=$535

b) on a $500 investment at 7% for 2 years: I = $500 ×.07 × 2= $70;
A= $500+$70=$570

c) on a $500 investment at 7% for $2\frac{1}{2}$ years: I = $500 ×.07 × 2.5= $87.50;
A= $500+$87.50=$587.50

If you have a total amount of $348 at the end of 2 years at an annual rate of 8%, what was you original investment? A= P + P ×.08 × 2; $348 = (1+.08 × 2) × P; P = $\frac{\$348}{1.16}$ = $300

2. Compound interest (principal $1, compounded annually)
How much money will you have after **3** years, with a $1 investment (the principal) at a 6% annual rate of interest, compounded annually (once a year)? $(1+.06)^3$ = $1.19

How much money will you have at the end of 7 years? $(1+.06)^7$ = $1.50

How much money will you have at the end of 100 years? $(1+.06)^{100}$ = $339.30

How much money will you have at the end of t years? $(1+.06)^t$

After how many years (nearest whole number) will you double your money? Since $(1+.06)^{11}$=$1.89 and $(1+.06)^{12}$=$2.01, it's closer to 12 years that will you double your money.

3. Compound interest (principal $5, compounded annually)
How much money will you have after **8** years, with a $5 investment (the principal) at a 6% annual rate of interest, compounded annually (once a year)? Write your answer as one number and as a binomial raised to some power. $5(1+.06)^8$ = $7.97

How much money will you have at the end of 200 years? $5(1+.06)^{200}$ = $575,629.52

How much money will you have at the end of t years? $5(1+.06)^t$

After how many years will you double your money? after 12 years the am't is
$5(1+.06)^{12}$ = $10.06

How much money will you have after 3 years, with a $5 investment (the principal) at a **7%** annual rate of interest, compounded annually (once a year)? $5(1+.07)^3$ = $6.13

How much money (**A**) will you have after **t** years, with an investment (the principal) of **P** dollars at an annual rate of interest of **r**, compounded annually (once a year)?
$$A = P(1+r)^t$$

4. Leading to a very important infinite sequence
Compound interest, changing the # times per year the money is compounded
How much money will you have after 1 year, with a $1 investment at an 6% annual rate of interest : **compounding the interest 1 time per year**, we end up with $1.06

compounded semi-annually (2 times a year) we end up with $(1 + \frac{.06}{2})^2 = \$ 1.0609$

compounded quarterly (4 times a year) we end up with $(1 + \frac{.06}{4})^4 = \$1.061363551$

compounded monthly (12 times a year) we end up with $(1 + \frac{.06}{12})^{12} = \$1.061677812$

compounded daily (365 times a year) we end up with $(1 + \frac{.06}{365})^{365} = \$1.061831311$

A program in <u>basic</u> that will calculate the amount you will have after 1 year, for any number of compound interest periods, n, at 6%.	10 input n 20 print (1+.06/n)^n 30 goto 10

compounded 1,000,000 times per year we end up with $(1 + \frac{.06}{10^6})^{10^6} = \$1.061836545$

Notice that we have an infinite sequence that approaches 1.061836545... This number turns out to be **e**$^{.06}$, where e is the base of the natural logarithms (2.7182818...); not only is it not a rational number, but it is called transcendental, like π.

$$\text{We say } \lim_{n \to \infty} \left(1 + \frac{.06}{n} \right)^n = 1.061836547... = e^{.06}$$

$$\text{and } e = e^1 = \lim_{n \to \infty} \left(1 + \frac{1}{n} \right)^n = 2.718281828...$$

So e is the limit of an infinite sequence $\left(1 + \frac{1}{n} \right)^n$ as n gets bigger and bigger.

The amount we will have if we invest $1 for 1 year, at **8%**, compounding the interest <u>continuously</u> will be:

$$\lim_{n \to \infty} \left(1 + \frac{.08}{n} \right)^n = 1.083287068... = e^{.08}$$

The amount we will have if we invest $1 for 1 year, at an annual interest rate of **r** compounding the interest **n** times per year.

$$\lim_{n \to \infty} \left(1 + \frac{r}{n} \right)^n = e^r$$

The amount we will have if we invest **$5** for 1 year, at **8%**, compounding the interest 1000 times per year.

$$A = \$5 \bullet \left(1 + \frac{.08}{1000} \right)^{1000} = \$5.416418007$$

Can you predict the amount we will have if we invest $5 for 1 year, at **8%**, compounding the interest <u>continuously</u>! Then calculate the number.

$$A = 5 \bullet \lim_{n \to \infty} \left(1 + \frac{.08}{n} \right)^n = 5 \bullet e^{.08}$$

The amount we will have if we invest **P** dollars for **1** year, at an annual interest rate **r**, compounding the interest **n** times per year.

$$A = P \bullet \lim_{n \to \infty} \left(1 + \frac{r}{n} \right)^n$$

The amount we will have after **3** years, with a $5 investment at a 6% annual rate of interest, compounded daily (365 times per year) is: $A = \$5 \bullet \left(1 + \frac{.06}{365} \right)^{3 \times 365} = \$5.99$

The amount we will have after **7** years, with a **$5** investment at a **6%** annual rate of interest, compounded daily is : $A = \$5 \bullet \left(1 + \frac{.06}{365} \right)^{7 \times 365} = \$7.61$

The amount we will have after **t** years with an investment of **P** dollars, at an annual rate of interest **r**, compounded **n** times per year $A = P \bullet \lim_{n \to \infty} \left(1 + \frac{r}{n} \right)^{t \bullet n}$

If you wanted to compute the number of years t, in which your investment would double, just solve this equation $2 = 1 \bullet \left(1 + \frac{r}{n} \right)^{t \bullet n}$ for t. Taking the ln of both sides we get

$\ln 2 = t \bullet n \bullet \ln(1 + \frac{r}{n})$ and $t = \dfrac{\ln 2}{n \bullet \ln\left(1 + \frac{r}{n} \right)}$. If we use 6% for r, n=1 (compounded annually), as

we did above, we get $t = \dfrac{\ln 2}{\ln\left(1.06 \right)} = 11.9$ years, which is what we figured before, about 12 years.

Amount you have after **t** years with an investment of **P** dollars, at an annual rate of interest **r**, compounded continuously

$$A = P \bullet \lim_{n \to \infty} \left(1 + \frac{r}{n} \right)^{t \bullet n} = P \bullet e^{r \bullet t}$$

5. Naming e^x with an infinite series

Write out the first 6 terms of the binomial expansion, then put 1 in for A and $\frac{.08}{n}$ in for B and see what you get.

$$(A+B)^n = 1 \bullet A^n + n \bullet A^{n-1} \bullet B^1 +$$
$$\frac{n(n-1)}{2!} \bullet A^{n-2} \bullet B^2 + \frac{n(n-1)(n-2)}{3!} \bullet A^{n-3} \bullet B^3 + \frac{n(n-1)(n-2)(n-3)}{4!} \bullet A^{n-4} \bullet B^4 +$$
$$\frac{n(n-1)(n-2)(n-3)(n-4)}{5!} \bullet A^{n-5} \bullet B^5 + \dots$$

$$\left(1+\frac{.08}{n}\right)^n = 1^n + n\bullet 1^{n-1}\bullet\frac{.08}{n} + \frac{n(n-1)}{2!}\bullet 1^{n-2}\bullet\left(\frac{.08}{n}\right)^2 + \frac{n(n-1)(n-2)}{3!}\bullet 1^{n-3}\bullet\left(\frac{.08}{n}\right)^3 +$$

$$\frac{n(n-1)(n-2)(n-3)}{4!}\bullet 1^{n-4}\bullet\left(\frac{.08}{n}\right)^4 + \frac{n(n-1)(n-2)(n-3)(n-4)}{5!}\bullet 1^{n-5}\bullet\left(\frac{.08}{n}\right)^5 +\dots \text{ since } 1 \text{ to any}$$

power is 1 and as $n\to\infty$ all the terms $\frac{n(n-1)(n-2)(n-3)(n-4)}{n!}\to 1$ and we get

$$e^{.08} = \lim_{n\to\infty}\left(1+\frac{.08}{n}\right)^n = 1 + \frac{.08^1}{1!} + \frac{.08^2}{2!} + \frac{.08^3}{3!} + \frac{.08^4}{4!} + \frac{.08^5}{5!} + \frac{.08^6}{6!} + \frac{.08^7}{7!} + \dots =$$

1.083287068...

If we put 1 in for A and $\frac{1}{n}$ in for B we get:

$$e = e^1 = \lim_{n\to\infty}\left(1+\frac{1}{n}\right)^n = 1 + 1 + \frac{1}{2!} + \frac{1}{3!} + \frac{1}{4!} + \frac{1}{5!} + \frac{1}{6!} + \frac{1}{7!} + \dots =$$

=2.718281828... (which is not repeating, not rational, but transcendental, like π).

We'll write the first 6 terms for e^x as an infinite series. In other words find

$\lim_{n\to\infty}\left(1+\frac{x}{n}\right)^n$ by starting with the binomial expansion, put $1\to A$ and $\frac{x}{n}\to B$, then

let $n\to\infty$.

$$(A+B)^n = 1\bullet A^n + n\bullet A^{n-1}\bullet B^1 +$$
$$\frac{n(n-1)}{2!}\bullet A^{n-2}\bullet B^2 + \frac{n(n-1)(n-2)}{3!}\bullet A^{n-3}\bullet B^3 + \frac{n(n-1)(n-2)(n-3)}{4!}\bullet A^{n-4}\bullet B^4 +$$
$$\frac{n(n-1)(n-2)(n-3)(n-4)}{5!}\bullet A^{n-5}\bullet B^5 + \dots$$

$$\left(1+\frac{x}{n}\right)^n = 1^n + n\bullet 1^{n-1}\bullet\frac{x}{n} + \frac{n(n-1)}{2!}\bullet 1^{n-2}\bullet\left(\frac{x}{n}\right)^2 + \frac{n(n-1)(n-2)}{3!}\bullet 1^{n-3}\bullet\left(\frac{x}{n}\right)^3 +$$

$$\frac{n(n-1)(n-2)(n-3)}{4!}\bullet 1^{n-4}\bullet\left(\frac{x}{n}\right)^4 + \frac{n(n-1)(n-2)(n-3)(n-4)}{5!}\bullet 1^{n-5}\bullet\left(\frac{x}{n}\right)^5 +\dots$$

Remember $\left(\frac{x}{n}\right)^2 = \frac{x^2}{n^2}$ and we can commute the product of n^2 and 2!

$$\left(1 + \frac{x}{n}\right)^n = 1 + x + \frac{n(n-1)}{n^2} \bullet \frac{x^2}{2!} + \frac{n(n-1)(n-2)}{n^3} \bullet \frac{x^3}{3!} +$$

$$+ \frac{n(n-1)(n-2)(n-3)}{n^4} \bullet \frac{x^4}{4!} + \frac{n(n-1)(n-2)(n-3)(n-4)}{n^5} \bullet \frac{x^5}{5!} + \ldots$$

Now let $n \to \infty$. The n-terms, like $\frac{n(n-1)}{n^2}$ will go to 1 and we get

$$e^x = \lim_{n \to \infty} \left(1 + \frac{x}{n}\right)^n = 1 + x + \frac{x^2}{2!} + \frac{x^3}{3!} + \frac{x^4}{4!} + \frac{x^5}{5!} + \ldots$$

6. Patterns with i

$i = i$
$i^2 = -1$
$i^3 = -i$
$i^4 = 1$
$i^5 = i$
$i^6 = -1$
$i^7 = -i$
$i^8 = 1$
$i^9 = i$

Since they repeat in groups of 4, and **i** to a power which is a multiple of 4 equals 1,

$i^{127} = i^{124} \bullet i^3 = -i$
$i = i$
$i^0 = 1$
$i^{-1} = \frac{1}{i} = \frac{i}{i^2} = -i$

$i^{-2} = \frac{1}{i^2} = \frac{i^2}{i^4} = \frac{-1}{1} = -1$

If you look at the graph of i^0 and i^1, how do you get from one point to the other? it's a rotation of 90° counterclockwise.

8. Using iteration to do the compound interest
Find how much money you will have after **10** years (iterate the function 10 times), with a **$1000** investment (P=1000) at a **8%** annual rate of interest, compounded annually? $2158.92 Ans.

9. One result of Ian playing with powers of powers was that he found

$$\lim_{x \to \infty} \left(\frac{(x+1)^{(x+1)}}{x^x} - \frac{x^x}{(x-1)^{(x-1)}} \right) = e$$

10. i^n plotted on the Argand plane turns out to be points on a circle.

$i^{\frac{1}{2}}$ must be between i^0 and i^1 and the same distance from the origin.

11. The graph of $(1+i)^n$ at the right is a spiral.

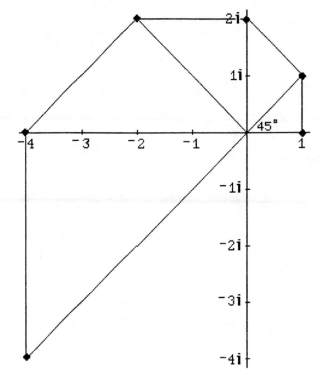

12. Getting back to **Ian's problem**..What would his Dad pay in monthly installments on a $10,000 home loan at 10% annual interest with a 30-year mortgage?

Ans. $<u>132.15</u>

Worksheet for **chapter 12**
"The Two Problems of the Calculus"

1. The derivative, or "rate of change", is used to describe how quickly quantities change. Historically, it helped deal with problems of how a pendulum swings, how planets move in their orbits (as well as space satellites), the velocity of a cannon shell, light, and electrons in a wire.

2. The integral, which turns out to be just the inverse of the derivative, historically dealt with finding the area under curves, the volume of fairly regular shapes, the work done in moving objects and the energy in light scattering.

Both problems involve infinite sequences and their limits. The derivative deals with an infinite sequence of slopes of lines, the integral deals with an infinite sequence of areas under a curve (which in turn involves an infinite series).

Archimedes (287-212 B.C.) essentially invented the integral calculus. We'll start there and find the area under curves different ways.

Question worksheets for **chapter 13**
"Area Under Curves--The Integral"

1. Area within shapes on a geoboard:
On the right is a picture of a geoboard -- a wooden board with a 5x5 square array of nails, 2" apart. Use colored rubber bands to make some shapes. Then assume figure A takes 1 can of paint to paint inside it (has an area of 1). How many cans of paint does it take to paint inside B and C and D?

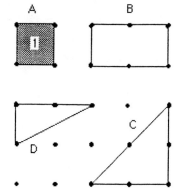

How many figures can you make with an area of 2?

Make up some shapes for a friend to find the area. Copy the spotty paper in the appendix.

How does the area of the triangles below change? Can you make up a rule about areas of triangles?

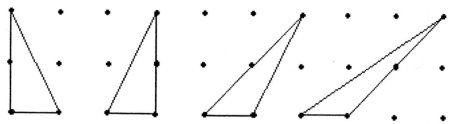

See if you can find, for any figure, a relationship between the number of nails touching the rubber band (t), the number of nails within the figure not touching the rubber band (i), and the area of the figure (A). The figure at the right, for example, has 4 nails touching the rubber band, 1 nail inside and has an area of 2. Have only 1 inside area and 1 outside for each figure. Make a table and keep track of this information in an orderly fashion.

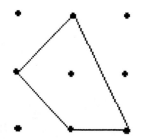

How many squares (with no diagonal sides) can you make on 2x2 geoboard? 3x3 geoboard? and so on. Find a rule that will give us the total number of squares you can make on an nxn geoboard.

2. How Archimedes found the area within a parabolic segment as shown in Fig. 1-
-the area enclosed by the parabola $y = x^2$ and the horizontal line segment:

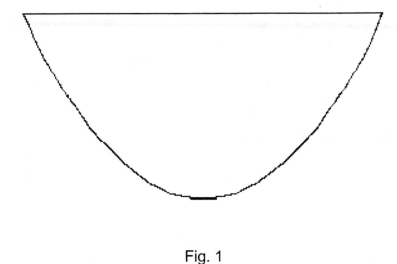

Fig. 1

Figure 2 shows a triangle of the same base and height as the parabolic segment.
Archimedes proved that the area of the parabolic segment is $\frac{4}{3}$ the area of this
triangle, say T.

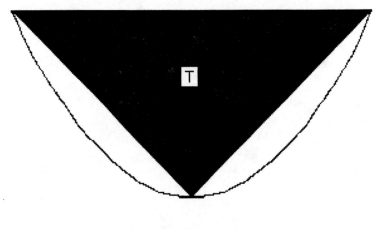

Fig. 2

Figure 3 shows the first step of my version of how Archimedes solved the problem. He built two smaller triangles between the big triangle and the parabola by constructing a perpendicular to AJ at its mid-point H, intersecting the parabola at a point, call it F. What is the area of these two smaller triangles in terms of T?

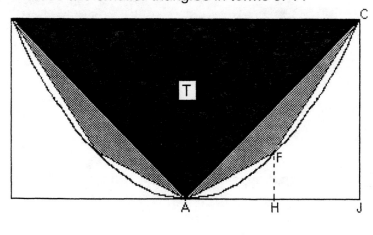

Fig. 3

Then Figure 4 shows his next step of making the 4 smaller triangles (spotted ones). He uses the mid-points of AH and HJ and again constructs the perpendiculars up to the parabola to locate the third vertices of these triangles. Find the area of these smallest triangles, then add to what we have so far, the large black triangle + the 2 smaller grey triangles + the 4 smallest triangles. Do you see a pattern? If we keep going forever, write down an infinite series for the area of the parabolic segment.

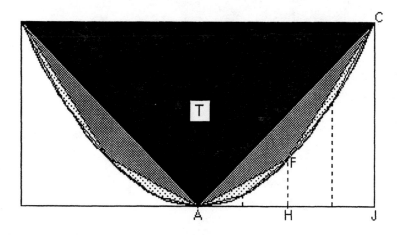

Fig. 4

3. Plotting points on a computer or calculator to find the area under curves:

I was browsing through a Scientific American "Computer Recreations" article in which it looked like they were filling in squares on a computer screen. I asked myself "Could I do that on our Casio FX7000G programmable graphics calculator?" After a couple of hours of trying things and making mistakes (I was never very good at programming), I was able to plot points on the screen to make a square. I plotted points as in the diagram at the right to make a 1x1 square. If you count the number of points, this number will be a measure of the area of the square. Try to write the program so it is possible to change the upper level of the points that are plotted, because the next thing you would want to do is to plot the points under a parabola, like x^2, or x^3, or a quarter-circle, a sine wave, or whatever. Very exciting!

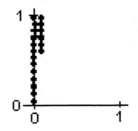

At the right is the figure formed by plotting points under the curve $y = x^2$ from $x = 0$ to 1, can you predict the area of this shaded portion of the 1x1 square?

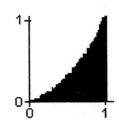

4. Finding the area under curves on graph paper

First predict what part of the area of the 1x1 square at the right below is under the curve $y = x^2$. Use the $\frac{1}{10}$" graph paper in appendix 4 to graph $y = x^2$ carefully from $x = 0$ to 1. Count the squares under the curve.

You'll have to approximate the squares.. do the best you can. Then count the squares in the 1x1 square. Find the ratio of no. of squares under the curve to the no. of squares in the 1x1 square. We'll call this the area under the curve $y = x^2$ from $x = 0$ to 1. What simple fraction is close to this number?

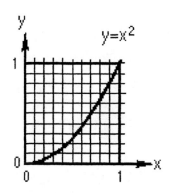

Area under $y = x^2$ from $x = 0$ to 1: _____

Now graph the curve $y = x^2$ from $x = 0$ to **2** like that at the right. Count the squares under the curve $y = x^2$ from $x = 0$ to **2** this time. (Notice that the "whole thing" surrounding the curve is not a square, but a rectangle of $2 \times 2^2 = 8 = 2^3$ units). What fraction of the rectangle is under this curve?

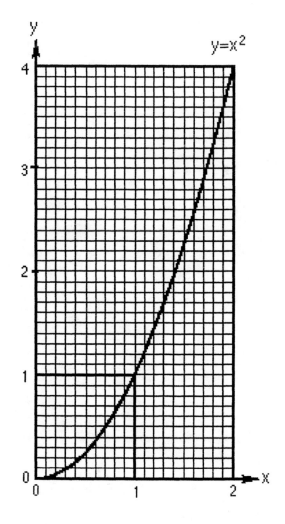

Matt, a 7 year-old, counted 32 squares, and $\frac{32}{100}$ of the 1x1 square as the area under the curve $y = x^2$ from x = 0 to 1. I asked him what simple fraction that is close to, he replied $\frac{1}{3}$. From x = 0 to 1 he correctly predicted $\frac{1}{3}$ of the $2x2^2$ rectangle = $\frac{1}{3} \cdot 2^3$. Sean counted an approximate 279 squares in going from 0 to 2, but was satisfied this was close enough. He figured there are 20•40 = 800 squares in the 2x4 rectangle (2x4=8 square units, and the area should be $\frac{1}{3}$ of 800 or 266.666... which is close to his 279). I don't like the normal integral notation for this work with young people. I'll introduce a little notation (not quite what they use in calculus courses): $\mathbf{A}_{0-1}\ x^2$ will mean the **A**rea under the curve $y = x^2$ from x = 0 to 1. And if we write the answers to find a pattern, things become simpler and we can generalize. For the area under the curve $y = x^2$ from x = 0 to **1** we'll write $\frac{1}{3} \cdot 1^3$, the 1^3 comes from a 1 x 1^2, then

$\mathbf{A}_{0-1}\ x^2 = \frac{1}{3} \cdot 1^3$ and

$\mathbf{A}_{0-2}\ x^2 = \frac{1}{3} \cdot 2^3$ and you can probably predict what will happen for

$\mathbf{A}_{0-3}\ x^2 =$

$\mathbf{A}_{0-4}\ x^2 =$ and generalizing,

$\mathbf{A}_{0-x}\ x^2 =$ it's not complicated if we look for patterns and not just write a number for an answer!

Now try the area under the following curves on the graph paper by counting squares, but predicting first: $y = 4$, $y = x$, $y = x^3$, $y = x^4$, $y = x^5$, and $y = x^n$. Write your generalizations in this form : $\mathbf{A}_{0-x}\ k =$ _____ ; $\mathbf{A}_{0-x}\ x =$ _____ ; $\mathbf{A}_{0-x}\ x^2 =$ ____ ; to $\mathbf{A}_{0-x}\ x^n =$ _____ .

Try some of these:

$y = 4$	$y = kx$	$y = kx^2$
$y = k$ (k is a constant)	$y = kx + m$	$y = 5x^2 + 7x$
$y = x$	$y = x^2$	$y = 5x^2 + 7x + 4$
$y = 2x$	$y = 3x^2$	$y = ax^2 + bx + c$

Sean's counting the squares under the curve $y = x^2$ from $x = 0$ to **2**

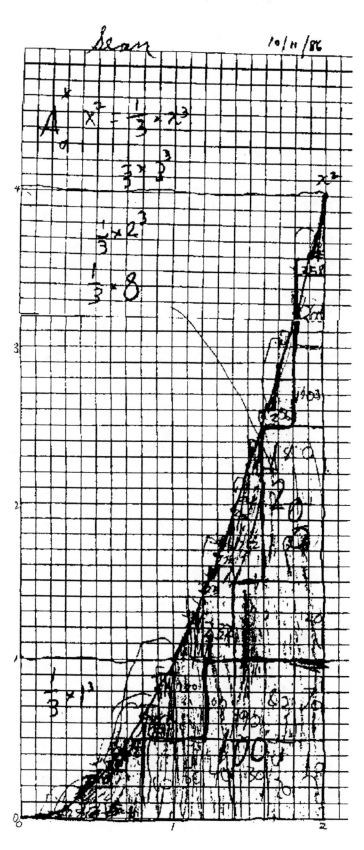

5. The rectangle method (the standard textbook method) of finding the area under curves.

We'll begin with finding the area under the curve (in this case a straight line) $y = x$ from 0 to 1. I know you can find the area of a triangle, which is what we have in the figure below. What we will do, however, is use the same strategy as if it were a curve. Our strategy is to fill the area under the curve with **rectangles** (hatched), then find the area of these, which you can do easily. We'll make the rectangles narrower and narrower so that the sum of the areas of these rectangles will get closer and closer to the area under the curve. We'll end up with an infinite series. The notation I'll use is: a_n (read as 'a sub n') is the sum of the area of the hatched rectangles under the curve in figure n; there are n-1 rectangles and $\frac{1}{n}$ is the width of each rectangle.

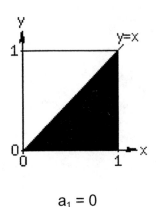 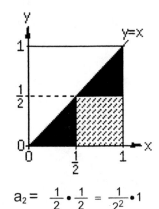 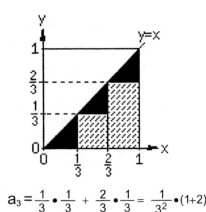

$$a_1 = 0 \qquad a_2 = \frac{1}{2} \cdot \frac{1}{2} = \frac{1}{2^2} \cdot 1 \qquad a_3 = \frac{1}{3} \cdot \frac{1}{3} + \frac{2}{3} \cdot \frac{1}{3} = \frac{1}{3^2} \cdot (1+2)$$

The picture for a_4 is at the right and the area of these rectangles is

$$a_4 = \frac{1}{4} \cdot \frac{1}{4} + \frac{2}{4} \cdot \frac{1}{4} + \frac{3}{4} \cdot \frac{1}{4} = \frac{1}{4^2} \cdot (1+2+3)$$ and generalizing

for the nth term in this sequence of partial sums $a_1, a_2, a_3, a_4, ..$ is

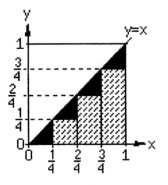

$$a_n = \frac{1}{n} \cdot \frac{1}{n} + \frac{2}{n} \cdot \frac{1}{n} + \frac{3}{n} \cdot \frac{1}{n} + \frac{4}{n} \cdot \frac{1}{n} + .. + \frac{n-1}{n} \cdot \frac{1}{n} =$$

$$\frac{1}{n^2} \cdot \left[(1+2+3+4+..+(n-1) \right]$$

From chapter 6 you can figure out the rule to get, $1 + 2 + 3 + 4 + .. n = \frac{n \cdot (n+1)}{2}$ and $1 + 2 + 3 + 4 + .. + (n-1) = \frac{n \cdot (n-1)}{2}$. So $a_n = \frac{1}{n^2} \cdot \frac{n \cdot (n-1)}{2}$. Now if $n \to \infty$, which means the number of rectangles gets bigger and bigger and the width of the rectangles gets smaller and smaller, $\frac{1}{n^2} \cdot n \cdot (n-1) \to 1$ (because as n->∞,

$n \cdot (n-1) \to n^2$ and $\frac{n^2}{n^2} \to 1$). So $\mathbf{A}_{0-1}$ x $= \underset{n\to\infty}{\text{limit}}\ a_n = \underset{n\to\infty}{\text{limit}}\ \frac{1}{n^2} \cdot \frac{n \cdot (n-1)}{2} = \frac{1}{2} \cdot 1^2$. I purposely wrote 1^2 because the area of the 1x1 square is 1^2, which is important for seeing patterns in what follows.

At the right is a_4 in finding the area under the curve $y = x$ from 0 to **2**

$a_4 =$

$\frac{1}{4} \cdot 2 \cdot \frac{1}{4} \cdot 2 + \frac{1}{4} \cdot 2 \cdot \frac{2}{4} \cdot 2 + \frac{1}{4} \cdot 2 \cdot \frac{3}{4} \cdot 2 =$

$a_4 = \frac{2^2}{4^2} \cdot (1+2+3)$. Use a_4 to help go back to

do a_1, a_2, a_3, and forward to generalize to a_n.

Then find the area under the curve

$y = x$ from 0 to **2** = $\mathbf{A}_{0-2}$ $x = \underset{n \to \infty}{\text{limit}}\ a_n$.

After that find the area under the curve $y = x$ from 0 to **3**, from 0 to **4**, then from 0 to x.

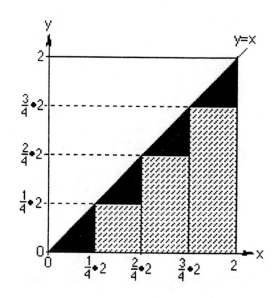

The area under the curve $y = x$ from $x = 0$ to $\mathbf{1} = \frac{1}{2} \cdot \mathbf{1}^2$

The area under the curve $y = x$ from $x = 0$ to $\mathbf{2} = \frac{1}{2} \cdot \mathbf{2}^2$

The area under the curve $y = x$ from $x = 0$ to $\mathbf{3} = \frac{1}{2} \cdot \mathbf{3}^2$

The area under the curve $y = x$ from $x = 0$ to $\mathbf{4} = \frac{1}{2} \cdot \mathbf{4}^2$ and

The area under the curve $y = x$ from $x = 0$ to $x = $???

Now comes a **new problem**, that is, the curve is changed, but the method of finding the area under it, is the same. Find the area under the curve $y = x^2$ (the dark area below), from $x = 0$ to **1**. Again we'll make rectangles (hatched), then find the area of these, get a sequence of partial sums as we make the width of the rectangles smaller, then we'll find the limit of this sequence, which will be the area we want. The area of the hatched rectangles will approach the area under the curve. We'll start with a_1 and a_2 below. Notice that the height of the rectangles are now square numbers because the curve is
$y = x^2$.

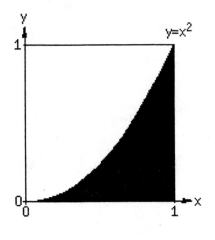

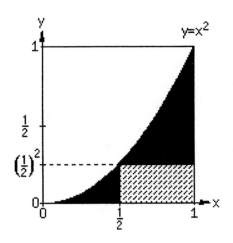

$$a_1 = 0 \qquad\qquad a_2 = \left(\frac{1}{2}\right)^2 \cdot \frac{1}{2} = \frac{1}{8}$$

Make the diagrams and find the areas of the rectangles for a_3 and a_4

Below are the diagrams for a_3 and a_4. Find the areas of the rectangles.

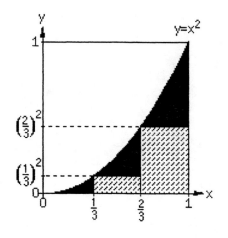

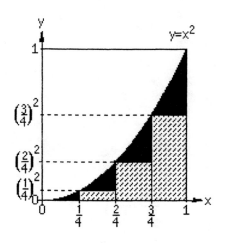

$a_3 =$ $a_4 =$

Can you generalize and write the nth term of the sequence of areas a_n.

Let's look at this sequence of areas $a_1, a_2, a_3, a_4, \ldots a_n, \ldots$ under the curve $y = x^2$, from $x = 0$ to **1**, as we change the width of the rectangles:

$a_1 = 0$

$a_2 = \left(\frac{1}{2}\right)^2 \cdot \frac{1}{2}$

$a_3 = \left(\frac{1}{3}\right)^2 \cdot \frac{1}{3} + \left(\frac{2}{3}\right)^2 \cdot \frac{1}{3}$

$a_4 = \left(\frac{1}{4}\right)^2 \cdot \frac{1}{4} + \left(\frac{2}{4}\right)^2 \cdot \frac{1}{4} + \left(\frac{3}{4}\right)^2 \cdot \frac{1}{4}$

$a_5 = \left(\frac{1}{5}\right)^2 \cdot \frac{1}{5} + \left(\frac{2}{5}\right)^2 \cdot \frac{1}{5} + \left(\frac{3}{5}\right)^2 \cdot \frac{1}{5} + \left(\frac{4}{5}\right)^2 \cdot \frac{1}{5}$ and generalizing

$a_n = \left(\frac{1}{n}\right)^2 \cdot \frac{1}{n} + \left(\frac{2}{n}\right)^2 \cdot \frac{1}{n} + \left(\frac{3}{n}\right)^2 \cdot \frac{1}{n} + \left(\frac{4}{n}\right)^2 \cdot \frac{1}{n} + \ldots + \left(\frac{n-1}{n}\right)^2 \cdot \frac{1}{n} =$

$a_n = \frac{1^3}{n^3} \cdot \left[\, 1^2 + 2^2 + 3^2 + 4^2 + \ldots + (n-1)^2 \right]$

Now we need to find a rule for the sum of the first n-1 squares. We'll get the sum of the first **n** squares by looking at the differences:

X 0 1 2   3   4   5   6

----

y 0 1 5 14 30 55 91   for x=2, y=1+4=5; for x=3, y=1+4+9=14, etc.
      1 4 9 16 25 36 → 1st differences
        3 5 7 9 11 → 2nd differences
         2 2 2 2 → 3rd differences

The 3rd differences are constant, therefore it is a 3rd degree function, like $ax^3 + bx^2 + cx + d$. d=0, since when x=0, y=0. This function turns out to be

$\frac{1}{6} \cdot n \cdot (n-1) \cdot (2n+1)$. The sum of the first **n-1** squares is $\frac{1}{6} \cdot n \cdot (n-1) \cdot (2n-1) = \frac{n^3}{3} - \frac{n^2}{2} + \frac{n}{6}$

So $a_n = \frac{1^3}{n^3} \cdot \left[\, 1^2 + 2^2 + 3^2 + 4^2 + \ldots + (n-1)^2 \right] = \frac{1^3}{n^3} \cdot \left(\frac{n^3}{3} - \frac{n^2}{2} + \frac{n}{6} \right) =$

and $a_n = \frac{1}{3} - \frac{1}{2n} + \frac{1}{6n^2}$

The area under the curve $y = x^2$, from $x = 0$ to **1** is

$$\boxed{\; A_{0-1}\; X2 = \lim_{n\to\infty} a_n = \lim_{n\to\infty} \left(\frac{1}{3} - \frac{1}{2n} + \frac{1}{6n^2} \right) = \frac{1}{3} = \frac{1}{3} \cdot 1^3 \;}$$ because as $n \to \infty$ both

the terms $\frac{1}{2n}$ and

$\frac{1}{6n^2} \to 0$. The $\frac{1}{3}$ is the same as what Sean and Matt and Archimedes got above. Again,

writing this as $\frac{1}{3} \cdot 1^3$ is important because it shows that the area is $\frac{1}{3}$ of a 1×1^2 rectangle.

Now let's find the area under the curve $y = x^2$, from $x = 0$ to **2** using the rectangle method. Find a_1, a_2, a_3, and a_4, using the diagrams below. a_3 is calculated below the diagrams:

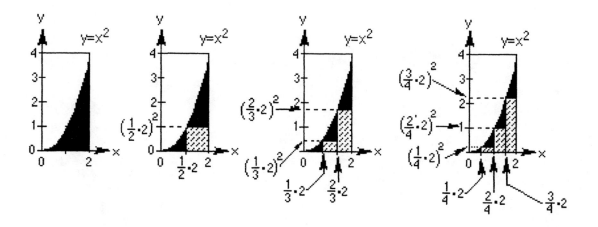

$a_1=$

$a_2 =$

$$a_3= \left(\frac{1}{3} \cdot 2\right)^2 \cdot \frac{1}{3} \cdot 2 + \left(\frac{2}{3} \cdot 2\right)^2 \cdot \frac{1}{3} \cdot 2 = \frac{2^3}{3^3} \cdot \left[1^2 + 2^2 \right]$$

$a_4=$

Generalize to a_n then find the limit of a_n as $n \rightarrow \infty$.

Now find the area under the curve $y = x^2$, from $x = 0$ to **3** or A_{0-3} x^2 using the rectangle method. First predict what you think it will be.

The diagram for a_4 is shown at the right.

$a_4 = \left(\frac{1}{4} \cdot 3\right)^2 \cdot \frac{1}{4} \cdot 3 + \left(\frac{2}{4} \cdot 3\right)^2 \cdot \frac{1}{4} \cdot 3 + \left(\frac{3}{4} \cdot 3\right)^2 \cdot \frac{1}{4} \cdot 3$

$a_4 = \frac{3^3}{4^3} \cdot \left[1^2 + 2^2 + 3^3 \right]$

Make the diagrams for a_1, a_2, and a_3. Then generalize to a_n and find the limit of a_n as $n \rightarrow \infty$.

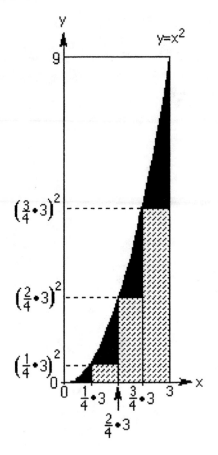

What are we trying to do? We're trying to find the area under the curve $y = x^2$, from $x = 0$ to **x** or A_{0-x} x^2 . What do we know so far?

The area under the curve $y = x^2$, from $x = 0$ to **1** or A_{0-1} $x^2 = \frac{1}{3} \cdot 1^3$

The area under the curve $y = x^2$, from $x = 0$ to **2** or A_{0-2} $x^2 = \frac{1}{3} \cdot 2^3$

The area under the curve $y = x^2$, from $x = 0$ to **3** or A_{0-3} $x^2 = $??

Can you generalize to
The area under the curve $y = x^2$, from $x = 0$ to **x** or A_{0-x} $x^2 = $??

Now look at the patterns under the area under different curves we have so far:

The area under the curve $y = x$ from $x = 0$ to x or A_{0-x} $x = \frac{1}{2} \bullet x^2$

The area under the curve $y = x^2$ from $x = 0$ to x or A_{0-x} $x^2 = \frac{1}{3} \bullet x^3$ ...now look for patterns

The area under the curve $y = x^3$ from $x = 0$ to x or A_{0-x} $x^3 = ?$

The area under the curve $y = x^4$ from $x = 0$ to x or A_{0-x} $x^4 = ?$

The area under the curve $y = x^n$ from $x = 0$ to x or A_{0-x} $x^n = ?$

Now try to find the area under these curves from $x = 0$ to x : $y = x^2 + 1$; $y = x^2 - 1$;
$y = 5x^2 + 7x$

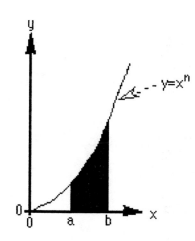

From what we've done so far, what do you think
would be the area under the curve
$y = x^n$ from $x = a$ to b ?

6. Two problems

Two seemingly unrelated problems ended up with interesting solutions.
PROBLEM 1. The area under the parabola $y = x^2$, from from $x = 0$ to 1.

PROBLEM 2. The ratio of $\dfrac{\text{the volume of a square pyramid}}{\text{the volume of a cube}}$, with the same base.

PROBLEM 1: Above we found the area under the parabola $y = x^2$, from from $x = 0$ to 1
which turns out to be $\frac{1}{3} - \frac{1}{2n} + \frac{1}{6n^2}$. As $n \to \infty$ the area goes to $\frac{1}{3}$.

PROBLEM 2: Find the ratio of $\dfrac{\text{the volume of a square pyramid}}{\text{the volume of a cube}}$ using the white rods

as in the picture below. n would equal the number of layers, then let n→ ∞. So for this arrangement, the volume of the pyramid is $1^2 + 2^2 + 3^2$ and the volume of the cube is 3^3; the ratio we're looking for is $\dfrac{1^2 + 2^2 + 3^2}{3^3}$. Now increase the number of layers to 4, 5, then n and see what happens to this ratio.

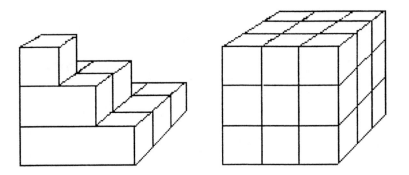

Write a program which will give us this ratio.

What do you notice about the answers in PROBLEM 1 and PROBLEM 2?

7. The natural logarithm is the area under a curve and an infinite series.

First, what is a logarithm? You know, $10^2 = 100$, 10 to the second power is 100. The log of 100, base 10 is 2, written $\log_{10}100 = 2$. In other words, **the logarithm is the exponent,** as simple as that.
Write a log statement for the following exponential statements: $2^5 = 32$; $x^3 = 216$; $a^x = y$
Write an exponential statement for the following log statements: $\log_{10}1000 = 3$; $\log_8 512 = x$; $\log_m F = w$
The natural log is the log of a number, base e, where e is 2.718... as described in chapter 11.

The logarithms were invented by Napier and independently by Burgi. They published in 1614 and 1620. Napier was trying to simplify computation. The astronomers Tycho Brahe and Kepler were the first beneficiaries of Napier's work, which changed multiplication problems to addition problems and made their work a lot simpler. Notice that $10^2 \cdot 10^3 = 10^5 = 10^{2+3}$, the exponents add when the powers are multiplied. Do similar things work for logs?

It would be very helpful, if you want to learn about how logs work, to make a table like the one below. **Write down your guess at the logs first** (they'll be wrong first), then write down what your calculator gives. Look for patterns as you go along!

logs, base 10		calculator gives (keep 3 decimal places):	write guess, first
log 1	=		
log 2	=		
log 3	=		
log 4	=		
log 5	=		
log 6	=		
log 7	=		
log 8	=		
log 9	=		
log 10	=		
log 20	=		
log 200	=		
log 2000	=		
log $\frac{1}{2}$	=		
log $\frac{1}{4}$	=		

How about $\log_{10}2 + \log_{10}5 = \log_{10}$?
        $0.301 + 0.699 =$?   What do you notice? Make up problems like these and generalize.

Try this: $3 \cdot \log_{10}2 = \log_{10}$?   What do you notice? Make up others like this and generalize.

Graph the equation $y = \frac{1}{x}$ from $x = 1$ to $x = 10$. Find the area under the curve from $x = 1$ to $x = 3$. Then find the area under the curve from $x = 3$ to $x = 6$. You can do it on the computer, using the program to plot points above or count the squares on the graph paper. This graph is part of an hyperbola which we came upon in chapter 6.

Using the program above to count the points, (changed to fit this graph), we found the area under the curve $y = \frac{1}{x}$ from $x = 1$ to $x = 3$ to be 1.0952. The $\log_e 3 = 1.0986$. The area from $x = 3$ to $x = 6$ turned out to be 0.6458 and the $\log_e 2 = 0.6931$. Adding these, we got the area from 1 to 6 which is 1.7410 and the $\log_e 6 = 1.7917$. The numbers we got by counting dots are close enough.

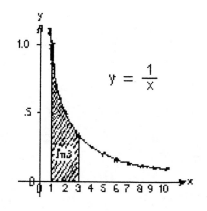

So $\mathbf{A}_{1-3}\ \frac{1}{\mathbf{x}} + \mathbf{A}_{3-6}\ \frac{1}{\mathbf{x}} = \mathbf{A}_{1-6}\ \frac{1}{\mathbf{x}}$ and this is the same as $\log_e 3 + \log_e 2 = \log_e 6 = \log_e(3 \cdot 2)$

You might try other areas, like $\mathbf{A}_{1-4}\ \frac{1}{\mathbf{x}} + \mathbf{A}_{4-7}\ \frac{1}{\mathbf{x}}$ and see if this is equal to $\mathbf{A}_{1-7}\ \frac{1}{\mathbf{x}}$.

The connection between the areas under curves and this property of logarithms, that is the log of the product equals the sum of the logs, was first noticed by A.A. de Sarasa in Gregory's published discovery about the areas in 1647.

Remember Ian's discovery $\frac{1}{1-\mathbf{x}} = 1 + \mathbf{x} + \mathbf{x}^2 + \mathbf{x}^3 + \mathbf{x}^4 + \mathbf{x}^5 + \ldots$

If we substitute $^-\mathbf{x}$ in for $\mathbf{x}$ above, what do we get?

We get $\frac{1}{1+X}$ = 1 - X + X^2 - X^3 + X^4 - X^5 + ... which converges for $^-$1< X < 1 .

The graph of $y = \frac{1}{1+X}$ at the right is an hyperbola

like $y = \frac{1}{X}$ except it is shifted 1 unit to the left. The

area under this curve from from X = 0 to X = a or

A_{0-a} $\frac{1}{1+X}$ = log$_e$(1 + a) and if we use the

generalizations from the section above, this will
equal the integral of the infinite series
1 - a + a^2 - a^3 + a^4 - a^5 + ... Doing each term

separately, we get A_{0-a} $\frac{1}{1+X}$ = log$_e$(1 + a) =

a - $\frac{1}{2}$•a^2 + $\frac{1}{3}$•a^3 - $\frac{1}{4}$•a^4 + $\frac{1}{5}$•a^5 - ... The natural

log then, is the area under the curve $y = \frac{1}{X}$ or

$y = \frac{1}{1+X}$ and it's the infinite series

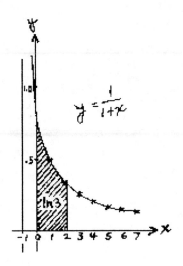

log$_e$(1 + a) = a - $\frac{1}{2}$•a^2 + $\frac{1}{3}$•a^3 - $\frac{1}{4}$•a^4 + $\frac{1}{5}$•a^5 - ... CAUTION: You just can't find the

log$_e$(1 + 2) by putting 2 in for a in the series above because this series converges only
when a is between $^-$1 and 1. Newton found logs of integers in a unique way. First he found
the log$_e$ 1.1 by putting .1 in for a in the series.

log$_e$(1 + .1) = .1 - $\frac{1}{2}$•(.1)^2 + $\frac{1}{3}$•(.1)^3 - $\frac{1}{4}$•(.1)^4 + $\frac{1}{5}$•(.1)^5 - ... = 0.0953, then similarly got

the logs of 1.2, 0.8, and 0.9 . He then said $2 = \frac{1.2•1.2}{0.8•0.9}$. Who else would think of writing 2

this way! Newton then proceeds to get the log$_e$2 by using the identities for logs:
log$_e$2= log$_e$ (1 + 0.2) + log$_e$ (1 + 0.2) - (log$_e$ (1 + $^-$0.2) + log$_e$ (1 + $^-$0.1)). This reinforces for
me, at least, that we have to write numbers different ways. Ever since I saw Sue Monell do
"number names for today's date" with 5 and 6 year-olds 30 some years ago, I thought it
was a great idea.

Write a program which will get this infinite series

log$_e$(1 + a) = a - $\frac{1}{2}$•a^2 + $\frac{1}{3}$•a^3 - $\frac{1}{4}$•a^4 + $\frac{1}{5}$•a^5 - ...

Part of this program will be a way to alternate signs; one way to do that is to get ($^-$1) to a
power one more than that for the power of a.

See if you can find log$_e$ 3 , log$_e$4 and others, using this same idea of Newton's (there must
be many ways to do each one).

One way I thought of for getting 3 is $3 = \dfrac{.6}{.2} = \dfrac{1 + {}^-0.4}{1 + {}^-0.8}$ then

$\log_e 3 = \log_e(1 + {}^-0.4) - \log_e(1 + {}^-0.8)$. I then put ${}^-0.4$ in for a in the program to calculate $\log_e(1 + {}^-0.4)$ which equals ${}^-0.510825624$. I put ${}^-0.8$ in for a in the program to calculate $\log_e (1 + {}^-0.8)$ which equals ${}^-1.609437911$. I subtracted ${}^-0.510825624 - {}^-1.609437911 = 1.098612287$ which should equal $\log_e 3$. I found the $\log_e 3$ on the calculator directly to check, and it was equal to 1.098612287.

8. Ian's method of finding the area under the normal distribution curve.
During the summer of 1987 I had a student who was getting ready for a course in statistics. I decided to write a program on my PC to plot points (as I had done on the FX7000G). This time I plotted points under the normal distribution curve whose

equation is $y = \dfrac{1}{\sqrt{2}} \cdot e^{\dfrac{{}^-x^2}{2}}$ and its graph is shown below.

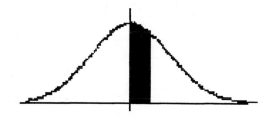

Find the area under this normal distribution curve.

The area under this curve between $x = a$ and $x = b$ is the probability that x lies between a and b. In the courses in statistics, the x is transformed into z, which is related to both the mean of the data and the standard deviation.

I had a little difficulty while writing the program to plot this diagram and asked Ian to help me. One of the things he did was to change from plotting points to drawing lines, measuring these then adding them up to obtain the area. By doing this, I think Ian invented a method very much the same as Cavalieri's method of indivisibles as described in his book "Geometria indivisibilibus" of 1635 (see Edwards, p.104).

Answer worksheets for chapter 13
"Area Under Curves--The Integral"

1. Area within shapes on a geoboard:

It takes 2 cans of paint for B. C takes $\frac{1}{2}$ + $\frac{1}{2}$ + 1 = 2 cans of paint. D is $\frac{1}{2}$ of 2 = 1.

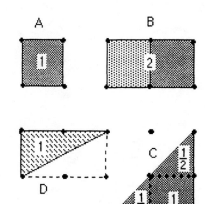

The area of each triangle below, is the same, 1.

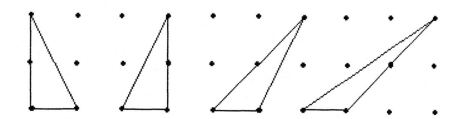

The rule for the area A within a figure with t nails touching and i nails inside is
$$A = \frac{1}{2}t + i - 1$$
See Don's website page at http://www.shout.net/~mathman/html/geoboard.html .
On a 3x3 geoboard there are four 1x1 squares and one 2x2 squares, 5 total. It turns out this will be the sum of the first n squares $1^2 + 2^2 + 3^2 + .. + n^2$ and this equals $\frac{n^3}{3} + \frac{n^2}{2} + \frac{n}{6}$.
This same rule comes up later in this chapter, in finding the area under a parabola!

2. My version of how Archimedes found the area within a parabolic segment is shown in Fig. 1. The area enclosed by the parabola $y = x^2$ and the horizontal line segment:

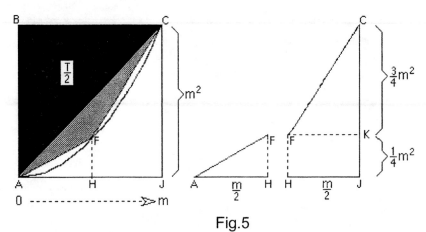

Fig.5

Figure 5 above shows $\frac{1}{2}$ of that in Fig. 3 in the question sheets. Let AJ = m, JC = m^2

since C is on the curve x^2, and the area of $\triangle$ABC is $\frac{T}{2}$. Since AH is $\frac{m}{2}$, and F is on

the curve x^2, FH is $\left(\frac{m}{2}\right)^2 = \frac{1}{4}m^2$, and the area of rectangle ABCJ = m•m^2 = m^3 = T

The area of one
grey triangle = area of $\triangle$ACJ - (area of $\triangle$AHF + quadrilateral HFCJ)

$\qquad\qquad$ = area of $\triangle$ABC - (area of $\triangle$AHF + $\quad$ $\triangle$FKC $\qquad$ + $\quad$ rect. HFKJ)

$\qquad$ = $\frac{T}{2}$ $\qquad\qquad$ - $\left(\frac{1}{2} \cdot \frac{m}{2} \cdot \frac{m^2}{4} \ + \ \frac{1}{2} \cdot \frac{m}{2} \cdot \frac{3}{4}m^2 \ + \ \frac{m}{2} \cdot \frac{1}{4}m^2\right)$

$\qquad$ = $\frac{T}{2}$ $\qquad\qquad$ - $\left(\frac{1}{16} \cdot m^3 + \frac{3}{16} \cdot m^3 + \frac{1}{8} \cdot m^3\right)$

$\qquad$ = $\frac{T}{2}$ - $\frac{3}{8} \cdot m^3$ = $\frac{T}{2}$ - $\frac{3}{8} \cdot$ T = $\frac{1}{8} \cdot$ T

The area of the **2** grey triangles, then = $\frac{1}{4} \cdot$ T

It turns out that the area of the four smallest triangles in figure 4 have an area of $\frac{1}{4} \cdot \frac{1}{4} \cdot$ T. Continuing this process we have the area of the parabolic segment =

T + $\frac{1}{4} \cdot$ T + $\left(\frac{1}{4}\right)^2 \cdot$ T + $\left(\frac{1}{4}\right)^3 \cdot$ T + $\left(\frac{1}{4}\right)^4 \cdot$ T +... = T + T•$\left(\frac{1}{4} + \left(\frac{1}{4}\right)^2 + \left(\frac{1}{4}\right)^3 + \left(\frac{1}{4}\right)^4 + ...\right)$

From chapter 1, the infinite series in the brackets converges, with limit $\frac{1}{3}$. So *the area of the parabolic segment* = T + $\frac{1}{3} \cdot$ T = $\frac{4}{3} \cdot$ T. At the time of Archimedes they didn't accept the idea of the infinite nor did he use the idea of limit, but instead showed that the area couldn't be bigger than $\frac{4}{3} \cdot$ T and it couldn't be smaller than $\frac{4}{3} \cdot$ T, so it had to be equal to $\frac{4}{3} \cdot$ T. In figure 5 above, the area of $\frac{1}{2}$ the parabolic segment is

$\frac{1}{2} \cdot \frac{4}{3} \cdot$ T = $\frac{2}{3} \cdot$ T = $\frac{2}{3} \cdot m^3$, so **the**

area under the parabola $y = x^2$ from 0 to m is $\frac{1}{3} \cdot m^3$. Another way to say this is that the **integral** of x^2 from 0 to m, is $\frac{1}{3} \cdot m^3$.

3. Plotting points on a computer or calculator to find the area under curves: The strategy for my program on the FX7000G to plot points to make a square was this: I plotted the point (0,1), subtracted a little from the **y**-coordinate, then plotted another point, continuing this until the y-coordinate went to 0. Then I added a little to the **x**-coordinate, and again plotted points from **y** = 1 to zero and so on, until **x** = 1, to make the 1x1 square. The program ended up looking like that at left (there are no line numbers needed but they are numbered for reference later).

1) Range ⁻2.35, 2.35, 1, ⁻1.55, 1.55, 1	(The range puts in the x min., x max., x scale, y min., y max., y scale. The 2.35 to 1.55 ratio is used to make a square grid on the non-square 95x63-dot display).	In <u>basic</u> 30 and 40 adjust for the way points are plotted on the screen
2) 0 →x:	(Sets the left side of the figure).	5 N =0
3) 0→N:	(N keeps count of the number of points plotted).	10 FOR x =0 TO 9 STEP .1
4) Lbl 3:	(Place to which Goto 3 returns).	
5) 1→y:	(Sets the top of the figure).	20 FOR y =0 TO 81
6) Lbl 4:	(Place to which Goto 4 returns).	30 t= 150+9 •x 40 v= 150- y
7) Plot x,y:	(Plots the point).	50 PSET (t,v)
8) 1 + N → N:	(adds 1 to the counter).	60 N=N+1
9) y - .07 →y:	(moves next point down. I had to play around to get .07 . If this number is too big all the spaces would not be filled in; if it was too small, the number of points plotted wouldn't be a minimum).	90 NEXT y moves next point up screen
10) y ≥0⇒Goto 4:	(Sets the bottom of the figure. If y ≥ 0 it jumps to Lbl 4 to plot another point, otherwise goes to step 11 to move to the right).	
11) x + .07→x:	(moves the plotting to the right)	100 NEXT x moves next point to right
12) x ≤1 ⇒Goto 3:	(sets the right end of the figure).	
13) "N = " : NΔ	Displays the number of points; hitting the G⇔T key shows the picture).	110 PRINT N 120 END

Running this program fills in a 1x1 square; the number of dots varies with the calculator or computer; on the FX7000G I got 400.

The next question I asked was "Could I find the area under the curve $y = x^2$ from 0 to 1?" With this program, easy. Just replace the 1 in line 5 with x^2, that's it! In the basic program just change the "for" statement from 81 to x^2. We got the picture at the right and N = 133 on the FX7000G. So the area under the curve $y = x^2$ from 0 to 1 was $\frac{133}{400}$, which is very

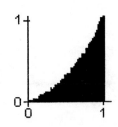

close to $\frac{1}{3}$ which is the integral of x^2, from 0 to 1. I was very excited about this and showed it to many people I work with, ages 6 to 45, as well as teachers, principals and parents. When I asked a couple of 6th graders what they would expect by just looking at the picture above, one said less than $\frac{1}{2}$ the 1x1 square, the other said $\frac{1}{3}$ of it. Students were able to get the area under x^3 from 0 to 1 to be $\frac{1}{4}$ (see a pattern.. what happens with x^4 ?; the area of within a circle of radius 1 by putting $\sqrt{1-x^2}$ in line 5 (gives $\frac{1}{4}$ of a circle), so at the end I multiplied N by 4, then divided by 400, which gave 3.18 (very close to 3.14 or π); the area of a quarter of an ellipse with semi-major axis 1 and semi-minor axis $\frac{1}{2}$ by putting $\sqrt{\frac{1}{4}\left(1-x^2\right)}$ in line 5. I was able to get the area between curves and the area under the normal distribution curve

$y = \frac{1}{\sqrt{2}} \cdot e^{\frac{-x^2}{2}}$ (which came out very close to 1!), by changing   to ⁻2.35 in line 2 and 2.35 in line 12.

Once I saw how simple this was, it gave me the impetus to get young people thinking about the integral. Now I realize this is not as "rigorous" as the "experts" want and expect, but if we start **young** people thinking about these really important ideas, then things will be a lot easier later. And my guess is that many more students will study math if they can see some sense to it, rather than memorizing a lot of formulas they don't understand, will soon forget and never want to use again.

The basic program in the right column above was written recently and gives an area under the parabola of .337; I thought this worked well. I haven't had a chance to find the area under these other curves but it should work.

4. Finding the area under curves on graph paper

The area under the curve $y = x^2$ from 0 to 1, 0 to 2 and so on, by counting squares on the graph paper

$\mathbf{A}_{0-1}\ x^2 = \frac{1}{3} \cdot 1^3$

$\mathbf{A}_{0-2}\ x^2 = \frac{1}{3} \cdot 2^3$ because the area is $\frac{1}{3}$ of the rectangle 2 by 2^2 or 2^3

$\mathbf{A}_{0-3}\ x^2 = \frac{1}{3} \cdot 3^3$ because the area is $\frac{1}{3}$ of the rectangle 3 by 3^2 or 3^3

$\mathbf{A}_{0-4}\ x^2 = \frac{1}{3} \cdot 4^3$ and generalizing,

$$A_{0-x} \ x^2 = \frac{1}{3} \cdot x^3$$

Under $y = 4$ the area is $A_{0-3} \ 4 = 4 \cdot 3 = 12$ and $A_{0-x} \ 4 = 4 \cdot x$ and $A_{0-x} \ k = k \cdot x$

Under $y = x$ the area is $A_{0-x} \ x = \frac{1}{2} \cdot x^2$

Under $y = x^2$ the area is $A_{0-x} \ x^2 = \frac{1}{3} \cdot x^3$

Under $y = x^3$ the area is $A_{0-x} \ x^3 = \frac{1}{4} \cdot x^4$

Under $y = x^4$ the area is $A_{0-x} \ x^4 = \frac{1}{5} \cdot x^5$

Under $y = x^5$ the area is $A_{0-x} \ x^5 = \frac{1}{6} \cdot x^6$ and generalizing

Under $y = x^n$ the area is $A_{0-x} \ x^n = \frac{1}{n+1} \cdot x^{n+1}$

Under $y = 2x$ the area is $A_{0-3} \ 2 \cdot x = 2 \cdot \frac{1}{2} \cdot 3^2$ and $A_{0-x} \ 2 \cdot x = 2 \cdot \frac{1}{2} \cdot x^2$ and

$$A_{0-x} \ k \cdot x = k \cdot \frac{1}{2} \cdot x^2$$

Under $y = k \cdot x^2$ the area is $A_{0-x} \ k \cdot x^2 = k \cdot \frac{1}{3} \cdot x^3$

Under $y = 5x^2 + 7x$ the area is $A_{0-x} \ 5x^2 + 7x = 5 \cdot \frac{1}{3} \cdot x^3 + 7 \cdot \frac{1}{2} \cdot x^2$

Under $y = 5x^2 + 7x + 4$ the area is $A_{0-x} \ 5x^2 + 7x + 4 = 5 \cdot \frac{1}{3} \cdot x^3 + 7 \cdot \frac{1}{2} \cdot x^2 + 4 \cdot x$

Under $y = ax^2 + bx + c$ the area is $A_{0-x} \ ax^2 + bx + c = a \cdot \frac{1}{3} \cdot x^3 + b \cdot \frac{1}{2} \cdot x^2 + c \cdot x$

As a teacher I need to try new things, do mathematics myself and look for ways to get my students into more difficult concepts, but at their level. I treat each student as an individual; I do different things with different students. And I don't wait until I completely understand everything about an idea before I'll get a student doing it-- that way I learn things along with my students. It's also why I encourage them to do things different ways. It makes teaching and learning enjoyable.

5. The rectangle method (the standard textbook method) of finding the area under curves.

In finding the area under the curve $y = x$ from 0 to **2**

$a_1 = 0$,

$a_2 = \frac{1}{2} \cdot 2 \cdot \frac{1}{2} \cdot 2 = \frac{2^2}{2^2} \cdot 1$,

$a_3 = \frac{1}{3} \cdot 2 \cdot \frac{1}{3} \cdot 2 + \frac{1}{3} \cdot 2 \cdot \frac{2}{3} \cdot 2 = \frac{2^2}{3^2} \cdot (1+2)$, (writing it this way, takes looking for patterns)

$a_4 = \frac{1}{4} \cdot 2 \cdot \frac{1}{4} \cdot 2 + \frac{1}{4} \cdot 2 \cdot \frac{2}{4} \cdot 2 + \frac{1}{4} \cdot 2 \cdot \frac{3}{4} \cdot 2 = \frac{2^2}{4^2} \cdot (1+2+3)$ and

$a_n = \frac{2^2}{n^2} \cdot [1+2+3+4+..(n-1)] = \frac{2^2}{n^2} \cdot \frac{n \cdot (n-1)}{2}$.

The area under the curve $y = x$ from 0 to **2** is

$$A_{0-2} \ x = \lim_{n \to \infty} a_n = \lim_{n \to \infty} \left(\frac{2^2}{n^2} \cdot \frac{n \cdot (n-1)}{2} \right) = \frac{1}{2} \cdot 2^2 .$$

The area under the curve y = x from 0 to **3** is

$$\mathbf{A}_{0-3} \; x = \lim_{n \to \infty} a_n = \lim_{n \to \infty} \left(\frac{3^2}{n^2} \cdot \frac{n \cdot (n-1)}{2} \right) = \frac{1}{2} \cdot 3^2 .$$

The area under the curve y = x from 0 to **4** is

$$\mathbf{A}_{0-4} \; x = \lim_{n \to \infty} a_n = \lim_{n \to \infty} \left(\frac{4^2}{n^2} \cdot \frac{n \cdot (n-1)}{2} \right) = \frac{1}{2} \cdot 4^2 .$$

The area under the curve y = x from 0 to **x** is

$$\mathbf{A}_{0-x} \; x = \lim_{n \to \infty} a_n = \lim_{n \to \infty} \left(\frac{x^2}{n^2} \cdot \frac{n \cdot (n-1)}{2} \right) = \frac{1}{2} \cdot x^2 ,$$ which is what we found before.

Now let's find the area under the curve y = x^2, from x = 0 to **2** using the rectangle method.

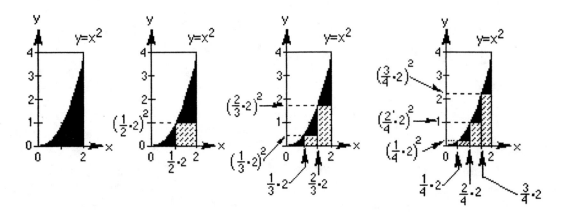

$$a_1 = 0 \qquad a_2 = \left(\frac{1}{2} \cdot 2 \right)^2 \cdot \frac{1}{2} \cdot 2 = \frac{2^3}{2^3} \cdot 1^2$$

$$a_3 = \left(\frac{1}{3} \cdot 2 \right)^2 \cdot \frac{1}{3} \cdot 2 + \left(\frac{2}{3} \cdot 2 \right)^2 \cdot \frac{1}{3} \cdot 2 = \frac{2^3}{3^3} \cdot \left[1^2 + 2^2 \right]$$

$$a_4 = \left(\frac{1}{4} \cdot 2 \right)^2 \cdot \frac{1}{4} \cdot 2 + \left(\frac{2}{4} \cdot 2 \right)^2 \cdot \frac{1}{4} \cdot 2 + \left(\frac{3}{4} \cdot 2 \right)^2 \cdot \frac{1}{4} \cdot 2 = \frac{2^3}{4^3} \cdot \left[1^2 + 2^2 + 3^2 \right] .. \text{ to}$$

$$a_n = \left(\frac{1}{n} \cdot 2 \right)^2 \cdot \frac{1}{n} \cdot 2 + \left(\frac{2}{n} \cdot 2 \right)^2 \cdot \frac{1}{n} \cdot 2 + \left(\frac{3}{n} \cdot 2 \right)^2 \cdot \frac{1}{n} \cdot 2 + .. + \left(\frac{n-1}{n} \cdot 2 \right)^2 \cdot \frac{1}{n} \cdot 2 =$$

$$a_n = \frac{2^3}{n^3} \cdot \left[1^2 + 2^2 + 3^2 + .. + (n-1)^2 \right] = \frac{2^3}{n^3} \cdot \left(\frac{n^3}{3} - \frac{n^2}{2} + \frac{n}{6} \right) =$$

$$\mathbf{A}_{0-2} \; x^2 = \lim_{n \to \infty} a_n = \lim_{n \to \infty} \left(\frac{1}{3} - \frac{1}{2n} + \frac{1}{6n^2} \right) \cdot 2^3 = \frac{1}{3} \cdot 2^3 , \text{ as we got before.}$$

Now let's find the area under the curve $y = x^2$, from $x = 0$ to **3** using the rectangle method. The diagrams for a_2, a_3 and a_4 are below.

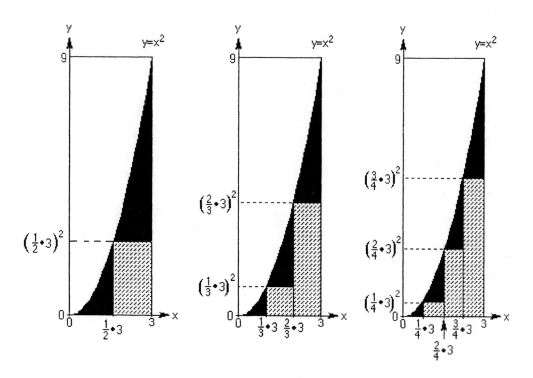

$$a_1 = 0 \qquad a_2 = \left(\frac{1}{2} \cdot 3\right)^2 \cdot \frac{1}{2} \cdot 3 = \frac{3^3}{2^3} \cdot 1^2$$

$$a_3 = \left(\frac{1}{3} \cdot 3\right)^2 \cdot \frac{1}{3} \cdot 3 + \left(\frac{2}{3} \cdot 3\right)^2 \cdot \frac{1}{3} \cdot 3 = \frac{3^3}{3^3} \cdot \left[1^2 + 2^2\right]$$

$$a_4 = \left(\frac{1}{4} \cdot 3\right)^2 \cdot \frac{1}{4} \cdot 3 + \left(\frac{2}{4} \cdot 3\right)^2 \cdot \frac{1}{4} \cdot 3 + \left(\frac{3}{4} \cdot 3\right)^2 \cdot \frac{1}{4} \cdot 3 = \frac{3^3}{4^3} \cdot \left[1^2 + 2^2 + 3^2\right] .. \text{ to}$$

$$a_n = \left(\frac{1}{n} \cdot 3\right)^2 \cdot \frac{1}{n} \cdot 3 + \left(\frac{2}{n} \cdot 3\right)^2 \cdot \frac{1}{n} \cdot 3 + \left(\frac{3}{n} \cdot 3\right)^2 \cdot \frac{1}{n} \cdot 3 + .. + \left(\frac{n-1}{n} \cdot 3\right)^2 \cdot \frac{1}{n} \cdot 3 =$$

$$a_n = \frac{3^3}{n^3} \cdot \left[1^2 + 2^2 + 3^2 + .. + (n-1)^2\right] = \frac{3^3}{n^3} \cdot \left(\frac{n^3}{3} - \frac{n^2}{2} + \frac{n}{6}\right) \text{ and as before}$$

$$\mathbf{A}_{0-3} \ x^2 = \lim_{n \to \infty} a_n = \lim_{n \to \infty} \left(\frac{1}{3} - \frac{1}{2n} + \frac{1}{6n^2}\right) \cdot 3^3 = \frac{1}{3} \cdot \mathbf{3}^3 .$$

Now look for patterns again!

The area under the curve $y = x^2$, from $x = 0$ to 1 or A_{0-1} $x^2 = \frac{1}{3} \cdot 1^3$

The area under the curve $y = x^2$, from $x = 0$ to 2 or A_{0-2} $x^2 = \frac{1}{3} \cdot 2^3$

The area under the curve $y = x^2$, from $x = 0$ to 3 or A_{0-3} $x^2 = \frac{1}{3} \cdot 3^3$

Generalizing...

The area under the curve $y = x^2$ from $x = 0$ to x or A_{0-x} $x^2 = \frac{1}{3} \cdot x^3$

The area under the curve $y = x$ from $x = 0$ to x or A_{0-x} $x = \frac{1}{2} \cdot x^2$

The area under the curve $y = x^2$ from $x = 0$ to x or A_{0-x} $x^2 = \frac{1}{3} \cdot x^3$

The area under the curve $y = x^3$ from $x = 0$ to x or A_{0-x} $x^3 = \frac{1}{4} \cdot x^4$

The area under the curve $y = x^n$ from $x = 0$ to x or A_{0-x} $x^n = \frac{1}{n+1} \cdot x^{n+1}$

The area under these curves from $x = 0$ to x :

$y = x^2 + 1$ the area is A_{0-x} $x^2 + 1 = \frac{1}{3} \cdot x^3 + x$;

$y = x^2 - 1$ the area is A_{0-x} $x^2 - 1 = \frac{1}{3} \cdot x^3 - x$;

$y = 5x^2 + 7x$ the area is A_{0-x} $5x^2 + 7x = 5 \cdot \frac{1}{3} \cdot x^3 + 7 \cdot \frac{1}{2} \cdot x^2$

The area under the curve $y = x^n$ from $x = a$ to b is just the difference between the area from $x = 0$ to b, and the area from $x = 0$ to a,

$$A_{a-b} \ x^n = \frac{1}{n+1} \cdot b^{n+1} - \frac{1}{n+1} \cdot a^{n+1}$$

6. Two problems

The two seemingly unrelated problems ended up with the same solution.

PROBLEM 1: Above we found the area under the parabola $y = x^2$, from from $x = 0$ to 1 which turns out to be $\frac{1}{3} - \frac{1}{2n} + \frac{1}{6n^2}$. As $n \to \infty$ the area goes to $\frac{1}{3}$.

PROBLEM 2: Find the ratio of using the white rods as in the picture on p. 256. n would equal the number of layers, then let $n \to \infty$. So for this arrangement, the volume of the pyramid is $1^2 + 2^2 + 3^2$ and the volume of the cube is 3^3;

the ratio we're looking for is $\dfrac{\text{the volume of a square pyramid}}{\text{the volume of a cube}} = \dfrac{1^2 + 2^2 + 3^2}{3^3}$. Now

increase the number of layers to n, we get $\dfrac{1^2 + 2^2 + 3^2 + .. + n^2}{n^3}$. From our work above the sum

of the first n squares is $\dfrac{n^3}{3} + \dfrac{n^2}{2} + \dfrac{n}{6}$. The ratio then is $\dfrac{\dfrac{n^3}{3} + \dfrac{n^2}{2} + \dfrac{n}{6}}{n^3} = \dfrac{1}{3} + \dfrac{1}{2n} + \dfrac{1}{6n^2}$ and

$\lim\limits_{n \to \infty} \left(\dfrac{1}{3} + \dfrac{1}{2n} + \dfrac{1}{6n^2} \right) = \dfrac{1}{3}$. Lo and behold this is the same answer as we got for

PROBLEM 1!

Richard and I wrote this program at the right. We got 1, .625, .518, .469, .440, .421, .408, .398, .390, .384, ... and for n=200 about .335, a slowly converging sequence approaching .333... or $\dfrac{1}{3}$.

Grace noticed the likeness of the 2 problems. This was very exciting!

Much of this discussion on the 2 problems was published in the Dec. 1979 issue of Mathematics Teaching, a journal of The Assn. of Teachers of Mathematics, in England.

A program in basic to get these ratios:

```
10 x =1
20 s = 0
30 s = x^2 + s
50 PRINT (s/x^3)
60 x = x+1
70 IF x>20 THEN STOP
80 GOTO 30
90 END
```

7. The natural logarithm is the area under a curve and an infinite series.

Write a log statement for the following exponential statements:

$2^5 = 32 \Leftrightarrow \log_2 32 = 5$

$x^3 = 216 \Leftrightarrow \log_x 216 = 3$

$a^x = y \Leftrightarrow \log_a y = x$

Write an exponential statement for the following log statements:

$\log_{10} 1000 = 3 \Leftrightarrow 10^3 = 1000$

$\log_8 512 = x \Leftrightarrow 8^x = 512$

$\log_m F = w \Leftrightarrow m^w = F$

base 10 logs	calculator values
log 1	0.000
log 2	0.301
log 3	0.477
log 4	0.602
log 5	0.699
log 6	0.778
log 7	0.845
log 8	0.903
log 9	0.954
log 10	1.000
log 20	1.301
log 200	2.301
log 2000	3.301
$\log \frac{1}{2}$	-0.301
$\log \frac{1}{4}$	-0.602

Notice $0.602 = 2 \cdot 0.301$

or $\log 4 = 2 \cdot \log 2 = \log 2^2$

and $0.903 = 3 \cdot 0.301$

or $\log 8 = 3 \cdot \log 2 = \log 2^3$

generalizing, we get $a \cdot \log b = \log b^a$

Also notice $0.301 + 0.477 = 0.778$, which is

$\log 2 + \log 3 = \log 6 = \log (2 \cdot 3)$ and

generalizing,

$\log r + \log s = \log (r \cdot s)$

How about $\log \frac{1}{2} = {}^{-}\log 2$ and generalizing,

$$\log\left(\frac{A}{B}\right) = {}^{-}\log\left(\frac{B}{A}\right)$$

and $\log\left(\frac{200}{2}\right) = \log 100 = \log 200 - \log 2 = 2.301 - 0.301$

$= 2$

generalizing, $\log\left(\frac{A}{B}\right) = \log A - \log B$

These generalizations (identities) hold for logs to any base.

A program which will get the infinite series for

$\log_e(1 + a) = a - \frac{1}{2} \cdot a^2 + \frac{1}{3} \cdot a^3 - \frac{1}{4} \cdot a^4 + \frac{1}{5} \cdot a^5 - \ldots$

FX7000G
```
?->X:
1->N:
0->S:
Lbl 8:
(-1)xʸ(N+1)x(XxʸN)÷N→A:
A+S→SΔ
N+1→N:
Goto 8
```

in Basic
```
10 input x
20 s=0
30 For x=1 to 20
40 s=(-1)^(n+1) x(x^n)/n + s
50 print s
60 Next N
```

Remember this series converges only for numbers between ${}^{-}1$ and 1.

See if you can find $\log_e 3$, $\log_e 4$ and others using this same idea of Newton's.

If you try to use the rule we found above to find the area under the curve $y = x^n$ from $x = 0$

to x or $\mathbf{A}_{0-x} x^n = \frac{1}{n+1} \cdot x^{n+1}$ to find the area under $y = \frac{1}{x}$ which is $y = x^{-1}$ you'll see what

Sean did, that the denominator of the fraction $\frac{1}{n+1}$ goes to 0 which makes the fraction

blow up. So the rule we found to find the area under the curve $y = x^n$ from $x = 0$ to x or

$\mathbf{A}_{0-x} x^n = \frac{1}{n+1} \cdot x^{n+1}$ doesn't work when n = ${}^{-}1$.

8. Area under the normal distribution curve.

The area under the normal distribution curve $y = \frac{1}{\sqrt{2}} \cdot e^{\frac{-x^2}{2}}$ is **1.**

Question worksheets for **chapter 14**
"Slopes and The Derivative"

1. Slope, rate and ratio. We started graphing in chapter 1 but the bulk of it is in chapter 6; the graphing is important because the derivative can best be shown this way. Let's look at the graph of 2x = y. Notice that if you go one unit to the right, you go up 2 units. **This ratio** of $\frac{2}{1}$, $\frac{\text{rise}}{\text{run}}$, is called **the slope of the graph.** The idea of slope appears in many contexts; for example, the slope of a mountain (see Alec's work later), the pitch of a roof (which is $\frac{1}{2}$ the slope of the roof), and the gradient of a road. If you were measuring the time an ant moved along the ground, you might let the x-axis represent the time and the y-axis represent the distance travelled by the ant. Then the slope of the graph, 2,

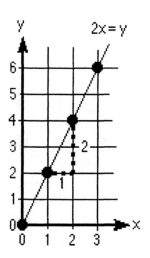

would represent the average rate of speed, $\frac{\text{distance}}{\text{time}}$, of the ant, say 2 centimeters per second. This idea of rate or ratio is used in many ways; for example-- interest rates, (# of dollars per 100 dollars, the word "per" means "divided by"), exchange rate, inflation rate, discount rate, pressure in tires (lbs. per sq. in.), typing speed, film speed, shutter speed, wind speed, population density (# of people per sq. km.), density of materials (mass per unit volume- g/cc), cost of food in price per g), frequency of electromagnetic radiation (hertz or cycles per second), speed of light, speed of sound, pollution rate (parts per million), postal rates, shipping rates, rpm (revolutions per minute of a car engine or turntable), pulse rate (beats per minute), crop yield (bu. per hectare), flow of a stream or blood, signal-to-noise ratio, gear ratios, trig ratios (sine, cosine, tangent), probability of an event, batting averages, e.r.a., and growth rates, just to mention a few.

x	y	
0	0	> 2
1	2	> 2
2	4	> 2
3	6	> 2
4	8	

The other thing we can say about the graph and data of the ant is that the distance the ant travels is a function of time. Of course we won't get a nice simple graph from real data. We talked about functions or guess the rule, in chapter 6. We should also look at the differences in the numbers. The y-number goes up by 2 as the x-number goes up by 1, which shows up as the slope on the graph!

2. Linear graphs and their slopes.

Find the slope and equation of each linear graph at the right and below and write its equation. Do you notice anything about the two lines below?

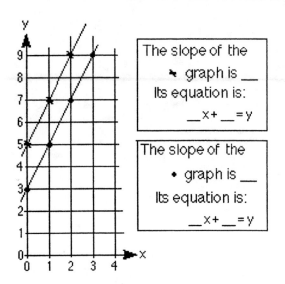

The slope of the
➤ graph is ___
Its equation is:
    ___ x + ___ = y

The slope of the
• graph is ___
Its equation is:
    ___ x + ___ = y

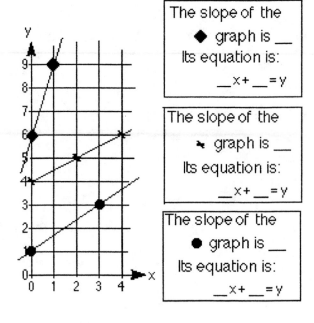

The slope of the
◆ graph is ___
Its equation is:
    ___ x + ___ = y

The slope of the
➤ graph is ___
Its equation is:
    ___ x + ___ = y

The slope of the
● graph is ___
Its equation is:
    ___ x + ___ = y

Find the slope and the equation of each graph at the right. What do you notice about the slopes?

Make up some other linear graphs of the form A•x + B = y for a friend to find the slopes and equations.

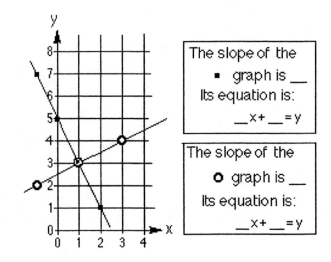

The slope of the
■ graph is ___
Its equation is:
    ___ x + ___ = y

The slope of the
○ graph is ___
Its equation is:
    ___ x + ___ = y

Find the slopes and equations for the two graphs below, then make up more equations and graphs to find the slopes. Make tables of numbers and how the numbers are related to the graph and to the equation.

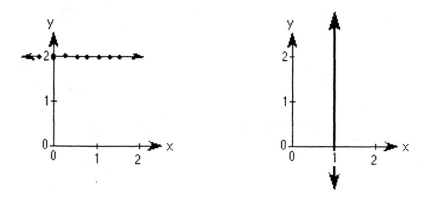

3. Alec's slopes of mountains and stairs

Alec, 13 years old at the time, made a scale drawing (numbers in feet) of the Illinois landscape from a topographic map of Champaign-Urbana:

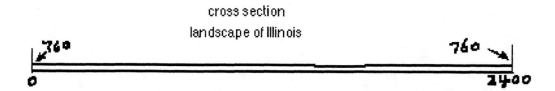

Using a topographic map of New Hampshire, he also found the slope of Mt. Washington. He found the elevation or height of the mountain from the map, measured to the approximate base of the mountain. He made a scale drawing, and found the slope to be 0.304 . The slope turns out to be the tangent of the angle of elevation. Using his dad's calculator -- he used tan^{-1} 0.304, the angle whose tangent is 0.304 or the inverse tangent of 0.304 (make sure you are in degree mode). He found the angle of elevation to be about 17° (Ian's legs think this is too low!).

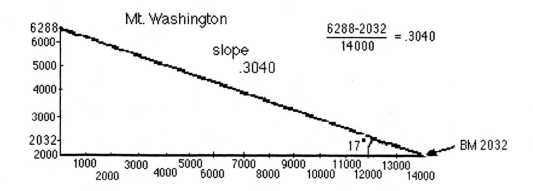

Alec also made scale drawings and found the slope and angle of elevation of a wheelchair access ramp and nearby stairs.

How about you doing a couple of these. Guess the slope first. Which of these do you think would have the larger slope? You might want to find the gradient (slope) of a portion of the state highway near you; try to find the slope of something of your own, in your house, part of your house, near your house. Compare your work with that of a friend or work together to do some.

4. Stories from graphs-The following are problems from "The Language of Functions and Graphs" published by The Shell Centre for Mathematical Education, University of Nottingham. They lead into the following problem of the derivative very nicely. Choose the best graph to describe each of the situations listed below. Copy the graph and label the axes clearly with the variables shown in brackets. If you cannot find the graph you want, then draw your own version and explain it fully.

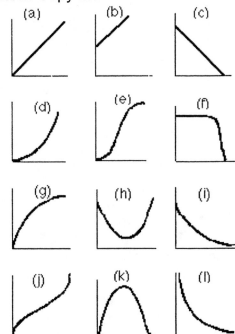

1) The weightlifter held the bar over his head for a few unsteady seconds, and then with a violent crash he dropped it. (height of bar/time)

2) When I started to learn the guitar, I initially made very rapid progress. But I have found that the better you get, the more difficult it is to improve still further. (proficiency/amount of practice)

3) If schoolwork is too easy, you don't learn anything from doing it. On the other hand, if it is so difficult that you cannot understand it, again you don't learn. That is why it is so important to pitch work at the right level of difficulty (educational value/difficulty of work)

4) When jogging, I try to start off slowly, build up to a comfortable speed and then slow down gradually as I near the end of a session. (distance/time)

5) "In general, larger animals live longer than smaller animals and their hearts beat slower. With twenty-five million heartbeats per life as a rule of thumb, we find that the rat lives for only three years, the rabbit seven and the elephant and whale even longer. As respiration is coupled with heartbeat--usually one breath is taken every four heartbeats--the rate of breathing also decreases with increasing size. (heart rate/life span)

6) As for 5, except the variables are (heart rate/breathing rate)

Now make up three stories of your own to accompany three of the remaining graphs. Pass your stories to your neighbor. Can they choose the correct graphs to go with the stories?

Jonathan's Mom wrote: "Jonathan suggested a story about tornadoes and low pressure areas; we ended up with the graph at the right:

note: we didn't know if this 'jives' with scientific fact, but we had fun with the discussion."

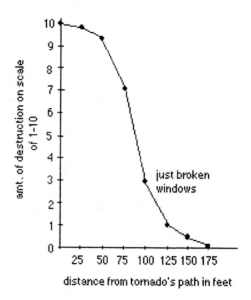

Give a simple number that will closely
approximate the slope of each of these lines:

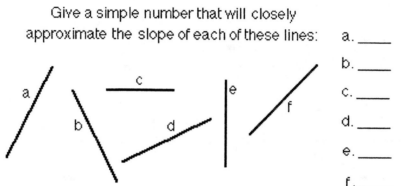

a. _____

b. _____

c. _____

d. _____

e. _____

f. _____

5. Use your pencil to approximate the slope of the tangent to various curves at certain points:

Now comes the big change. We've been finding the slopes of straight lines, now the question is what is the slope of a curved line?

Well it changes, right? So what we do is find the slope of the straight line that touches the curve at one point or we say is tangent to the curve at that point.

Shown at the right is the graph of $y = x^2$. Put your pencil (the dark line) next to the curve at various points and try to approximate the slopes of these lines. At (1,1) the slope is about 2.

At the right is the graph of the X-coordinate of the point above vs the approximate slope of the tangent line at that point. So at (1,1) the slope is about 2, so we plot the point (1,2). Plot more points on this graph.

What do you notice?

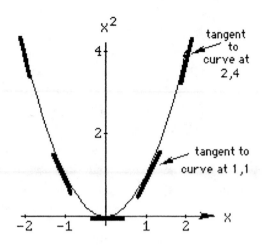

Approximate slopes of tangents to the curve x^2

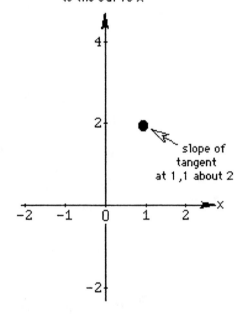

Shown below is the graph of $y = e^x$. Put your pencil next to the curve at various points and try to approximate the slopes of these lines.

Shown below is the graph of $y = \ln x$ Put your pencil next to the curve at various points and try to approximate the slopes of these lines.

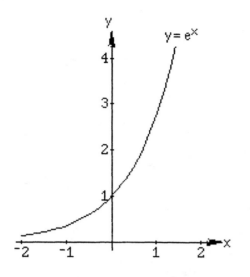

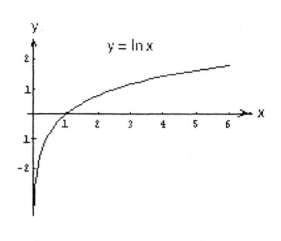

Sketch the graph of approximations to the slopes of the tangents at various points on the curve $y = e^x$ above.

Sketch the graph of approximations to the slopes of the tangents at various points on the curve $y = \ln x$ above.

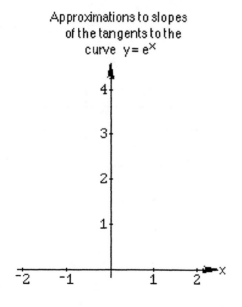

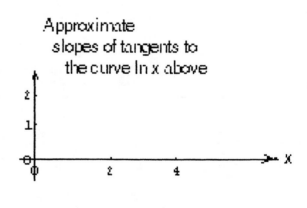

Shown below is the graph of y = sin x. Put your pencil next to the curve at various points and try to approximate the slopes of these lines.

Shown below is the graph of y = cos x. Put your pencil next to the curve at various points and try to approximate the slopes of these lines.

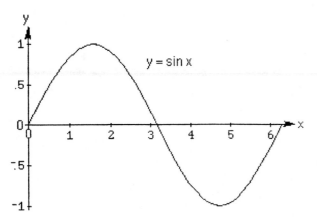

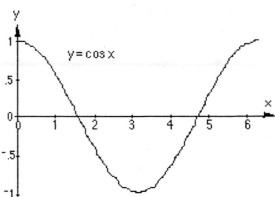

Sketch the graph of approximations to the slopes of the tangents at various points on the curve y = sin x above.

Sketch the graph of approximations to the slopes of the tangents at various points on the curve y = cos x above.

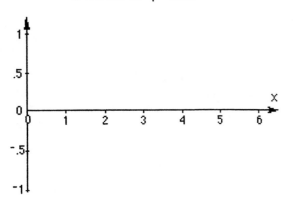

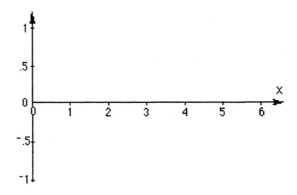

6. Using the computer to "zoom in" on a curve at a point and then finding the slope of the tangent to the curve at that point.

At the right are pictures of a computer screen in *Derive*, reduced in size, starting with the graph of $y=x^2$ with the cross at the point (1,1) and a scale of x:1, y:1.Each dot is 1 unit apart vertically and horizontally. We then "zoom in" on the graph, at the point (1,1). What does "zooming in" essentially do? It changes the scale on the axes.

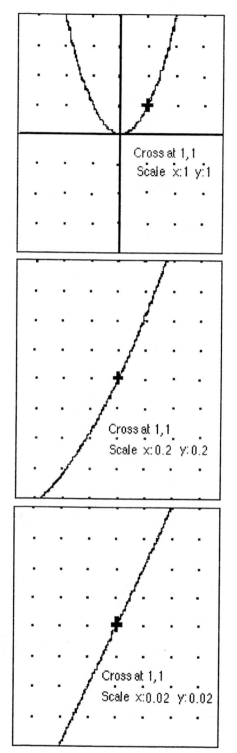

Cross at 1,1
Scale x:1 y:1

Cross at 1,1
Scale x:0.2 y:0.2

Cross at 1,1
Scale x:0.02 y:0.02

The second graph shows the same curve, again centered at (1,1), but the scale is x:0.2, y:0.2

The third graph ends up 0.02 of a unit apart . Notice what happens. In this small portion of the graph, the curve looks like a straight line, as far as the eye can see! The slope of this line then is essentially the **slope of the curve** or the slope of the line tangent to the curve at the point (1,1). Using the dots on the screen, we can find the slope of this line, which is 2, the slope of the tangent to the curve at (1,1). As far as I know, this idea was first done using *Derive* by my partner in The Math Program, Jerry Glynn.

We can then do the same thing at various points on the curve $y=x^2$ and try to find a rule relating the x-coordinate of the point to the slope of the tangent to the curve at that point. This rule you find will be the derivative of x^2. I think this idea makes the derivative, which I used to think was a difficult concept, into something very simple.

We'll do one more example of the zooming in on a curve, then we'll see how we can do this without the computer. This is exciting.

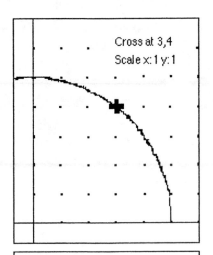

At the right are 3 computer screens in *Derive* with part of the graph of $y = \sqrt{25 - x^2}$, or part of the top half of the circle $x^2 + y^2 = 25$ whose center is at (0,0) with a radius of 5 units. We then zoom in on that curve at the point (3,4).

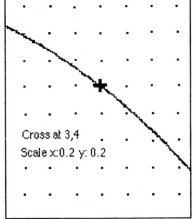

The second screen picture is of the same curve, with the cross still at (3,4), but the scale is 0.2 this time.

The third screen picture is of the same curve, with the cross still at (3,4), but the scale is 0.01 this time.

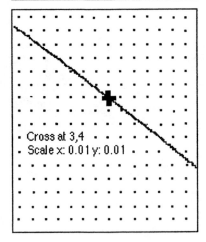

What do you get for the slope of this "straight" section of the curve?

How is the slope related to the coordinates of the point?

Could you predict the slope of this curve at the point (4,3)?

Would you predict the slope of the tangent to the curve at the point (x,y)?

Suppose you don't have a computer to "zoom in" on the curve, can you do this? Sure! Just change the scale on your graph paper; actually I just drew a diagram like the one shown at the right using 0.001 as the distance my points are apart. What I did was to say I was zooming in on the curve $y = x^2$ at the point $(2, 2^2)$. I then found the the slope of the almost straight line segment from the point $(1.999, 1.999^2)$ to $(2.001, 2.001^2)$ using a calculator. I got 4.000000000 as the slope of this line, close to the tangent to the curve $y = x^2$ at the point $(2, 2^2)$.

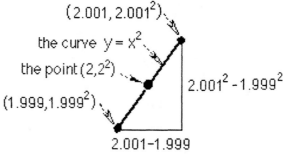

Zooming in on the curve $y = x^2$
at the point $(2, 2^2)$

$(2.001, 2.001^2)$

the curve $y = x^2$

the point $(2, 2^2)$

$(1.999, 1.999^2)$

$2.001^2 - 1.999^2$

$2.001 - 1.999$

$$\text{slope}_{1.999-2.001} = \frac{2.001^2 - 1.999^2}{2.001 - 1.999} = 4.000000000$$

Going from $(2, 2^2)$ to $(2.001, 2.001^2)$,

the slope of the line is $\frac{(2 + .001)^2 - 2^2}{(2 + .001) - 2}$ = 4.001, very close to 4. If you want to get a better approximation, try going from $(2, 2^2)$ to $(2.0001, 2.0001^2)$.

"Zoom in" on the curve $y = x^2$ at the point $(3, 3^2)$, using the slope of the line from $(3, 3^2)$ to $(3.001, 3.001^2)$ and also from $(2.999, 2.999^2)$ to $(3.001, 3.001^2)$ to see how they differ; then do a similar thing for $(4, 4^2)$ and $(10, 10^2)$ to find the slope of line which is close to the tangent to the curve at each point.

Fill in table below showing the x-coordinate and the slope of the tangent at that point

X-coordinate	1	2	3	4	5	.....	10	..	X
slope of tangent		4							

Find a rule relating the x-coordinate of each point and the slope of the tangent at that point?
This rule is the derivative of x^2.

Why do you think the slope of the line, when you go the same distance either side of the target point, is exactly the same as the slope of the tangent at that target point?

Now zoom in on the curve $y = x^3$ at the points $(1, 1^3)$, $(2, 2^3)$, and a few others. Make a table like we did above. See if you can figure out the derivative of x^3 this way.
..and x^4?

7. Derivatives as done in textbooks

At some point when Ian was 11 years old, he and I went through the following discussion to get the derivative of x^2, which is the slope of the tangent to the curve $y=x^2$ at any point (x, x^2). This then led to the derivative of x^n and other functions.

We found the slopes of the curves above in 2 ways, by putting our pencil next to the curve and approximating the slopes of these lines, then we zoomed in on the graph at certain points and calculated the slope of a line very close to the tangent to the curve.

Now our strategy will be to find the slopes of lines from point A, to points to the right of it on the curve, like B, then from A to C and so on, getting closer and closer to point A. We will get an **infinite** sequence of slopes of lines which will approach the slope of the tangent. The limit of this sequence will be the slope of the tangent to the curve at the point A.

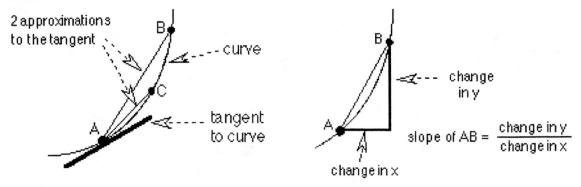

The scales on the following graphs will be distorted in order to show the straight lines clearly. Once we do one of these infinite sequences of slopes, the rest of them will be easy, because there will be patterns, as usual, which will make it possible to predict others.

The first problem will be to find the slope of the tangent to the curve $y = x^2$ at the point $(1,1^2)$, shown below.

The slope of the line from the point $(1,1^2)$ to $(2,2^2)$ is

$$\text{slope } x^2_{(1,1^2)} = \frac{2^2-1^2}{2-1} = 3$$

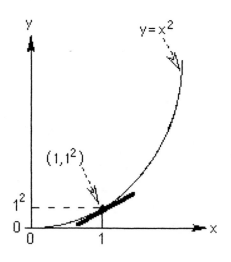

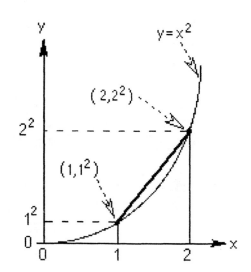

Now we'll find the slope of the straight line from $(1, 1^2)$ to $(1\frac{1}{2}, 1\frac{1}{2}^2)$:

Now we'll find the slope of the straight line from $(1, 1^2)$ to $(1\frac{1}{3}, 1\frac{1}{3}^2)$:

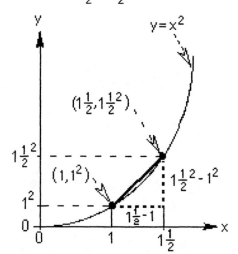

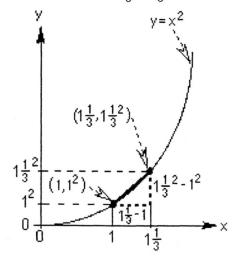

$$\text{slope } x^2_{(1,1^2)} = \frac{\left(1+\frac{1}{2}\right)^2-1^2}{\left(1+\frac{1}{2}\right)-1} = \frac{1\frac{1}{4}}{\frac{1}{2}} = 2+\frac{1}{2}$$

$$\text{slope } x^2_{(1,1^2)} = \frac{\left(1+\frac{1}{3}\right)^2-1^2}{\left(1+\frac{1}{3}\right)-1} = \frac{\frac{7}{9}}{\frac{1}{3}} = 2+\frac{1}{3}$$

Look at what's happening to the slopes; we have $3, 2\frac{1}{2}, 2\frac{1}{3}$, or $2 + 1, 2 + \frac{1}{2}, 2 + \frac{1}{3}$.

Predict what you would get for the slope of the straight line from $(1, 1^2)$ to $\left(1\frac{1}{4}, 1\frac{1}{4}^2\right)$.

Draw the picture, then find the slope to see if your prediction is right.

If we extend this sequence of slopes, and call **h** the number we add to the x-coordinate of our point (1,1), what happens to this sequence as h gets closer and closer to zero?

Generalizing this sequence of slopes of straight lines approaching the slope of the tangent to the curve $y = x^2$ at the point $(1, 1^2)$, we get $\underset{(1,1^2)}{\text{slope}} x^2 = \dfrac{(1+h)^2 - 1^2}{(1+h)-1}$.

From chapter 9, to get $(1 + h)^2$, we can use the identity $(A + B)^2 = A^2 + 2AB + B^2$ and substitute 1 in for A and **h** in for B.

Now we want the limit of this sequence as $h \to 0$, which we'll write as $\underset{h \to 0}{\text{limit}} \dfrac{(1+h)^2 - 1^2}{(1+h)-1} = ?$

What do you get for the limit of this sequence?

Now find the slope of the tangent to the curve $y = x^2$ at the point $(2, 2^2)$ in the same way as we found the slope of the tangent at the point $(1, 1^2)$. Draw the diagrams, then find the slopes of the lines from $(2, 2^2)$ to $(3, 3^2)$ and from $(2, 2^2)$ to $\left(2+\frac{1}{2},\left(2+\frac{1}{2}\right)^2\right)$ and from $(2, 2^2)$ to $\left(2+\frac{1}{3},\left(2+\frac{1}{3}\right)^2\right)$. The first 2 pictures look like these:

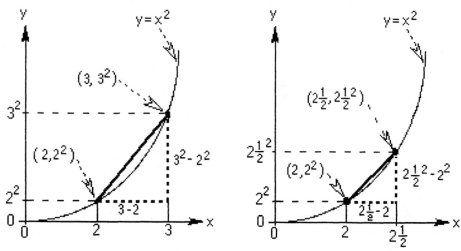

So what do you get for these slopes?
Predict what you would get for the slope of the straight line from $(2, 2^2)$ to $\left(2+\frac{1}{4},\left(2+\frac{1}{4}\right)^2\right)$. Draw the picture, then find the slope to see if your prediction is right.

If we extend this sequence of slopes, and call h the number we add to the x-coordinate of our point $(2, 2^2)$, what happens to this sequence as h gets closer and closer to zero?

Look at what's happening to the slopes from $(2, 2^2)$: we have $5, 4\frac{1}{2}, 4\frac{1}{3}$, or $4 + 1, 4+\frac{1}{2}$, $4+\frac{1}{3}$.

Generalizing this sequence of slopes of straight lines approaching the slope of the tangent to the curve $y = x^2$ at the point $(2, 2^2)$, we get $\underset{(2,2^2)}{\text{slope } x^2} = \dfrac{(2+h)^2 - 2^2}{(2+h)-2}$.   Now we want the

limit of this sequence as h→0, which we'll write as $\underset{h\to 0}{\text{limit}} \dfrac{(2+h)^2 - 2^2}{(2+h)-2} = ?$

What do you get for the limit of this sequence?

Now find the slope of the tangent to the curve $y = x^2$ at the point **($3, 3^2$)** in the same way as we found the slope of the tangent at the point $(1, 1^2)$. Draw the diagrams, then find the slopes of the lines from $(3, 3^2)$ to $(4, 4^2)$, from $(3, 3^2)$ to $\left(3+\frac{1}{2}, \left(3+\frac{1}{2}\right)^2\right)$, from

$(3, 3^2)$ to $\left(3+\frac{1}{3}, \left(3+\frac{1}{3}\right)^2\right)$, and generalize to $\underset{h\to 0}{\text{limit}} \dfrac{(3+h)^2 - 3^2}{(3+h)-3} = ?$

What is your prediction for the slope of the tangent to the curve $y = x^2$ at the point **($4, 4^2$) ? ($5, 5^2$) ?**

Fill in table below showing the x-coordinate and the slope of the tangent at that point from what we've done so far:

X-coordinate	1	2	3	4	5	.. 10	.. X
slope of tangent	2	4					

In general then, the slope of the tangent to the curve $y = x^2$ at the point **(x, x^2)** is the limit of the sequence of slopes of straight lines and is written as

$$\underset{h\to 0}{\text{limit}} \frac{(x+h)^2 - x^2}{(x+h)-x}$$

and what would this be equal to?

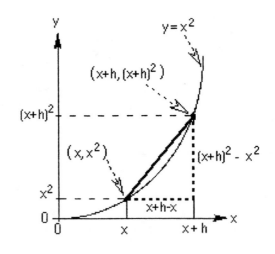

8. Tickertape -- application of derivative

For this next problem you will need the tickertape or recording timer; see the bibliography under materials.

The problem is to see what happens when an object is dropped and **find its speed after 4 ticks** of time.

Clamp the timer to a table, near its edge. Attach a weight to the paper tape, start the timer, let the object fall to the ground. Marks are made on the tape by the timer at **equal time intervals**.Try different size objects (a brick, a bolt..). Try just pulling the tape through the timer to make the dots the same distance apart; further apart but the same distance apart. Just experiment first. How can you tell from the dots on the tape about how fast the object moves?

Now get the data we'll graph. Take one object and get the marks on the tape as the object falls to the ground. The time between dots is the same.Tear off the tape. It will look something like this:

Tape   0 1 2 3   4   5   6   7   8   9

Measure the distance from the first point (do the best you can here, because it's sometimes hard to tell where the first point is), to each of the points on the tape. Make a table to keep track of the data:

After tick #	0	1	2	3	4	5	6	7	8	9	10	11	12	13
The distance weight fell (mm)	0													

Graph the distance vs time from the table above, with the time (in ticks) on the horizontal axis and the distance on the vertical axis. What do you notice?

Measure the distance between the marks on the tape, or the differences in the distances from the table above. Then graph the change in distance vs. the time, which is the average speed vs. time graph. On the vertical axis put the change in distance, the time on the horizontal axis. What do you notice?

Calculate the change in speed between ticks, the second differences from the table above and represents the acceleration of the object as it falls. Then graph the change in speed vs the time in ticks.

Using these graphs, find the speed of the falling object after 4 ticks.

Graphing real data, never gives perfect graphs such as $y = x^2$, $y = 2x$ and $y = 2$. The thing about the mathematics vs say, physics, is that the mathematics, although theoretical, describes physical reality close enough to enable us to predict very precisely, many things. That's why mathematics is so important to understand, both as a discipline unto itself, and for its applications in so many other fields.

Where do we stand on the derivatives, the slopes of the curves so far?
The slope of $y = 2$ is 0 (a horizontal line has a slope of 0)
The slope of $y = 3x$ is 3; the slope of $y = mx + b$ is m
The slope of the tangent to the curve $y = x^2$ is $2x$

Find the slope of the tangent to each of the following curves (the derivative): $y = 5x^2$;
$y = x^2 + 3x + 7$

9. Now let's find the slope of the tangent to the curve $y = x^3$ at the point $(5,5^3)$. What is your prediction first?_____

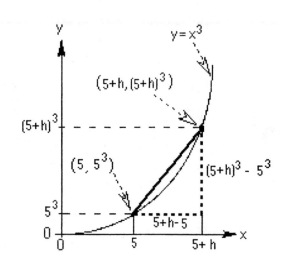

The slope of the line from

$(5,5^3)$ to $\left(5+1, \left(5+1\right)^3\right)$,

= slope $x^3 \bigg|_{(5,5^3)} = \dfrac{(5+1)^3 - 5^3}{(5+1)-5}$ = 9 1

Find the slope of the line from $(5,5^3)$ to

$\left(5+\frac{1}{2}, \left(5+\frac{1}{2}\right)^3\right)$

Find the slope of the line from $(5,5^3)$ to

$\left(5+\frac{1}{3}, \left(5+\frac{1}{3}\right)^3\right)$

Find the slope of the line from $(5,5^3)$ to

$\left(5+ .0001, \left(5+ .0001\right)^3\right)$

In general, find the slope of the line from $(5,5^3)$ to $\left(5+h, \left(5+h\right)^3\right)$, as $h \to 0$, in other words, find

the slope of the tangent to the curve $y = x^3$ at the point $(5,5^3)$. It is $\displaystyle \lim_{h \to 0} \dfrac{(5+h)^3 - 5^3}{(5+h)-5} = ?$

What would the slope of the tangent to the curve $y = x^3$ at the point $(6,6^3)$ be?
What would the slope of the tangent to the curve $y = x^3$ at the point (x,x^3) be? This will be the derivative of x^3.

Fill in the table at the right with the functions and their derivatives you've found so far. Look for some patterns.

function	its derivative
$y = 2$	0
$y = ax$	a
$y = x^2$	$2x$

10. Rectangles of a constant perimeter of 20

One other application of the derivative which I think is important, besides velocity and acceleration, is using it to find the maximum and minimum of a function. One simple example (which can be done without the calculus as well), is to find the length of the rectangle with the largest area, that has a perimeter of, say 20.

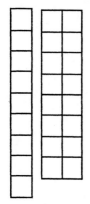

First, draw some rectangles with a perimeter of 20, like the 1x9 and 2x8 ones at the left.

Fill in the table at the right with the length (L), width (W) and the area (A) of each rectangle.

Graph the length vs area as shown at the far right. Find the equation of your graph. To help, use the relationship between L and W in the perimeter, which is 20.

At the maximum point of the graph the tangent to it is horizontal and its slope = 0. Find the derivative of this function, set that = 0 and solve the resulting equation for L, the answer to the problem.

L	W	A
1	9	9
2	8	16
3		
4		
5		
6		
7		
8		
9		

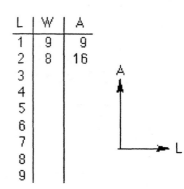

Answer worksheets for **chapter 14**
"Slopes and The Derivative"

2. Linear graphs and their slopes

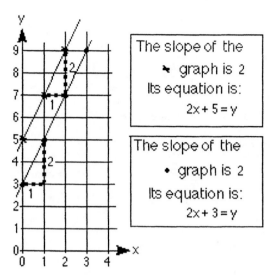

The slope of the

↖ graph is 2

Its equation is:

$2x + 5 = y$

The slope of the

• graph is 2

Its equation is:

$2x + 3 = y$

The slope of the

◆ graph is 3

Its equation is:

$3x + 6 = y$

The slope of the

↖ graph is $\frac{1}{2}$

Its equation is:

$\frac{1}{2}x + 6 = y$

The slope of the

● graph is $\frac{2}{3}$

Its equation is:

$\frac{2}{3}x + 1 = y$

Notice if the slopes are the same, the lines are parallel.

The graphs of $^-2x + 5 = y$ and $\frac{1}{2}x + 2\frac{1}{2} = y$ are perpendicular and their slopes are negative reciprocals of each other or the product of the slopes is $^-1 = {}^-2 \cdot \frac{1}{2}$. With a negative slope you go left 1 and up 2 or $\frac{^+2}{^-1} = {}^-2$, or you can go down 2 and right 1 or $\frac{^-2}{^+1} = {}^-2$, either way. For the fractional slope of $\frac{1}{2}$ you can think of this as going 1 to the right and up $\frac{1}{2}$ for $\frac{\frac{1}{2}}{\frac{1}{1}}$ or going 2 to the right and 1 up for $\frac{1}{2}$. In either case you get a slope of $\frac{1}{2}$.

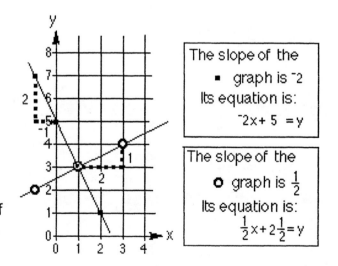

The slope of the

■ graph is $^-2$

Its equation is:

$^-2x + 5 = y$

The slope of the

○ graph is $\frac{1}{2}$

Its equation is:

$\frac{1}{2}x + 2\frac{1}{2} = y$

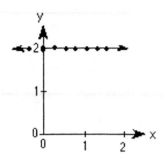 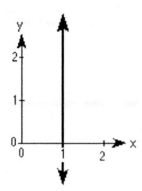

For the horizontal line at the left above the slope is 0, and one can write the equation as $0 \cdot x + 2 = y$ or $y = 2$. No matter what value you put in for x, the y value will be always be 2.

For the vertical line at the right above, the slope doesn't exist, but one can write the equation as $x = 1$ or $0 \cdot y + 1 = x$, no matter what you put in for y, the x value will be 1. Notice that the x and y are interchanged in their position in the equation...hmm. Raises new questions!

3. Alec's slopes of a wheelchair access ramp and nearby stairs.

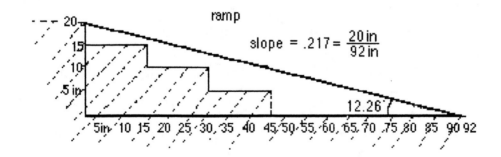

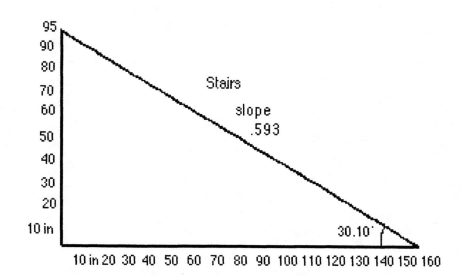

4. Stories from graphs

Story #1→ graph f; #2 → g; #3 → k; #4 → e; #5 → c; #6 → a

Jonathan thought that (h) would be good to illustrate the stock market, especially the recent crash (written 8-12-89). He said the vertical axis could be the # of sales & the horizontal could be months.

the slope of each of these lines is: a. __2__

b. __-2__

c. __0__

d. __$\frac{1}{2}$__

e. __infinite__

f. __1__

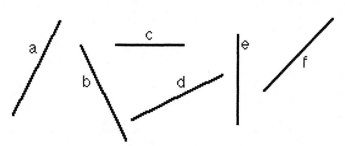

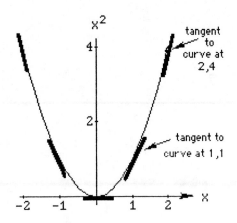

Approximate slopes of tangents
to the curve x^2

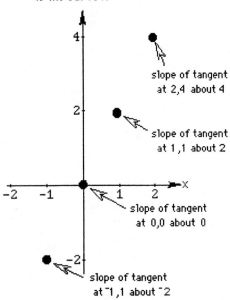

The derivative of x^2 is the line 2X.

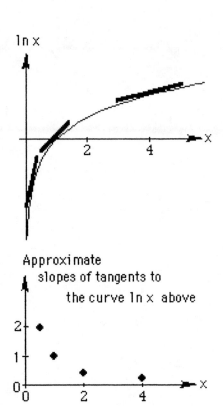

The derivative of ln x is this curve which is

$\frac{1}{X}$

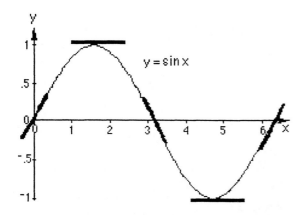

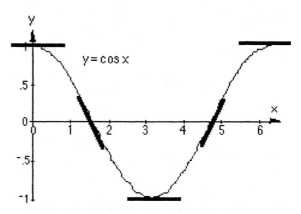

Approximate slopes of tangents
to the curve $y = \sin x$

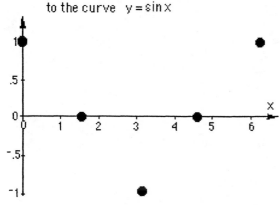

Approximate slopes of tangents
to the curve $\cos x$

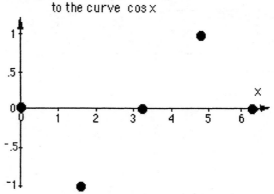

Watch out for the scale. The slope of the first pencil line looks bigger than 1, but because of the scale, it is 1. This graph turns out to be the cos x , so the derivative of the sin x is the cos x.

This graph turns out to be the opposite of the sin x, so the derivative of the cos x is ⁻sin x.

6. Zooming in on the curve $y = x^2$

"Zoom in" on the points $(3, 3^2)$, $(4, 4^2)$ and $(10, 10^2)$ to find the slope of the line which is close to the tangent to the curve at each point

Going from $(3, 3^2)$ to $(3.001, 3.001^2)$: slopex^2 $= \dfrac{3.001^2 - 3^2}{3.001 - 3} = 6.001$ **or**
$\quad\quad\quad\quad\quad\quad\quad\quad\quad_{(3,3^2)}$

Going from $(2.999, 2.999^2)$ to $(3.001, 3.001^2)$:

slopex^2 $= \dfrac{3.001^2 - 2.999^2}{3.001 - 2.999} = \dfrac{(3 + .001)^2 - (3 - .001)^2}{(3 + .001) - (3 - .001)} = 6.00000000.001$
$_{(3,3^2)}$

Going from $(4, 4^2)$ to $(4.001, 4.001^2)$: slope$x^2 = \dfrac{4.001^2 - 4^2}{4.001 - 4} = 8.001$ **or**
$\quad\quad\quad\quad\quad\quad\quad\quad\quad_{(4,4^2)}$

Going from $(3.999, 3.999^2)$ to $(4.001, 4.001^2)$:

$$\text{slope}\, x^2_{(4,4^2)} = \frac{4.001^2 - 3.999^2}{4.001 - 3.999} = \frac{(4+.001)^2 - (4-.001)^2}{(4+.001)-(4-.001)} = 8.00000000 .$$

Going from $(10, 10^2)$ to $(10.001, 10.001^2)$: $\text{slope}\, x^2_{(10,10^2)} = \frac{10.001^2 - 10^2}{10.001 - 10} = 20.001$ **or**

Going from $(9.999, 9.999^2)$ to $(10.001, 10.001^2)$:

$$\text{slope}\, x^2_{(10,10^2)} = \frac{10.001^2 - 9.999^2}{10.001 - 9.999} = \frac{(10+.001)^2 - (10-.001)^2}{(10+.001)-(10-.001)} = 20.00000000$$

The table showing the x-coordinate and the slope of the tangent at that point is below:

X-coordinate	1	2	3	4	5	..10	.. X
slope of tangent	2	4	6	8	10	..20	.. 2X

The slope of the tangent to the curve $y=x^2$ at the point (x, x^2) is 2x. The derivative of x^2 then, is 2x.

Why does the slope of the line joining 2 points whose x-coordinates are equidistant from the one we are finding the tangent to, turn out to be exactly equal to the slope of the tangent?
In general the slope of this line (no matter how big or small h is) is

$$\frac{(x+h)^2 - (x-h)^2}{(x+h)-(x-h)} = \frac{\left(x^2 + 2xh + h^2\right) - \left(x^2 - 2xh + h^2\right)}{2h} = \frac{4xh}{2h} = 2x$$

Does this work for any other curve of higher power than x^2? No.

Now zoom in on the curve $y = x^3$ at the points $(1, 1^3)$, $(2, 2^3)$ and a few others. Make a table like we did above. See if you can figure out the derivative of x^3

Going from $(1, 1^3)$ to $(1.001, 1.001^3)$: $\text{slope}\, x^3_{(1,1^3)} = \frac{1.001^3 - 1^3}{1.001 - 1} = 3.00300100$

Going from $(2, 2^3)$ to $(2.001, 2.001^3)$: $\text{slope}\, x^3_{(2,2^3)} = \frac{2.001^3 - 2^3}{2.001 - 2} = 12.0060010$

Going from $(3, 3^3)$ to $(3.001, 3.001^3)$: $\text{slope}\, x^3_{(3,3^3)} = \frac{3.001^3 - 3^3}{3.001 - 3} = 27.0090010$

Going from $(10, 10^3)$ to $(10.001, 10.001^3)$: $\text{slope}\, x^3_{(10,10^3)} = \frac{10.001^3 - 10^3}{10.001 - 10} = 300.0300000$ **or**

Going from $(9.999, 9.999^3)$ to $(10.001, 10.001^3)$:

$$\text{slope}\, x^3_{(10,10^3)} = \frac{10.001^3 - 9.999^3}{10.001 - 9.999} = \frac{(10+.001)^3 - (10-.001)^3}{(10+.001)-(10-.001)} = 300.0000005 \text{ This time we get a much}$$

closer answer to 300, but not exactly 300. So this going either side of the target point gets us a better approximation to the slope of the tangent to the curve.

The table showing the x-coordinate and the slope of the tangent at to the curve $y = x^3$ at that point is shown below:

X-coordinate	1	2	3	10	..	x
slope of tangent	3	12	27	300	..	$3x^2$

The derivative of x^3 then, is $3x^2$

Zooming in on the upper half of the circle $y = \sqrt{25 - x^2}$ at the point (3,4) we get $\frac{-3}{4}$

for the slope of the tangent. At the point (4,3) we get $\frac{-4}{3}$ for the slope of the tangent.

In general, the derivative is $\frac{-x}{y}$. Looking at patterns certainly makes things much simpler.

7. Derivatives as done in textbooks

From Feb. 1982 to Feb. 1983 Ian went through a very prodigious period mathematical discovery (not to diminish his earlier and now I can say, his later work). He is presently in his sophomore year at Oberlin College, developing new theorems in graph theory. He also tells me he is doing things in his calculus class like using the properties of the Nautilus shell, that of constant ratio of distances from the center and constant angle (as Yao did in chapter 6), to show it is a logarithmic curve. In January of 1982, at age 11, upon my suggestion, he started reading W. W. Sawyer's "What is Calculus About?". During this year he figured out the derivative of x^n and discovered the fundamental theorem of the calculus. He did some work on Maclaurin's Theorem, as well as all his work on the binomial theorem (see chapter 9). My role as the teacher was one of giving a few suggestions. I always felt I was not really teaching Ian much at all, but providing an atmosphere in which he could "learn to learn" as he put it. He was always raising questions, pondering the mathematics. I dare say, through about age 14, Ian spent more time thinking about mathematics than 90% of us do in our lifetime, combined! Although Ian is an unusual young man, I have worked with a many others, including girls, who are capable of much more than I ever thought possible. If we believe young people can do great things, they will do it -- I am convinced of that. But I am also convinced there has to be a big change in **how** this is done with young people. I think all too often curricular changes come from textbook salesmen and college professors, neither of whom have ever worked with young people. That's why what Bob Davis did in the 60's and 70's was so important, he did it with young people and showed me the way! Get a hold of Davis' books in the bibliography.

In finding the slope of tangent to the curve $y = x^2$ at the point $(1,1^2)$, we found the slopes of the lines from $(1,1^2)$ to $(2,2^2)$, $(1,1^2)$ to $(1\frac{1}{2},1\frac{1}{2}^2)$, $(1, 1^2)$ to $(1\frac{1}{3},1\frac{1}{3}^2)$ we get 3, $2\frac{1}{2}$, $2\frac{1}{3}$, or $2 + 1$, $2 + \frac{1}{2}$, $2 + \frac{1}{3}$. The picture at the right shows the straight line from $(1,1^2)$ to $\left(1\frac{1}{4},1\frac{1}{4}^2\right)$; its slope is

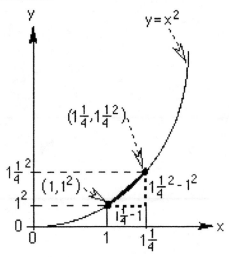

$$\frac{\left(1+\frac{1}{4}\right)^2 - 1^2}{\left(1+\frac{1}{4}\right) - 1} = \frac{\frac{9}{16}}{\frac{1}{4}} = 2 + \frac{1}{4}.$$

Let h be how much we add to the x-coordinate of our point $(1, 1^2)$. We will have h decrease. We can extend this sequence of slopes 3, $2\frac{1}{2}$, $2\frac{1}{3}$, $2\frac{1}{4}$, $2\frac{1}{5}$, $2\frac{1}{6}$, ... or $2 + 1$, $2 + \frac{1}{2}$, $2 + \frac{1}{3}$, $2 + \frac{1}{4}$, .. $2 + h$, ... What's happening as h goes to zero? The limit of this infinite sequence of slopes is 2, or more formally,

$$\lim_{h \to 0} \frac{(1+h)^2 - 1^2}{(1+h) - 1} = \lim_{h \to 0} \frac{1 + 2h + h^2 - 1}{1 + h - 1} = \lim_{h \to 0} \frac{2h + h^2}{h} = \lim_{h \to 0} (2 + h) = 2$$

So the slope of the tangent to the curve $y = x^2$ at the point $(1, 1^2)$ is 2.

Look at what's happening to the slopes from $(2, 2^2)$: we have 5, $4\frac{1}{2}$, $4\frac{1}{3}$, or $4 + 1$, $4 + \frac{1}{2}$, $4 + \frac{1}{3}$.

Generalizing this sequence of slopes of straight lines approaching the slope of the tangent to the curve $y = x^2$ at the point $(2, 2^2)$, we get $\text{slope} \, x^2_{(2,2^2)} = \frac{(2+h)^2 - 2^2}{(2+h) - 2}$.   Now to get the slope of the tangent, we want the limit of this sequence as h→0,

$$\lim_{h \to 0} \frac{(2+h)^2 - 2^2}{(2+h) - 2} = \lim_{h \to 0} \frac{4 + 4h + h^2 - 4}{2 + h - 2} = \lim_{h \to 0} \frac{4h + h^2}{h} = \lim_{h \to 0} (4 + h) = 4$$

Generalizing this sequence of slopes of straight lines approaching the slope of the tangent to the curve $y = x^2$ at the point $(3, 3^2)$, we get $\text{slope} \, x^2_{(3,3^2)} = \frac{(3+h)^2 - 3^2}{(3+h) - 3}$.

The limit of this sequence as h→0, $\lim_{h \to 0} \frac{(3+h)^2 - 3^2}{(3+h) - 3} = \lim_{h \to 0} \frac{9 + 6h + h^2 - 9}{3 + h - 3} =$

$\lim_{h \to 0} \frac{6h + h^2}{h} = \lim_{h \to 0} (6 + h) = 6 = $ the slope of the tangent to the curve at $(3, 3^2)$.

Filling in the table below showing the x-coordinate and the slope of the tangent at that point, looks like this:

X-coordinate	1	2	3	4	5	..	10	..	X
slope of tangent	2	4	6	8	10	..	20	..	2X

In general then, the slope of the tangent to the curve y = x^2 at the point **(x, x^2)** is

$$\lim_{h \to 0} \frac{(x+h)^2 - x^2}{(x+h) - x} = \lim_{h \to 0} \frac{x^2 + 2xh + h^2 - x^2}{x + h - x} = \lim_{h \to 0} \frac{2xh + h^2}{h} = \lim_{h \to 0} (2x + h) = 2x$$

8. Tickertape -- application of derivative

The following was from a student's work. The tape is shown below.

Tape   0 1   2   3   4   5   6   7   8   9

As the weight fell, the time between the ticks stayed the same and the marks spread further apart.

After tick #	1	2	3	4	5	6	7	8	9	10	11	12	13
The weight fell (mm)	6	14.5	25	37	53	72.5	94.5	121.5	153	191	235	285	342

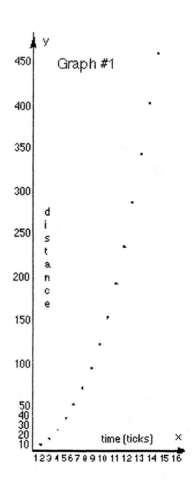

Graph #1

The graph #1 at the right ---the distance (in mm.) from the starting point vs. time (in ticks) turns out to look very much like a parabola. The distance travelled increases in each time unit as the weight falls. Galileo first recorded data like this and found that the distance is proportional to the time squared; in other words, in 1,2,3, etc. seconds, the distance it travels will be some multiple of 1^2, 2^2, 3^2, ... Galileo used his pulse to measure the time in his experiments! The rule that fits this data is a parabola, like s = $\frac{1}{2}$•at^2, where t is the time in sec., s the distance in cm, and a the acceleration due to gravity, 980 cm/sec^2.

The graph #2 at the right shows the change in distance with the change in time. It was obtained by measuring the distance between the marks on the tape. This graph is very close to a straight line such as 2X, which we found for the derivative of X^2. Its slope is about 3.9 mm/tick, so the average velocity v = 3.9•t.

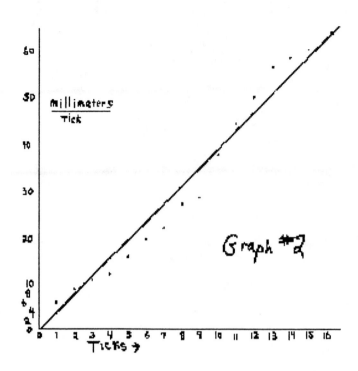

The graph #3 at the right is the change in speed vs. time or the average acceleration, whose equation is a = 3.9 mm/tick^2.

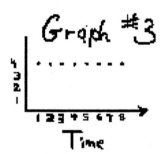

We found the speed after 4 ticks 3 ways:

 Method 1. From graph #1: The distance covered between ticks 3 and 4 was 12 mm. The distance between ticks 4 and 5 was 16 mm., so the speed after 4 ticks was between 12 and 16 mm/tick.

Method 2. We went to the graph of change in distance vs. change in time (graph #2). The graph shows the speed after 4 ticks was about 15.6 mm/tick.

Method 3. According to graph #3, the object accelerates about 3.9 mm/tick each tick. Therefore, after 4 ticks, its speed is 4•3.9 = 15.6 mm/tick.

The slope of the tangent to $y = 5X^2$ is 10X;   to $y = X^2 + 3X + 7$ it is 2X + 3

9. The slope of the tangent to the curve $y=X^3$ at the point $(5,5^3)$. Find The slope of the

line from $(5,5^3)$ to $\left(5 +1, (5 + 1)^3 \right)$ = 91

The slope of the line from $(5,5^3)$ to $\left(5 +\frac{1}{2}, \left(5 +\frac{1}{2}\right)^3\right)$ = $82\frac{3}{4}$

The slope of the line from $(5,5^3)$ to $\left(5 +\frac{1}{3}, \left(5 +\frac{1}{3}\right)^3\right)$ = $80\frac{1}{9}$

The slope of the line from $(5,5^3)$ to $\left(5 + .0001, (5 +.0001)^3\right)$ = 75.0015

We get a sequence $91, 82\frac{3}{4}, 80\frac{1}{9}, .. 75.0015, ...$ which approaches 75 or $3\cdot5^2$ as its limit.

We'll use the binomial expansion, putting $5\to A$ and $h\to B$ to get
$$(5+h)^3 = 5^3 + 3\cdot5^2\cdot h + 3\cdot5^1\cdot h^2 + h^3$$

The slope of the tangent to the curve $y = x^3$ at the point $(\mathbf{5,5^3})$ is

$$\lim_{h\to0} \frac{(5+h)^3 - 5^3}{(5+h)-5} = \lim_{h\to0} \frac{5^3 + 3\cdot5^2\cdot h + 3\cdot5^1\cdot h^2 + h^3 - 5^3}{h} =$$

$$\lim_{h\to0} 3\cdot5^2 + 3\cdot5^1\cdot h + h^2 = \mathbf{3\cdot5^2}$$

The slope of the tangent to the curve $y = x^3$ at the point $(\mathbf{6,6^3})$ is

$$\lim_{h\to0} \frac{(6+h)^3 - 6^3}{(6+h)-6} = \lim_{h\to0} \frac{6^3 + 3\cdot6^2\cdot h + 3\cdot6^1\cdot h^2 + h^3 - 6^3}{h} =$$

$$\lim_{h\to0} 3\cdot6^2 + 3\cdot6^1\cdot h + h^2 = \mathbf{3\cdot6^2}$$

Generalizing further,

The slope of the tangent to the curve $y = x^3$ at the point $(\mathbf{x,x^3})$ is

$$\lim_{h\to0} \frac{(x+h)^3 - x^3}{(x+h)-x} = \lim_{h\to0} \frac{x^3 + 3\cdot x^2\cdot h + 3\cdot x^1\cdot h^2 + h^3 - x^3}{h} =$$

$$\lim_{h\to0} 3\cdot x^2 + 3\cdot x^1\cdot h + h^2 = \mathbf{3\cdot x^2}$$ | So the derivative of x^3 is $3\cdot x^2$ |

The table of functions and their derivatives is shown at the right. Below you can see the patterns Ian found.

function	its derivative
$y = 2$	0
$y = a\,x$	a
$y = x^2$	$2x$
$y = 5x^2$	$10x$
$y = x^2 + 3x + 7$	$2x + 3$
$y = x^3$	$3x^2$

At age 11, Ian realized that he could go up and down, starting with $y = x^4$ and used the following notation to show this:

$$y^{-2'} = \frac{x^6}{30}$$
$$y^{-1'} = \frac{x^5}{5}$$

he started here $y^{0'} = x^4$

$$y^{1'} = 4x^3$$
$$y^{2'} = 12x^2 \quad \text{Ian's notation for the 2nd derivative was } y^{2'}$$
$$y^{3'} = 24x^1$$
$$y^{4'} = 24$$
$$y^{5'} = 0$$

Going down from x^n we get nx^{n-1}, going up we get $\frac{x^{n+1}}{n+1}$. The first is the derivative of x^n, the second is the integral (or antiderivative) of x^n. That was exciting!

Ian also made up the generalization that the n + 1st derivative of x^n is 0; as he showed above, the 5th derivative of x^4 is 0. This is a nice beginning for Taylor's Theorem.

10. Rectangles of a constant perimeter of 20

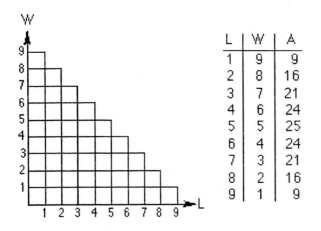

L	W	A
1	9	9
2	8	16
3	7	21
4	6	24
5	5	25
6	4	24
7	3	21
8	2	16
9	1	9

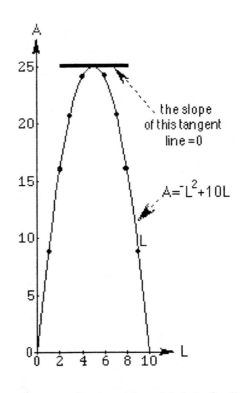

The perimeter of a rectangle = 2•L + 2•W = 20, so W = 10 - L. The area A = L•W. Substituting for W,
A = L•(10 - L) = $^-$L^2 + 10•L. The graph of this equation, a parabola (shows up again), is at the right. Notice that as the length increases the area increases, reaches a maximum, then decreases. If we take the derivative of the area with respect to the length, which is finding the slope of the tangent to the curve, we get $^-$2•L + 10. At the maximum point the slope of the tangent is 0, because at the point where we go from increasing to decreasing area (as a function of L) we are getting no change in area. So we set
$^-$2•L + 10 = 0. Solving this equation for L, we get L= 5. So the rectangle with the maximum area has a length of 5, which is a square. This idea of maximum area also applies in 3-D, to surface area.

What about the other problem, for a given area, of say 36, which rectangle would have the smallest perimeter?

Appendix 1 --The important mathematics

I keep saying we should be doing important mathematics with young people. What do I include in this category of important mathematics?

Infinite series

from coloring in squares, from cookie-sharing (Brad's method--special scissors), convergent, divergent, limit of, as a name for a fraction, for π, for e^x, for sin x, for cos x

Infinite sequences-- convergent, divergent, limit of-- from solving equations, ratios of successive fibonacci numbers, in finding square roots, of partial sums

Infinite continued fractions

for π, for phi, for **e**, for $\sqrt{2}$, graphs of

Renaming numbers -- like $\frac{4}{6}$ is a name for $\frac{2}{3}$ and so is $\frac{1}{2}+\frac{0}{4}+\frac{1}{8}+\frac{0}{16}+...$

Counting

rows on a pineapple $\rightarrow$ the Fibonacci numbers $\rightarrow$ the golden mean
leaves on a sunflower stalk $\rightarrow$ the Fibonacci numbers $\rightarrow$ the golden angle
as used in cookie-sharing to find how many of a piece makes a whole cookie and thus naming the piece
squares to find the area on a geoboard and under a curve on graph paper

Fractions

addition, multiplication
equivalent fractions
complex fractions
continued fractions,
infinite continued fractions
division as related to fractions
changing fractions to decimals and bimals
changing infinite repeating decimals (and bimals) to simple fractions
in making linear graphs
from sharing cookies
within infinite series and infinite sequences
$\frac{SA}{Vol}$ ratio of white to orange rods to show why
rodents are nocturnal animals

slope of a line $\rightarrow$ slope of tangent to a curve
$\rightarrow$ the derivative
ratio of $\frac{\text{diagonal of a regular pentagon}}{\text{the side of a regular pentagon}} \rightarrow$ Golden mean
ratios of successive Fibonacci numbers
ratio of $\frac{\text{perimeter of inscribed polygon}}{\text{diameter of the circle}} \rightarrow \pi$
velocity as a ratio of $\frac{\text{distance}}{\text{time}}$
rate of interest, %
sine function

Guessing functions--linear, quadratic, exponential, and their differences

Graphing

linear graphs $\rightarrow$ fractions, negative numbers, slope and intercept
quadratic $\rightarrow$ moving parabolas, from distance/time experiment and length/area of rectangle of constant perimeter of 20; quadratic equation; graphing iterations
partial sums of an infinite series; infinite sequences.

Angles

of whorling leaves on a sunflower stalk
central angle in a circle $\rightarrow \pi$
sum of the angles of a polygon

Area, perimeter, and volume

on geoboard -- area of shapes, # of squares$\rightarrow$ sum of squares
perimeter of the snowflake curve (involves divergent series) and area of the snowflake
curve (involves convergent series)
finding the surface area of 6 cubes
surface area and volume of rods $\rightarrow \frac{SA}{Vol}$ ratio (involves convergent sequence)
volume of pyramid, volume of cube
area under curves $\rightarrow$ the integral
area of rectangles with constant perimeter of 20 $\rightarrow$ derivative

Binomial expansion -- Pascal's triangle (obtaining it 3 or 4 ways), Ian's way, its relation to
infinite series,
finding the cube root of 2, in compound interest

Interest

simple, compound $\rightarrow \mathbf{e} \rightarrow$ sin x and cos x $\rightarrow$ $\mathbf{e}^{i\pi}$ + 1 = 0

Solving equations

linear -- like 2x + 3 = 17, 2x + 3 = 18, 5x + 3 = 2x + 21-- by guessing,
by balance pictures, using transformations
quadratic--by guessing, sum and product of roots, by iteration a
number of ways, by graphing, by quadratic formula
cubic -- by iteration, by computer

Iterating functions

to solve equations
to find compound interest

to find the square root of a number by
averaging
to find the square root of square root...

Computer programs -- see appendix 3

There are other important mathematical topics not included in this book, notably
Pythagoras, geometric transformations with matrices, making 3D models, multiplying 12x13
in your head, sine waves, and number theory.

Appendix 2 -- Activities for a Parent and/or Teacher Workshop

Try to find patterns in all your work. Graph everything possible!

1. Add up these fractions...*forever!* $\frac{1}{2} + \frac{1}{4} + \frac{1}{8} + \frac{1}{16} + \frac{1}{32} + \cdots$

Color in an 8x8 square on **graph paper** as you add each one. What happens to the sum?
Then try $\frac{1}{3} + \frac{1}{9} + \frac{1}{27} + \frac{1}{81}$ ... What is this sum going to? Do others. Find a rule.

2. Share 6 cookies with 7 people so that each person gets the same amount. How many
cookies does each person get ? **Use 3x5 cards.** Do it another way. Do it Brad's way (your
scissors can only cut into 2 **equal** pieces, and keep track of sizes of pieces). Do it another
way similar to Brad's.

3. Solve for x :

$$\sqrt{x + \sqrt{x + \sqrt{x + \sqrt{x + \ldots}}}} = 3$$

4. Find the perimeter and area of the snowflake curve. You'll need the **snowflake sheets**.
What happens as we go forever?

5. Now try the harmonic series:

$$\frac{1}{2} + \frac{1}{3} + \frac{1}{4} + \frac{1}{5} + \frac{1}{6} + \ldots \text{Use your } \textbf{calculator}! \text{ What's happening?}$$

6a. Find the $\frac{\text{Surface Area}}{\text{Volume}}$ ratio of each of the white to orange **Cuisenaire rods**. Graph

Length vs SA, L vs Vol., L vs $\frac{\text{Surface Area}}{\text{Volume}}$ ratio. Use this information to show why rodents
are nocturnal animals.

6b. **Graph** (find pairs of numbers to make this true, then plot a point for each pair) $x + y = 7$ and $x + y = 8$, etc. for first or second graders, then $2x + 3 = y$ and $3x + 3 = y$, etc.
for older students, but try to find patterns in the points, in either case.

6c. Play guess my rule.

7a. Use the sunflower stalk or the pineapple to find its phyllotaxis numbers to generate the
Fibonacci numbers. Find the next ten numbers in the infinite Fibonacci sequence: 1, 1, 2, 3,
5, 8, 13, 21, . . .

Find the ratios of the $\frac{\text{larger}}{\text{smaller}}$ numbers from the sequence, like

$\frac{1}{1} =$ $\frac{2}{1} =$ $\frac{3}{2} =$ $\frac{5}{3} =$ and show each as a mixed number and as a

decimal, to the maximum number of places shown on your **calculator**. **Graph** these
numbers.

7b. Make a Fibonacci spiral using the **graph paper**.

7c. Find the length of the segment AC if point C cuts AB such that

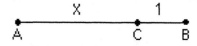

$\frac{\text{the whole segment AB}}{\text{the larger segment AC}} = \frac{\text{the larger segment AC}}{\text{the smaller segment CB}}$. Let the larger segment AC =x , the

smaller segment CB = 1, and the whole segment AB = x +1. From the above proportion
write an equation in x and solve it.

8a. Solve this quadratic equation (that is, make it true): $x^2 - 5x + 6 = 0$. Try guessing, try
some algebraic transformations, graph it. See how many ways you can solve it.

8b. Graph $y = 5 - \dfrac{6}{x}$ and $y = 5 - \dfrac{6}{5 - \frac{6}{x}}$. Where do these intersect?

8c. Iterate $5 + \dfrac{x}{2}$.

9. Find $(a + b)^2$, $(a + b)^3$ . . . , by drawing a square, then a cube, *or* In how many ways can 3, 4, .. **coins** come up heads and tails ? *or* How many trains can you make as long as a purple, .. **rod**? *or* On **spotty paper,** how many routes can you find from point A to point B.. ?

10a. Use a calculator to find successive approximations to $\sqrt{40}$ using the iterative

(feedback) - averaging method: $\dfrac{G + \frac{40}{G}}{2}$ = new Guess no.

10b. Find successive square roots of any number, like 40. What happens?

10c. On separate **circle dot cards** make an equilateral triangle, a hexagon and a dodecagon. **Measure** (in mm) the perimeter of each polygon and the diameter of the circle then find the $\dfrac{\text{perimeter of polygon}}{\text{diameter of circle}}$ ratio in each case. What's happening?

11. Don't do any arithmetic, but keep a careful record of your work: find the amount of money you will have after 1 year if you invest $100 at an annual interest rate of 7%, compounded quarterly. Same problem but compounded 12 times a year. Compounded daily. What happens if . . . ?

13. Find the area under the curve $y = x^2$ from $x=0$ to $x =1$. You will need the $\frac{1}{10}$" **graph paper**.

14. Find the slope of the line $3x + 5 = y$. Find the slope of the curve $y = x^2$ at the point (2,4).

Materials needed:

Paper, pencil, Cuisenaire rods, calculator, rulers, scissors, 3x5 cards, graph paper, 12-dot circle cards, nautilus shell, area under curve sheets, snowflake curve sheets, pentagon sheet, pineapple, and sunflower stalk. Don's book, "Calculus By and For Young People (ages 7, yes 7 and up)". Overhead projector, videotape player (VHS) with color monitor to view Don's videotapes, chalkboard, and tables for participants to work at. Also see Don's website at http://www.shout.net/~mathman for more student works.

Appendix 3 --
On writing computer programs and the use of calculators and computers

These programs are really not that complicated (they all say that, right?). Perhaps if we look carefully at the problems we're studying, it will help with the programming. Just remember this, there are many ways to write a program and your way is probably just as good, if not better than mine. As long as we get the same result. And I want to get young people started quickly, so I go for simplicity, which may not be the most efficient way. The problems we are working with are:

1. To generate a sequence of numbers, then determine if the sequence converges or diverges. With a slight change one can use this program to print out multiples of any number as well as other jobs like this.

    a. We need to be able to describe, with some kind of a rule, how to get the numbers.
    b. We need to get the first number.
    c. We need to print out the first number
    d. We need to change something so that
    e. When we go back to the rule, we'll get the second number.
    f. Then just continue this process to get as many terms in the sequence as we want.

Suppose we want to print out a sequence of powers of $\frac{1}{2}$. We want $\left(\frac{1}{2}\right)^1$, $\left(\frac{1}{2}\right)^2$, $\left(\frac{1}{2}\right)^3$ ...

We'll write these as $\left(\frac{1}{2}\right)^n$, have n start at 1, calculate and print out the answer, increase n by 1, go back to the rule, calculate the next number, print it out, and continue this process. We then have the sequence we want. The program, or set of instructions will vary with the language we use. To start with n as 1, in Basic we write n=1 (and need instruction or line numbers), for the FX7000G we just write 1→N with a colon to separate instructions. In the first column below I've written the instructions for the FX7000G. The Δ in the language of the FX7000G means to display the previous number on the screen. In the second column is a Basic program in which I used a "for, next" loop, which changes N from 1 to 20 and does the instructions inbetween the "for" and "next" with the new N. The answers produced in these first 2 programs will be the decimal form. The last 2 columns show how to get Derive and *Mathematica* to print out the common fractions.

FX7000G	Basic	*Derive*	*Mathematica*
1→N:	10 for N=1 to 20	vector((1/2)^n,n,3)	Table[(1/2)^n,{n,1,3}]
Lbl 6:	20 print (1/2)^N	..will print out	..will print out
(1÷2)x^{y}NΔ	30 next N	$\frac{1}{2}$, $\frac{1}{4}$, $\frac{1}{8}$	$\frac{1}{2}$, $\frac{1}{4}$, $\frac{1}{8}$
1+N→N:			
Goto 6			

1a. To generate the sequence of partial sums of an infinite series and to determine if the series converges or diverges: Start with a number, change it, add this new number to the old one, and print the sum. Then repeat this process.

We are trying to get: $\frac{1}{2}$, $\frac{1}{2}+\left(\frac{1}{2}\right)^2$, $\frac{1}{2}+\left(\frac{1}{2}\right)^2+\left(\frac{1}{2}\right)^3$, and $\frac{1}{2}+\left(\frac{1}{2}\right)^2+\left(\frac{1}{2}\right)^3+\left(\frac{1}{2}\right)^4+,\cdots$

The following program calculates the partial sums of a geometric series

$\frac{A}{B}+\left(\frac{A}{B}\right)^2+\left(\frac{A}{B}\right)^3+\left(\frac{A}{B}\right)^4+\cdots$ where you put in whatever top number (A) and bottom number (B) you want; both programs will print the answers as decimals:

    FX7000G   Basic

? → AΔ	Put in a # for A, displays it	10 input A; print A
? → BΔ	Put in a # for B, displays it	20 input B; print B
0 → S:	start the sum S=0	30 S=0
1 → N:	start N, the exponent, =1	40 For N =1 to 20
Lbl 3:	come here from the Goto 3	
(A÷B) x^{y}N + S → SΔ	raises the fraction f(A,B) to the N th power, adds this to the previous sum S to get the new sum and displays it	50 S = (A/B)^N + S 60 Print S
N + 1 → N: Goto 3	add 1 to N go back to repeat this process	70 Next N

1b. To generate the Fibonacci sequence,
obtained by adding the last 2 numbers 1, 1,2, 3, 5, 8,...

Computer programs to give the Fibonacci sequence for the FX 7000G and in Basic are shown at the right. The key thing we need to do here is to make the sum into the second number and the second number into the first before repeating the process of adding the two numbers.

FX 7000G	Basic
1 → X:	10 X=1
1 → Y:	20 Print X
Lbl 7:	30 Y=1
X+Y→ ZΔ	40 Print Y
Y → X:	50 Z=X+Y
Z->Y:	60 Print Z
Goto 7	70 X=Y
	80 Y=Z
	90 Goto 50

1c. To generate a sequence of numbers by iterating a function: Start with a function, put a number in for x, calculate the result, print it, put this result back in for x and repeat this process. Did you hear the difference between this process and the others? We calculate the result, then put this result back in for x in the function.

From Chapter 8:	FX 7000G	Mathematica	Basic
Computer programs to iterate the function	? → X: Lbl 5:	g[x_]:=5-6/x N[NestList[g,1,20],10]	10 N=0 20 INPUT X
$5 - \dfrac{6}{x}$ on the FX7000G,	5-6÷X→XΔ Goto 5		30 X=5-6/X 40 Print X

in Mathematica and in BASIC (to show 20 numbers).		(you define the function, start with 1→X, iterates 20 times and gives 10 digits in each answer)	50 N=N+1
			60 IF N<20
			      THEN
			      GOTO 30
			70 STOP

2. Graphing-- used in ch. 13 to find the area under a curve by plotting points under the curve, counting these points and finding the ratio of the number plotted to the number filling a 1x1 square:

3. To change a fraction to a bimal -- used in ch. 2

The follow list shows the chapter numbers and the program(s) used:

Ch 1: Print out a sequence of partial sums of an infinite series to determine if the series converges or diverges.

Ch 2: To change a fraction to its bimal.

Ch 3: None

Ch 4: None

Ch 5: Print out a sequence of partial sums of the harmonic series

Ch 7: Print out the Fibonacci sequence and their successive ratios

Ch 8: #1. Iterate the function $5 - \dfrac{6}{x}$. This one, shown above, enables you to iterate at least 3 other functions used in this chapter.

#2. Iterate $\dfrac{6}{5-A}$ to find the numbers that make $5 - \dfrac{6}{x}$ go to zero.

#3. Iterate the function $\dfrac{x}{3} + \dfrac{10}{3}$ to solve a linear equation

Ch 9: None

Ch 10: #1. To get π similar to way Kholer and Achimedes did it.

#2. To get π using a program in Wells' book

#3. To get π using the Gregory-Leibnitz series

#4. To iterate ... $\sqrt{\sqrt{\sqrt{n}}}$

#5. Gayla's (a 6th grader) program to find the first 20 approximations for $\sqrt{N}$ using the averaging and iteration method

Ch 11: Iterating to get the compound interest for any number of years, t.

Ch 12: None

Ch 13: #1. To find the area under a curve by plotting points under the curve, counting these points and finding the ratio of the number plotted to the number filling a 1x1 square.

#2. To find the ratio of the volume of a pyramid to the volume of a cube with the same base and height

#3. To find logs using an infinite series

Ch 14: None

Note: There are 16 programs given in the worksheets, but other programs are talked about and it would be possible to write programs for other problems (like finding the golden angle in ch 7). **All the programs are written in basic** with most also in the language for the FX7000G. Other, newer, programmable calcuolators could also be used.

Why use computers and calculators with young people?

I had three experiences in the last few years that made me realize how important it is for people to use calculators and computers, besides just for word processing and to "check answers". One was I learned about iteration (the basis of fractals and chaos theory) to solve quadratic equations. Second, the exciting realization, for me, that i^i is a real number. The third was that I wrote a program on the FX7000G calculator which plotted and counted the points under a curve, the integral -- and I could then get young people to do these things without the calculator!

The calculators and computers give **me** a way to do tedious things quickly and easily and it enables me to try things I would never have done before. I can ask questions and get feedback quickly and easily. In working on the mathematics there were many calculations I had to do by hand before I saw a pattern. I wouldn't use a computer to teach the graphing of $x + y = 7$ to a 7 year-old because the 7 year-old needs to make mistakes, needs to put the numbers on the axes wrong, needs time to think about what she/he is doing. I tend to get young people using the calculator or computer **after** I see they can do things with pencil and paper, **after** they have seen some patterns. In fact I want to see my students able to do lots of calculations in their head without pencil and paper and without a calculator. For example, if I want a youngster to learn about iteration, I might give her $5 + \frac{x}{2}$ to start with. I would go step by step the first few iterations, to make sure she can divide a fraction by 2. Then after this experience I might say, use a calculator to go on, and keep track of what you get. Then I might get her to write a program to do the iterations and compare the results obtained before by hand. Teaching is not simple.

Appendix 4 -- Sheets to be copied
Along with the shell on page Q103 and people tiles on page Q189
.5 " graph paper for chapters 1, 6 with young people

.25 " graph paper for ch. 6 (graph functions), ch. 7 (spiral), and ch. 8 (sierpinski curve).

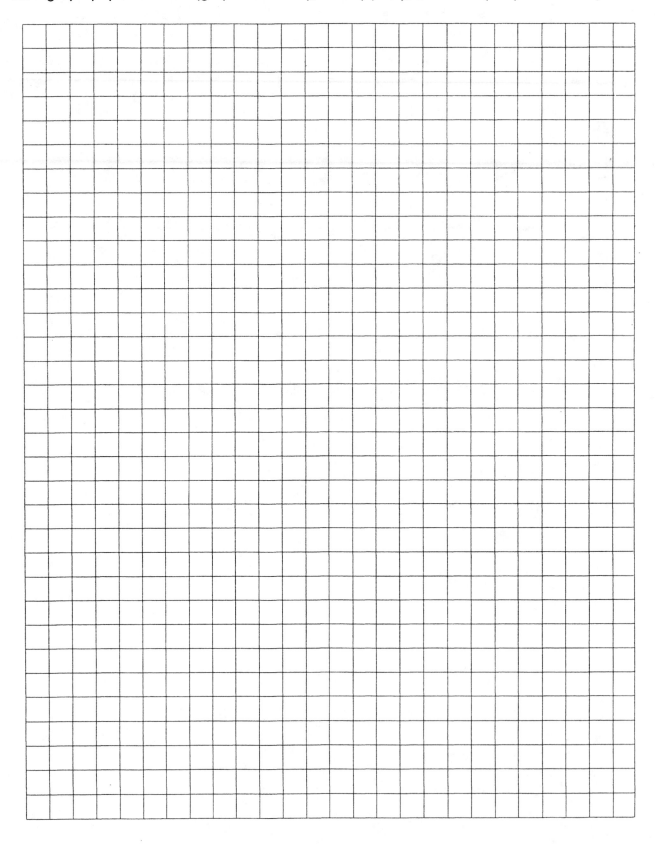

0.1" for area under curves in chapter 13

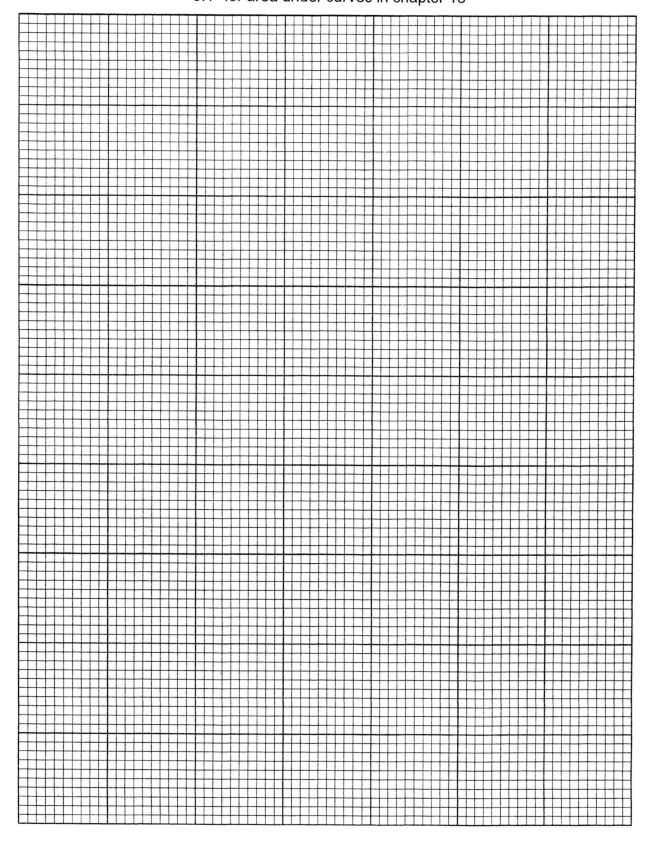

Plain triangular graph paper for snowflake curve in chapter 4

4th snowflake for chapter 4

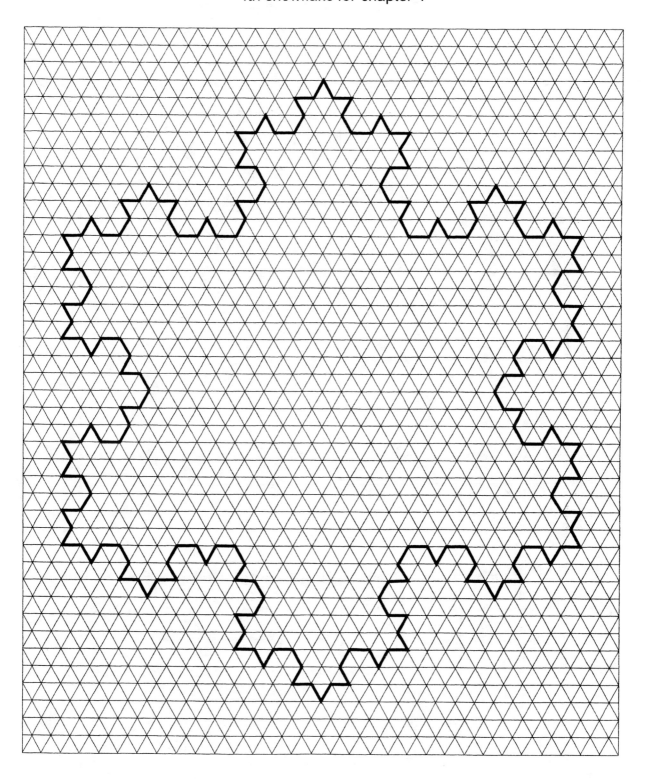

4th sierpinski curve for chapter 4

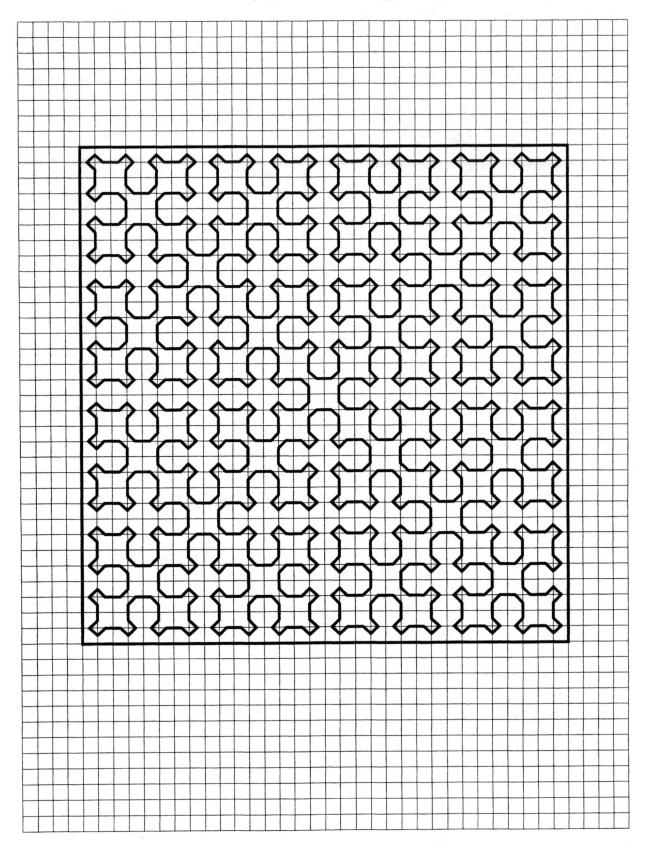

12-dot circles for chapter 10

The regular pentagon for chapter 7.

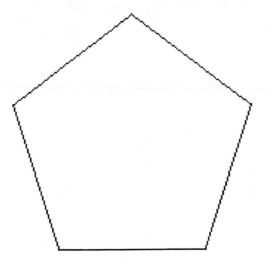

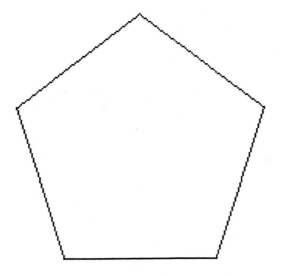

Spotty paper for finding routes in ch. 9, and area in ch. 13

Bibliography
Books & Journals

The Association of Teachers of Mathematics; Mathematics Teaching (Journal) and Micromath (Journal); 7 Shaftesbury St., Derby DE3 8YB, England

Beard, Col. R.S.; Patterns in Space; Creative Publications; Palo Alto, CA; 1973

Beckman, Petr; A History of Pi; St. Martin's Press, NYC; 1971

Boyer, Carl B.; A History of Mathematics; John Wiley & Sons: NYC

Boyer, Carl B.; A History of Calculus; Dover Publications, Inc., NY

Cohen, Don; Calculus By and For Young People (ages 7, yes 7 and up); Don Cohen; Rev. 1989

Cook, Theodore A.; The Curves of Life; Dover Publications, Inc., NY; 1914

Coxeter, H.S.M.; Introduction to Geometry; John Wiley & Sons, NY; 1961

Cundy, H.M. and Rollett, A.P.; Mathematical Models; Oxford U. Press; 1961

Davis, Robert B.; Discovery in Mathematics; Cuisenaire Co. of America, New Rochelle, NY 10802

Davis, Robert B. ; Explorations in Mathematics; & Discovery in Mathematics –both out of print(?)

Dunham, William; Journey Through Genius, The Great Theorems of Mathematics; John Wiley & Sons; 1990

Edwards, C.H., Jr.; The Historical Development of the Calculus; Springer-Verlag, NY; 1979

Feynman, Leighton and Sand; The Feynman Lectures on Physics, Vol. 1; Ch. 22; Addison Wesley: Menlo Pk., CA; 1963

Garland, Trudi Hammel; Fascinating Fibonaccis; Dale Seymour Pub.; Palo Alto, CA

Gardner, Martin; many books , like: Penrose Tiles To Trapdoor Ciphers; W.H. Freeman and Co., NY; '89

Gleick, James; Chaos; Viking Penquin Inc., NYC; 1987

Glynn, Jerry; Exploring Math From Algebra to Calculus With Derive®; http://www.derive.com

Gray, Theodore and Glynn, Jerry; The Beginner's Guide to Mathematica Ver.3; 1997;   Cambridge U. Press

Griffiths, P.L.; Mathematical Discoveries- 1600-1750; Stockwell, Ltd., England; 1977

Hemmings, R. and Tahta, D (Leapfrogs Group); Images of Infinity; England; 1984

Huntley, H. E.; The Divine Proportion; Dover Publications, Inc., NY; 1970

The Illinois Council of Teachers of Mathematics; The Illinois Mathematics Teacher

Land, Frank; The Language of Mathematics; Doubleday, NY; 1963

Mandelbrot, Benoit B.; The Fractal Geometry of Nature; W. H. Freeman and Co.; CA

Olds, C.D.; Continued Fractions; Random House, Inc.; 1963

Peoples' Great Math; The Math Program; 809 Stratford Dr., Champaign, IL, 61821

Polya, George; Mathematical Methods in Science; Math'l Assn of America; 1529 18th St. NW, Washington, DC 20036; 1977

Polya, George; How to Solve It; Doubleday & Co.; Garden City, NY; 1957

Polya, George; Mathematical Discovery; 2 Vols; John Wiley & Sons, NY; 1962

Sawyer, W.W.; The Search for Pattern; Penguin Books, Baltimore, MD;1970

Sawyer, W.W.; IMC Book C; Bell and Hyman; London, England; 1982

Sawyer, W.W.; IMC Book C2; Bell and Hyman; London, England

Sawyer, W.W.; Mathematician's Delight; Penguin Books, Baltimore, MD; 1943

Sawyer, W.W.; What Is Calculus About?; Mathematical Assn of America; 1529 18th St, N.W., Washington, DC 20036

Shell Centre For Mathematical Education; The Language of Functions and Graphs; Univ. of Nottingham, England

Stevens, Peter; Patterns in Nature; Little, Brown, Boston; 1974

Thompson, D'Arcy; On Growth and Form; Cambridge U. Press; 1917

Materials

Calculator: Casio, TI (graphics, programmable, scientific)

Cuisenaire Rods- (starter set + 1000- $1cm^3$ rods); ETA/Cuisenaire; 1-800-445-5985; www.etacuisenaire.com

Geoboard: wood, square array of 5 nails x 5nails; ETA

Mathematics Calendar; Math Products Plus; P.O. Box 64, San Carlos, CA 94070

Mirrors (2), plastic, 4"x6"; ETA

Nautilus Shell; Shell World, 5684 International Dr., Orlando, FL 32819-8509; 1-407-370-3344; Fax:1-407-396-2244; email: flashells@aol.com; http://www.shellworld.com

Pineapple (a Fibonacci one - go to your market and count the rows..8, 13, 21! People will look at you a little funny).

Shuttle Puzzle (haven't found this- see chapter 6 to make it yourself)

Sunflower stalk and/or head-- start planting!

Ticker-tape (Acceleration Timer): Central Scientific Co.; Franklin Park, IL; 1-800-262-3626; #72702-21

Topographic maps-- a U.S. Geological Survey Dept., some bookstores

Tower Puzzle: ETA

Videotapes

"Infinite Series By and For 6 year-olds and up"; Running time 24 min.; produced by Don Cohen

"Iteration to Infinite Sequences with 6 to 11 year-olds"; Running time 38 min.; produced by Don Cohen

Websites of note

IES wonderful Java applets at http://www.ies.co.jp/math/java/
with Don's ideas used in 3 of these at:
http://www.ies.co.jp/math/java/comp/itoi/itoi.html (from Ch. 11-a WOW!) and
http://www.ies.co.jp/math/java/trig/sixtrigfn/sixtrigfn.html all 6 trig functions
at once
http://www.ies.co.jp/math/java/misc/magbox/Magbox1.html Maggie's difference
of 2 cubes
The Math Forum, the best MathED site on the www!
http://mathforum.org/
Ron Knott's fine work on Fibonacci numbers and the golden mean at
http://www.mcs.surrey.ac.uk/Personal/R.Knott/Fibonacci/fib.html
Xah Lee's great work on curves -especially the equiangular spiral! at
http://xahlee.org/SpecialPlaneCurves_dir/EquiangularSpiral_dir/equiangularSpira
l.html

Computer Software

Derive®, http://education.ti.com/product/software/derive/features/features.html
Logo
Mathematica; Wolfram Research Inc., Champaign, IL 61820; http://www.wri.com
Microsoft Basic; Microsoft Corp., Redmond, WA; 1-800-227-4679
DPGraph; by David Parker; http://www.dpgraph.com/subscribe.html

About the author:

Donald Cohen was born in Jersey City, N.J. He has taught students of all ages and abilities for 49 years, the last 27 of these as co-founder and teacher of The Math Program, with his partner Jerry Glynn. He lives in Champaign, IL.

After 7 years of teaching in a junior high school, he realized there must be a more enjoyable and effective way to teach math. He searched for alternatives. This lead to designing new curriculum for NY State; learning about mathematics and creativity from Dr. Robert B. Davis with The Madison Project; learning what real teaching is about by observing great teachers such as Sue Monell; teaching teachers; working on Plato (a computer-based education system started at the U of IL); all before Don and Jerry invented The Math Program.

One of the most exciting and satisfying events in Don's life was the completion of his book
"Calculus By and For Young People
(ages 7, yes 7 and up)"

which was reviewed in the Dec.1988 issue of **Scientific American**, as well as in many other places. The Japanese translation of this book was published by Kodansha Ltd. on August 20, 1998, and they sold 22,336 copies in 3 1/3 years! He then produced two videotapes to go with the book
"Infinite Series By and For 6 year-olds and up"
and
"Iteration to Infinite Sequences with 6 to 11 year-olds";

this book of worksheets, which is also on a CD-ROM in Japanese and English, and
"A Map To Calculus" - a poster or flowchart or overview;
and his latest book
"Changing Shapes With Matrices" ; the Japanese translation of this book was
published on April 20, 2001 by Kodansha Ltd. and sold 5,490 in 8 months!

The last few years Don has worked hard to develop his website at URL
http://www.shout.net/~mathman , with email: mathman@shout.net and has worked with students around the world via IM. These are the good old days!

Don has been blessed with a wonderful wife, three fine sons, and 6 terrific grandchildren and 2 greatgrandchildren. He is a watercolor artist (see cover) and as a friend said, "he takes time to smell the flowers and gives them to people".

"We have not succeeded in answering all your problems. The answers we have found only serve to raise a whole set of new questions. In some ways we feel we are as confused as ever, but we believe we are confused on a higher level and about more important things". -- from an unknown source, but certainly a kindred spirit.